Table of Contents

Month 1 Checklist

Hands-on activities to help your child in school!

NUMBERS

Counting Numbers 1-10: pages 5-15, 32
Counting Numbers 1-20: pages 16-20, 32
Writing Numbers: pages 1-20: 6, 9, 14, 18

Communicating about numbers through counting, reading, or writing is essential for all work in mathematics. This month's worksheets provide practice with reading, writing, and counting numbers through 20, forward and backward.

- ❑ Complete the worksheets.
- ❑ Count collections of things around the house: windows, doors, beds, etc. Then, challenge your child to find things to count in a specific room, such as the kitchen (plates, mugs, or various food items).
- ❑ Make a counting book with your child. Staple or clip 10 pieces of paper together. Have your child write "1" on the first page, "2" on the second page, and so on, and then draw objects on each page that match the number—for example, 3 flowers on the "3" page. Encourage your child to read the completed book to you and other family members.
- ❑ Play "What's Next?" Begin a number sequence, such as 5, 6, 7 and have your child say the next three numbers. Then switch roles. Vary the game by counting backward: simply begin a sequence with 10, 9, 8, and have your child say the next three numbers.
- ❑ Make number flash cards. Write the number word on one side of the card and have your child write the number on the other side. Review by having your child read the word name and then looking at the number, or vice versa.

NUMBERS continued

Before, After, and Between: pages 28-30, 32
Comparing Numbers: pages 21-27, 31, 32

Learning to write numbers before, between, and after other numbers, ordering numbers, and finding amounts that are more or less than a given amount are important skills that are the focus of the following activities:

- ❑ Complete the worksheets.
- ❑ Display a collection of 4 plates, 6 cups, and 8 spoons. Ask your child to order the collections from least number of items to greatest number. Repeat the activity for other household collections.
- ❑ Play a guessing game. Make a number line from 1 to 20 for reference. Then say, "I am thinking of a number between 1 and 20. What is the number?" Offer clues by saying, "This number is greater than ___" or "This number is less than ___" in response to your child's guesses. Continue until the number is guessed. Reverse roles and play again.

Dot Count

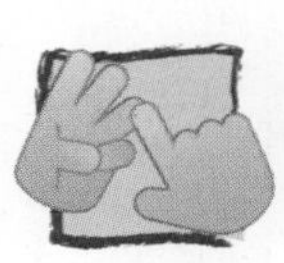
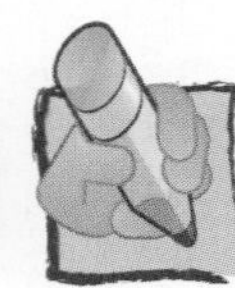

Count the dots. Trace and write the numbers.

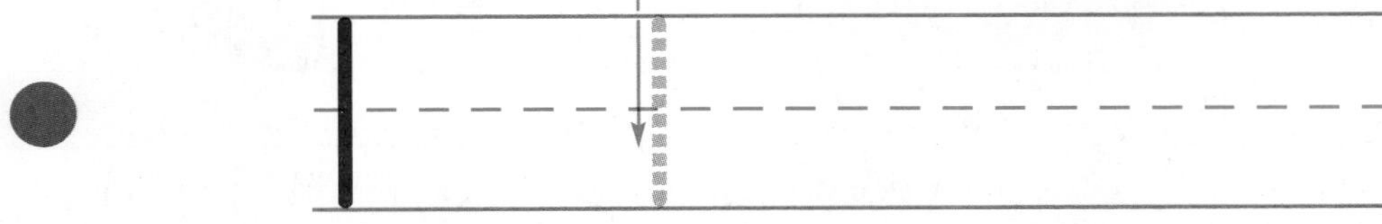

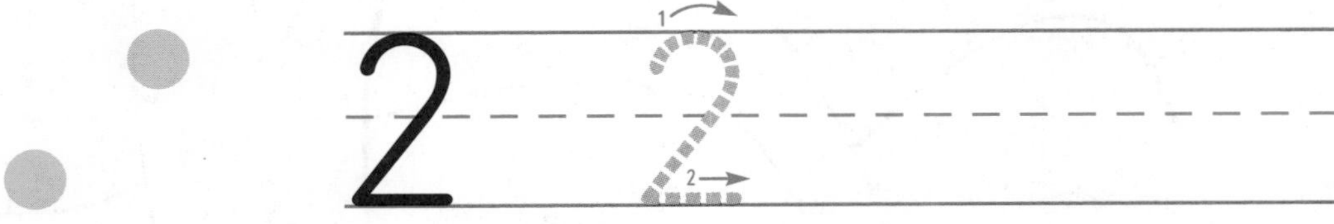

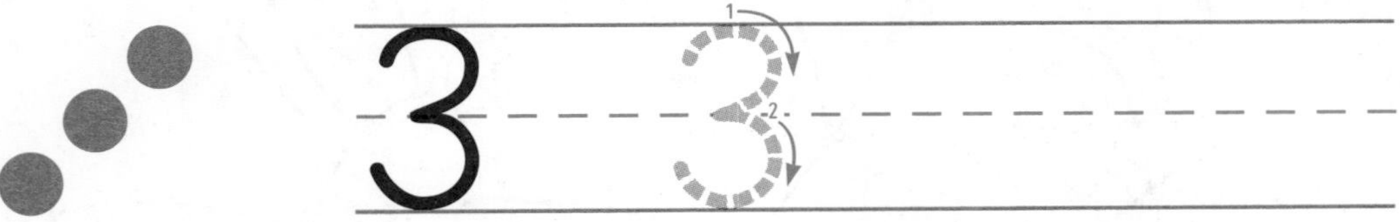

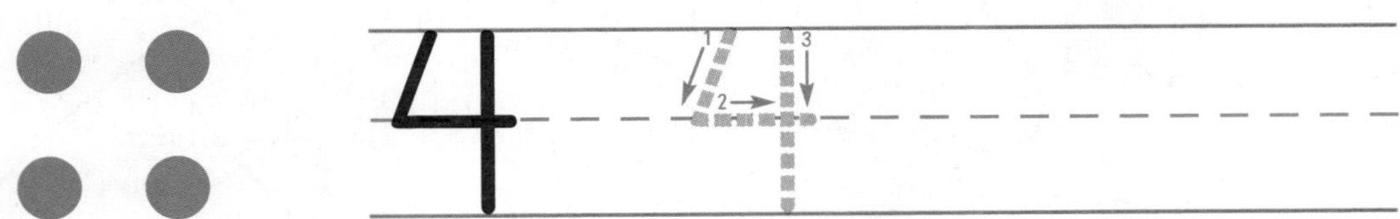

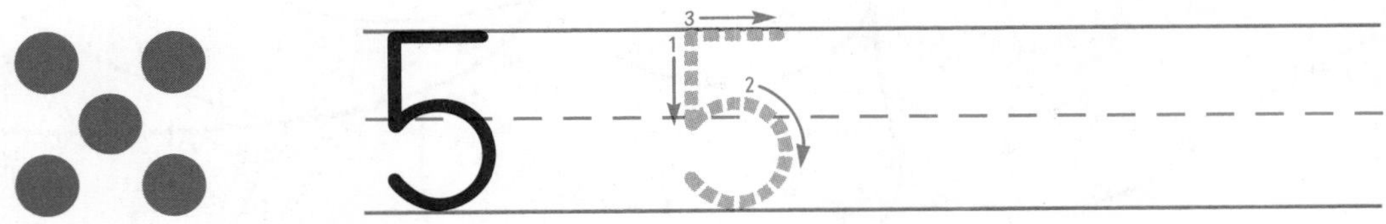

Who's Hiding?

1 = 

2 = 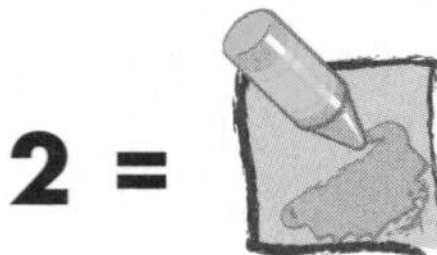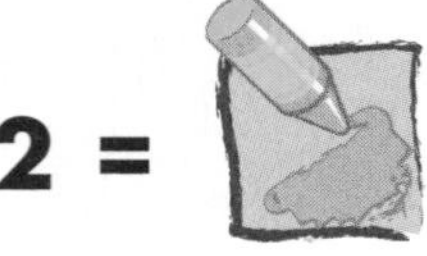

3 = 

4 = 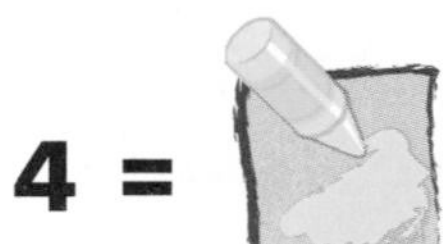

5 = 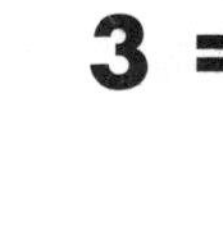

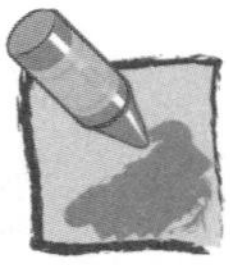

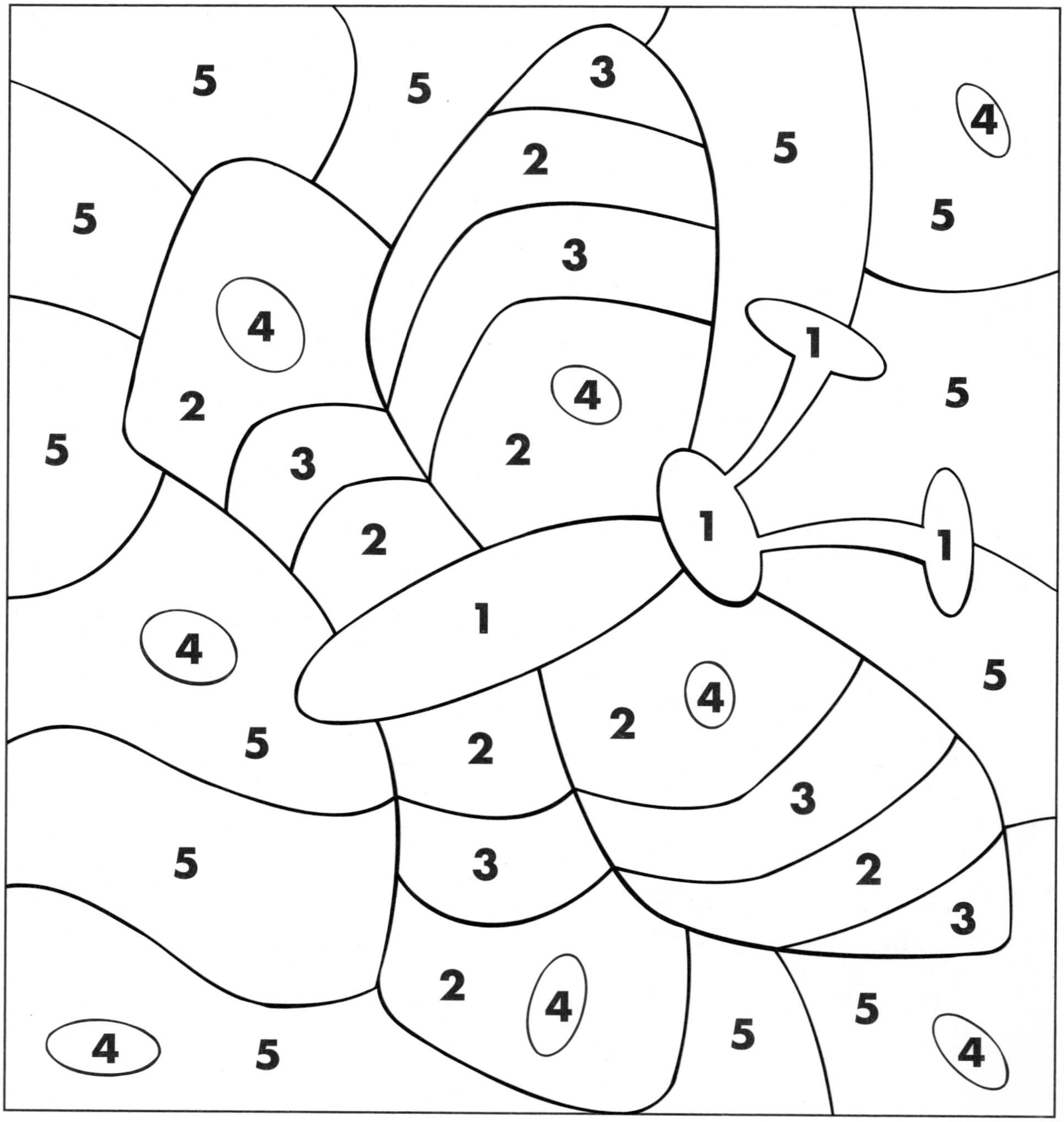

In The Garden

1

2

3

4

5

Count.
Circle the right number.

1 4 2

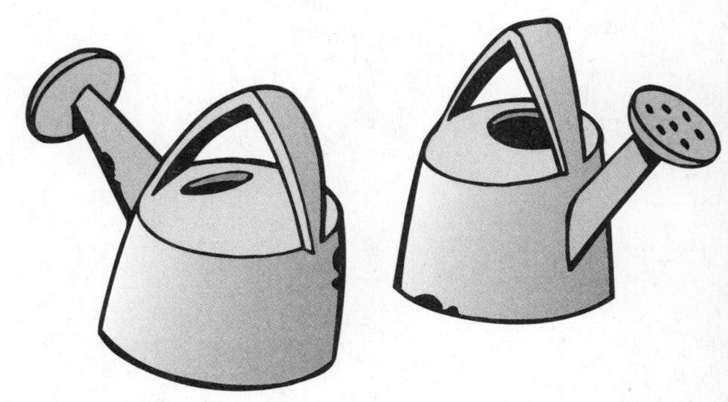

2 5 3

3 1 5

2 4 5

At the Beach

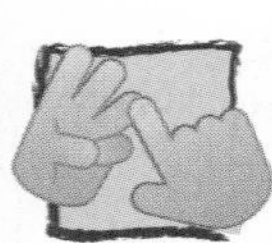

Count.
Write how many.

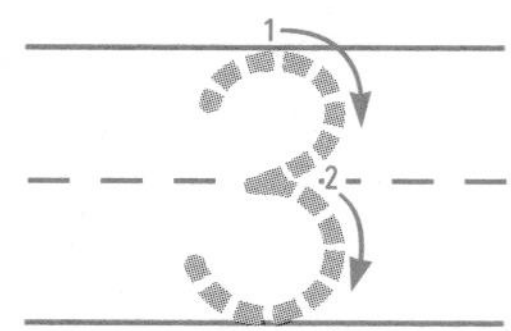

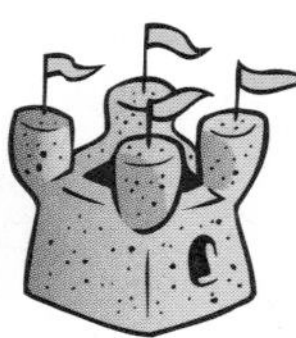

Star Count

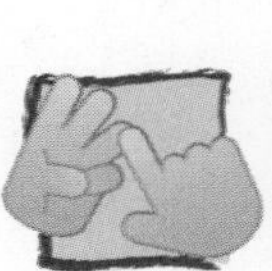
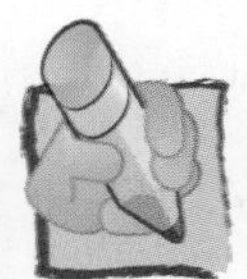

Count the stars. Trace and write the numbers.

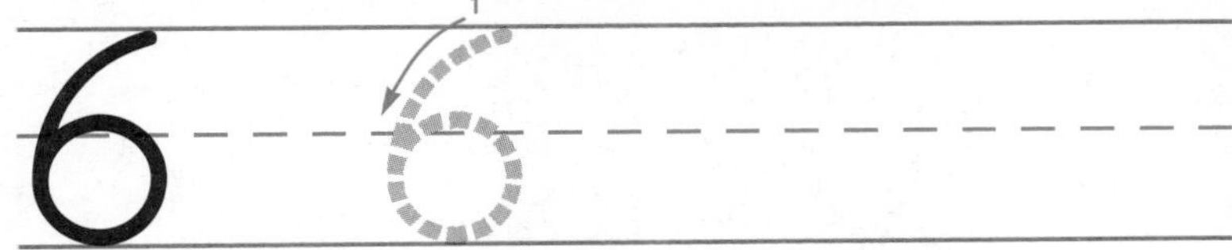

★★★★
★★★

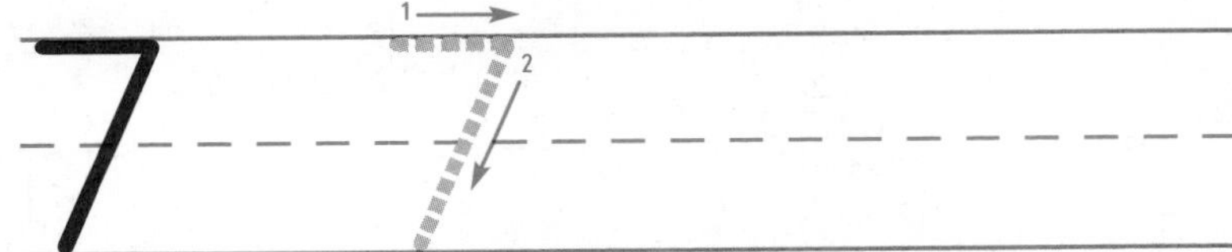

★★★★
★★★★

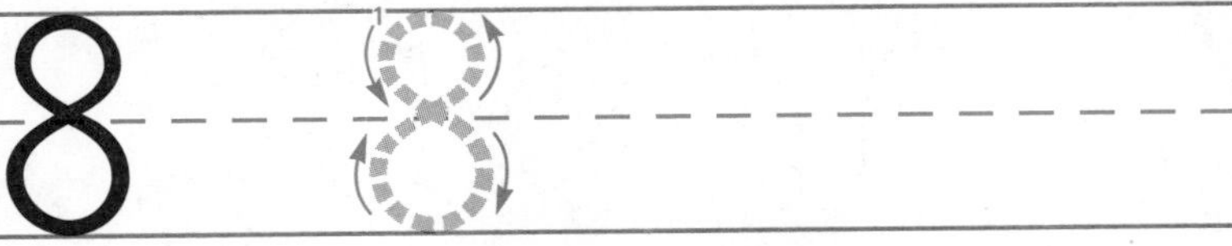

★★★★★
★★★★

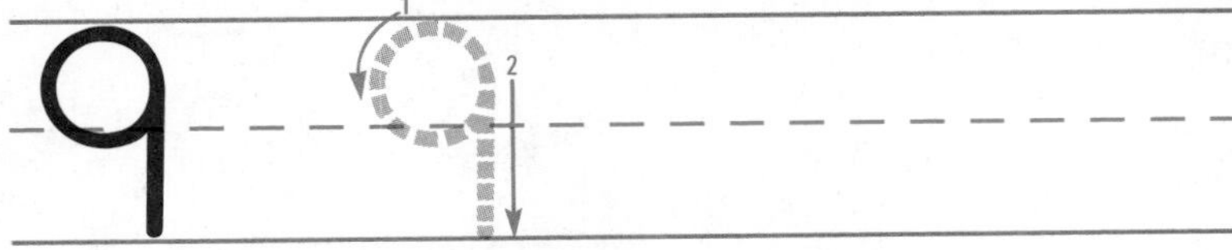

★★★★★
★★★★★

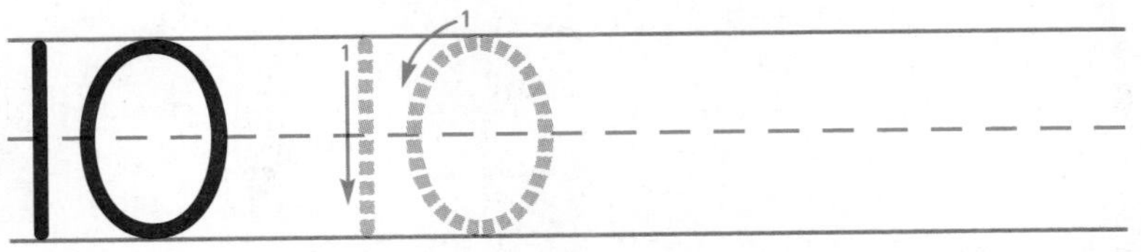

How Many Animals?

Count. Draw lines to match.

6

7

8

10

How Many Toys?

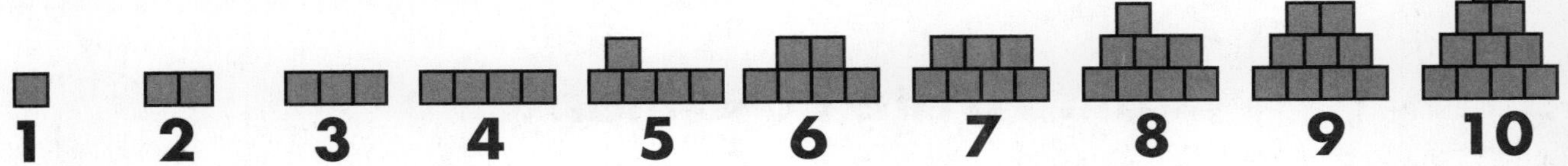

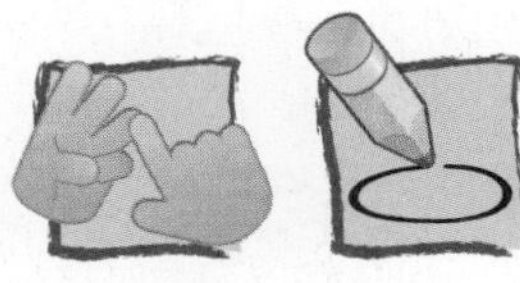

Count. Write how many.

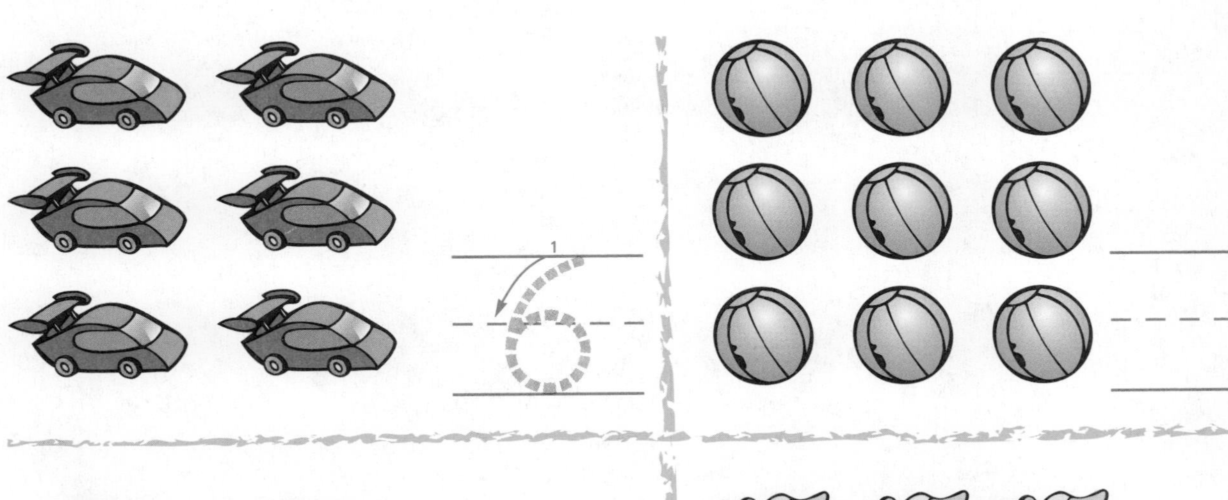

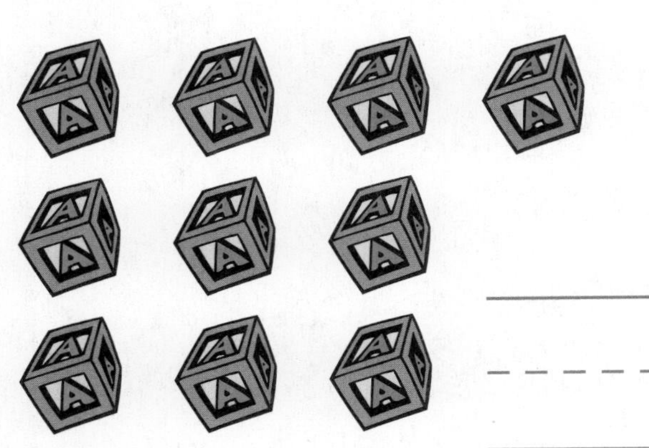

Spin and Roll

Count. Write how many.

8

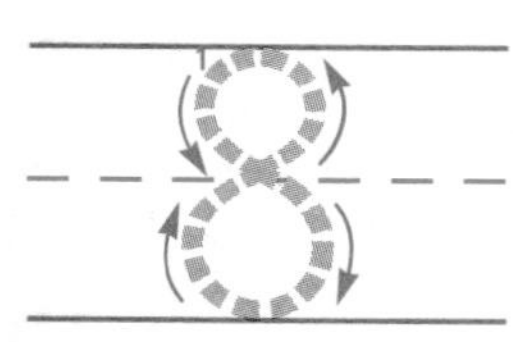

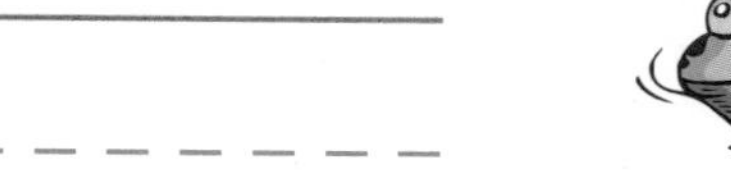

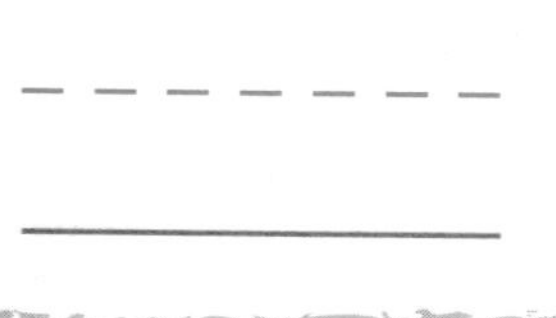

In The Sky

Color to show the number.

9

7

5

10

6

8

Hidden Numbers

Find the numbers 1-10 hidden in the picture. Circle each number.

1 2 3 4 5 6 7 8 9 10

Recognizing numerals 1 to 10; using visual discrimination

1 to 10, 10 to 1

Count to 10 and back again.

1 2 3 4 5 6 7 8 9 10 9 8 7 6 5 4 3 2 1

Write 1 to 10.

1 3 5

6 10

Write 10 to 1.

10 9 6

5

Count up the ladder.
Then count down.

10 9 8 7 6 5 4 3 2 1

NUMBERS

Sweet Treats

Draw lines to match.

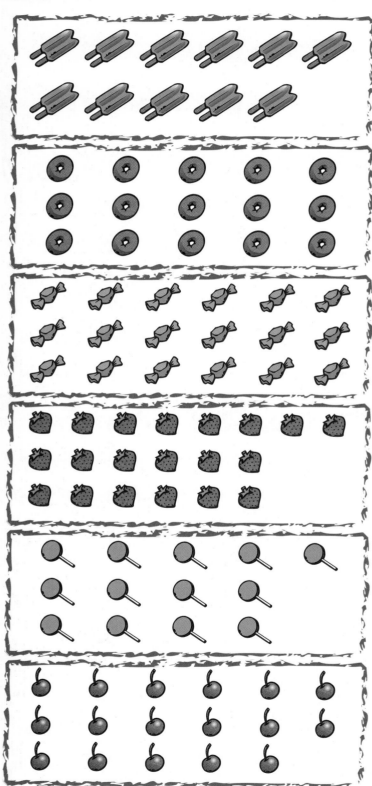

Counting objects and matching numerals 11-20

At School

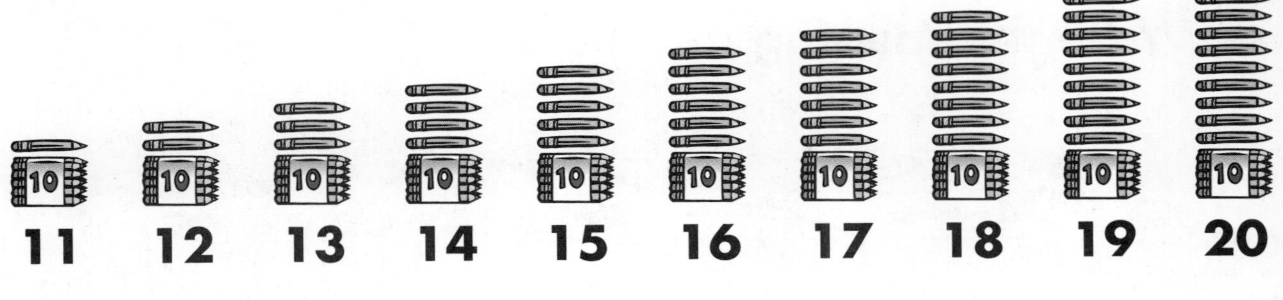

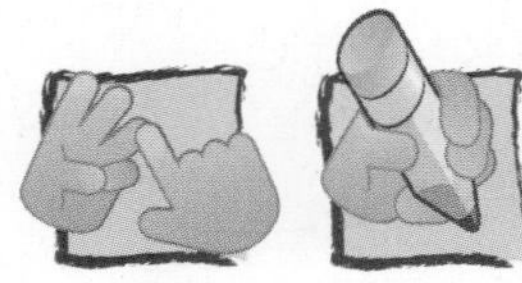

Count. Write how many.

12

Counting objects and writing numerals to 20

Counting Fun

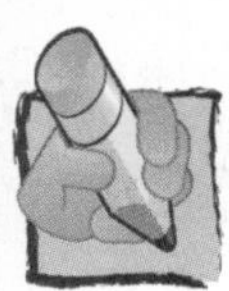

Write the missing numbers.

1 2 3 4

7 8

10

13 15

17 19

Counting and writing numbers in sequence through 20

Dot's Great!

Connect the dots from 1 to 20.
Color the picture.

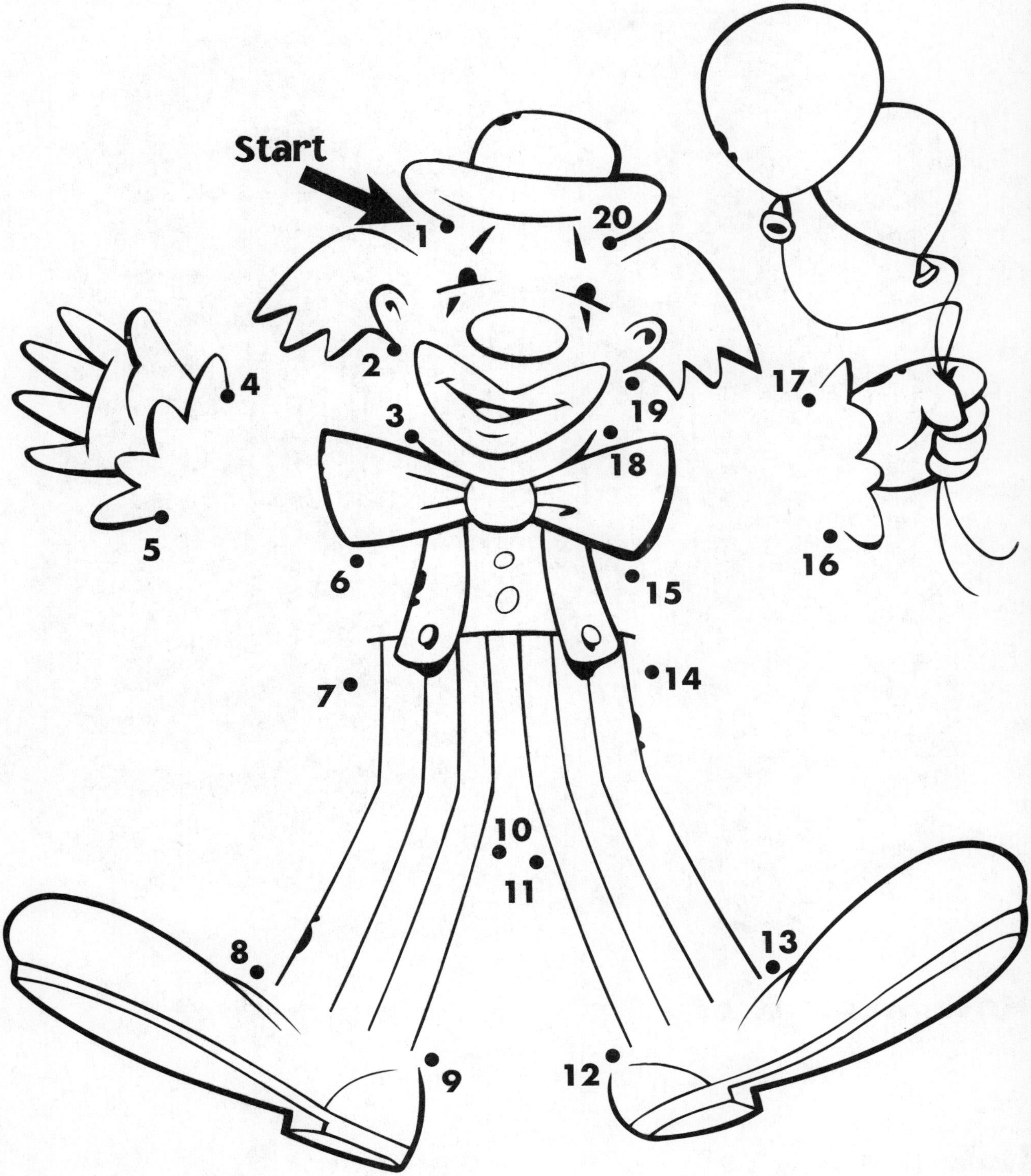

Review

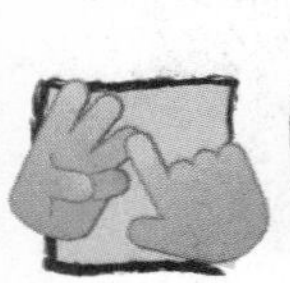

Count. Write how many.

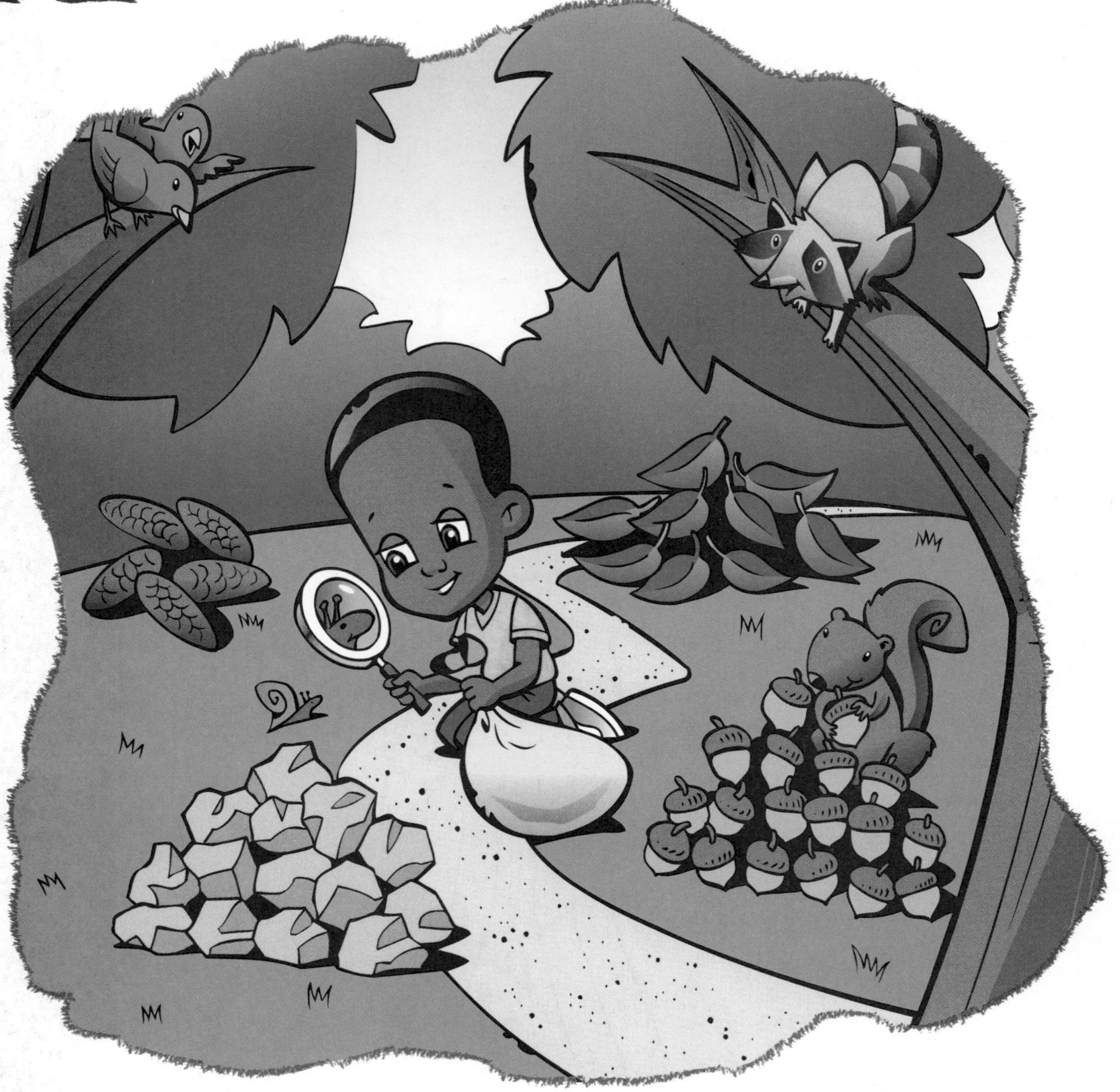

How many s? ______

How many s? ______

How many 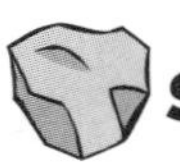s? ______

How many s? ______

Give the Dog a Bone

Match.

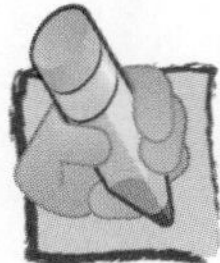

Write the answer.

How many [bone]s did the dogs find?

Matching sets showing the same number of objects

More or Fewer

more

fewer

Circle the set that shows **more** for each row.

Circle the set that shows **fewer** for each row.

One More, One Fewer

8 is one more than 7.
7 is one fewer than 8.

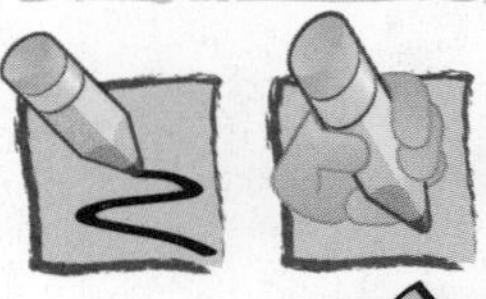

Draw one more. Write the number.

How many?

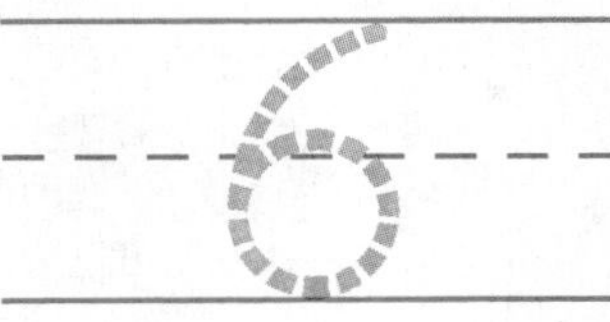

How many?

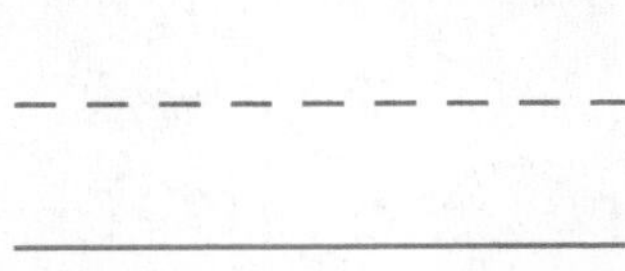

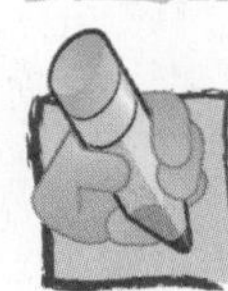

Show one fewer. Write the number.

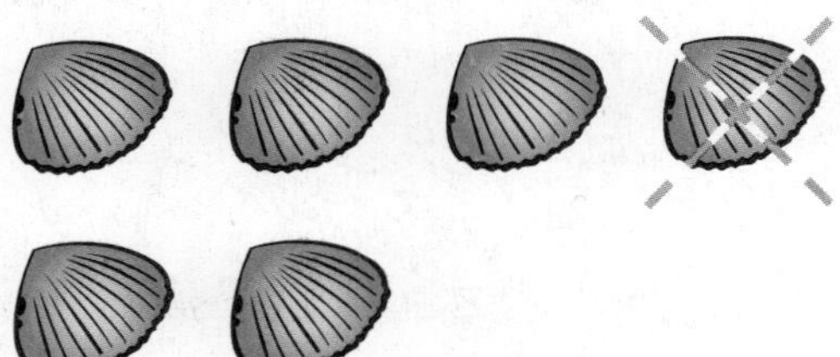
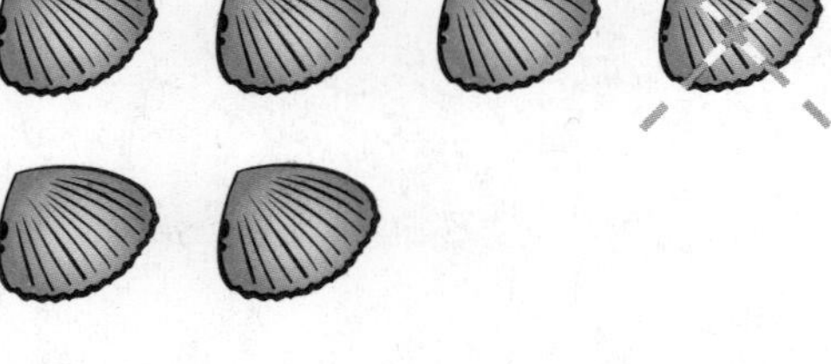

How many?

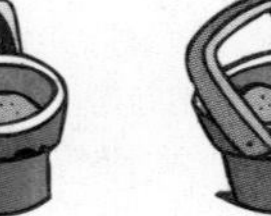

How many?

It's a Party

Circle the set in each row that shows more.

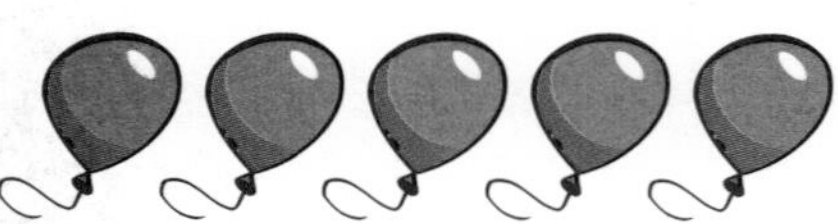

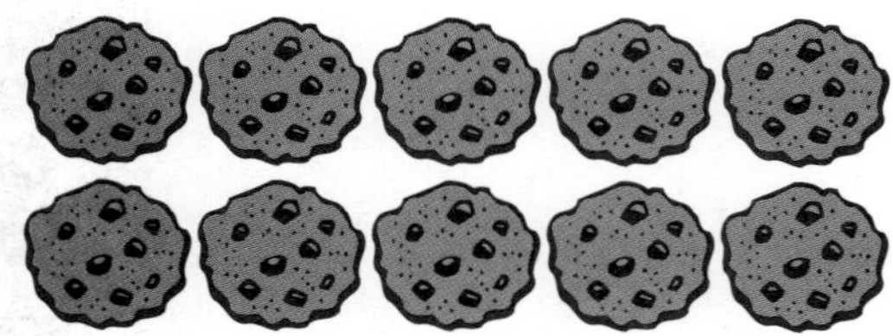

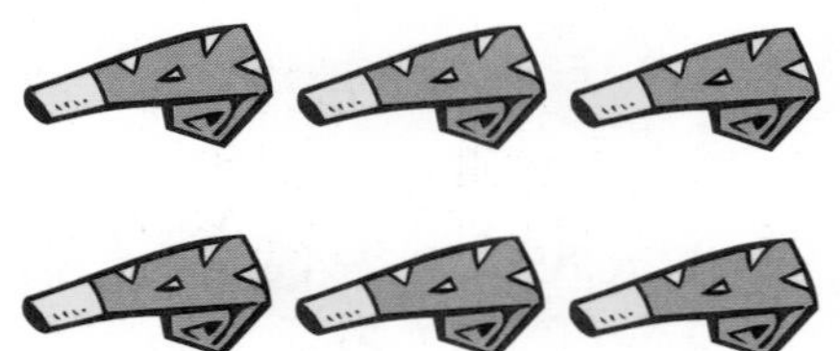

What to Wear?

Circle the set in each row that shows fewer.

NUMBERS

Counting Flowers

7 is more than 4.

Circle the number that is more.

3 5

7 2

8 6

4 7

11 9

10 13

Identifying the set that shows more

Counting Fruit

6 is less than 8. A smaller number means fewer pieces

Circle the number that represents fewer pieces.

3 

5 

9

6

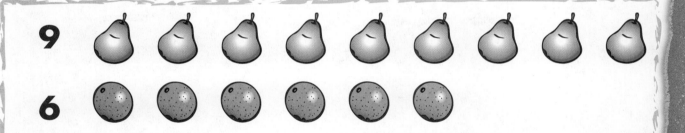

10

11

15

17

NUMBERS

What's Before?

1 comes before 2.

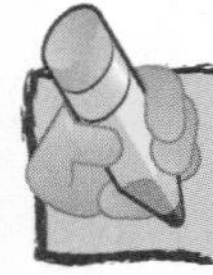

Write the number that comes before.

9

6

4

12

16

3

What's After?

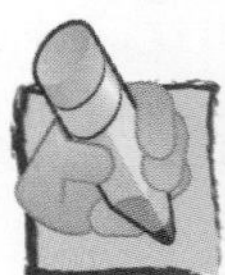

Write the number that comes after.

8 comes after 7.

NUMBERS

What's Between?

5 comes between 4 and 6.

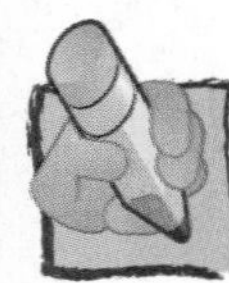

Write the number that comes between.

4	11	8
___	___	___
2	9	6

18	15	20	7
___	___	___	___
16	13	18	5

Pick It

8 is the larger number.
5 is the smaller number.

Circle the larger number.

2 5	10 8	6 4
15 11	6 9	14 15

Circle the smaller number.

10 12	3 5	16 18
7 6	13 19	20 17

Practice Test

How many?

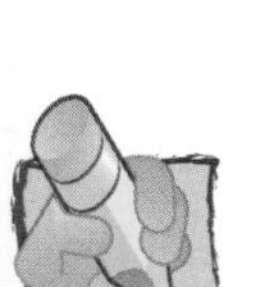

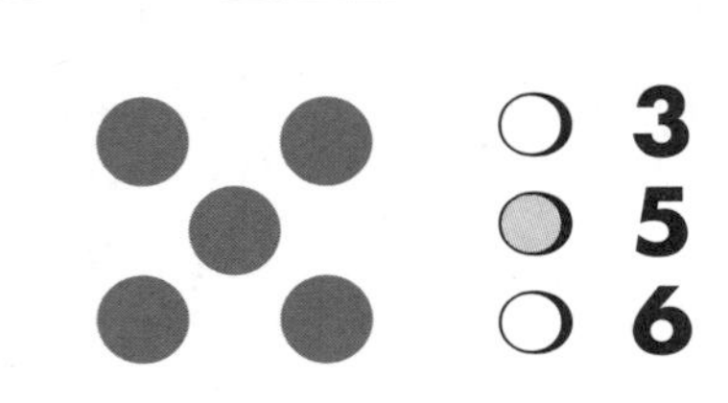

- ❍ 3
- ❍ 5
- ❍ 6

1. How many?

- ❍ 6
- ❍ 7
- ❍ 8

2. How many?

- ❍ 9
- ❍ 10
- ❍ 11

3. What comes before?

______, 5, 6

- ❍ 3
- ❍ 7
- ❍ 4

4. What comes between?

11, ______, 13

- ❍ 10
- ❍ 12
- ❍ 14

5. How many?

- ❍ 19
- ❍ 16
- ❍ 13

6. How many?

- ❍ 8
- ❍ 11
- ❍ 13

7. Which is more than 7?

- ❍ 8
- ❍ 7
- ❍ 6

8. Which number means fewer than 16?

- ❍ 18
- ❍ 17
- ❍ 15

Month 2 Checklist

Hands-on activities to help your child in school!

ADDITION WITH SUMS THROUGH 8

Add 0-5: pages 35-42
Add 0-8: pages 43-51
Solving Problems with Addition: page 47

Understanding the concept of addition sometimes just takes a little practice. The activities below will help your child master the basics:

❑ Complete the worksheets.

❑ Play "Penny Drop." Drop 5 pennies, one at a time, into an empty jar. Have your child count aloud as your drop them. Then have your child *count on* as you drop 2 more pennies into the jar. Ask your child to tell how many in all. Spill the pennies out so your child can verify that the sum is correct. Repeat the game as time and interest permit.

❑ Display 4 buttons, and have your child write as many different combinations as possible that make 4. The list should include 3 + 1, 2 + 2, and 1 + 3. Repeat the activity for 5 through 8.

❑ Using a favorite picture book, have your child make up an addition story based on one of the illustrations. For a page from *Goldilocks and the Three Bears*, for example, your child may say, "2 parent bears and 1 baby bear are equal to 3 bears in all."

SUBTRACTION FROM NUMBERS THROUGH 8

Subtract 0-5: pages 52-57
Subtract 0-8: pages 58-64

Once your child has a basic understanding of addition, the concept of subtraction can be introduced. Tell your child that in addition, amounts are joined; and in subtraction, one amount is separated, or taken away, from another. The activities below provide excellent practice and reinforcement of these concepts.

- ❑ Complete the worksheets.
- ❑ Have your child hold up a total of no more than 8 fingers, using fingers on both hands. Ask him or her to tell how many fingers are up in all. Then have your child put one hand behind his or her back and tell how many fingers are (a) hidden and are (b) still showing. You may wish to write a subtraction sentence that matches the finger play. Repeat several times.
- ❑ Play "What's Under the Cup?" Show your child up to 8 buttons and drop them into a paper cup. While your child covers his or her eyes, spill the buttons out and hide some under the cup. Then say, "Open your eyes. How many buttons can you see now? How many must be hiding under the cup?" Repeat the game several times.
- ❑ Tell a story, such as: "There were 5 apples on the counter. 2 were eaten. There are 3 apples left." Have your child write the subtraction sentence that describes the story. Repeat a few more times. Next, write a subtraction sentence such as $6 - 4 = 2$ and have your child make up a story to go with it.

Flying High

 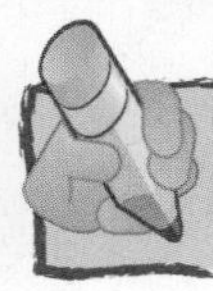

Count. Write how many in all.

in all

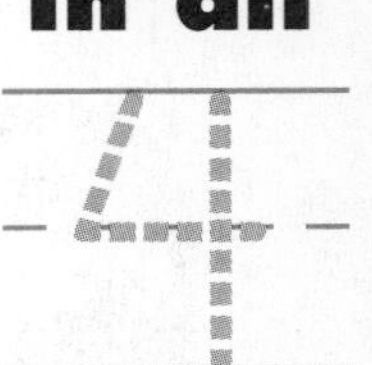

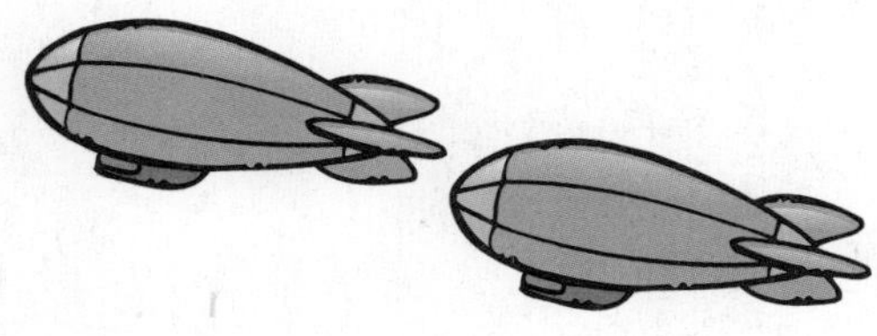 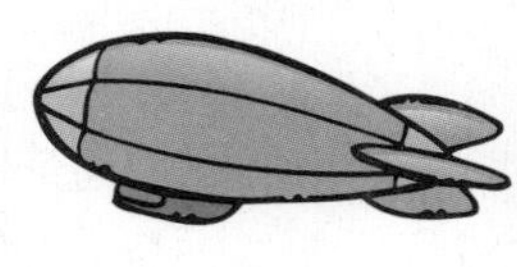

in all

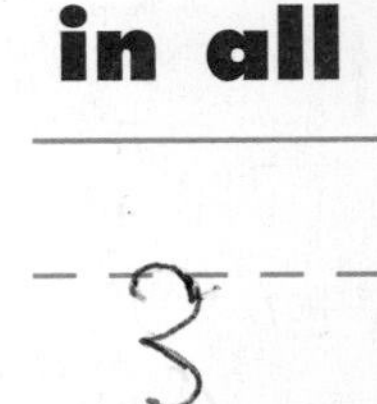

in all

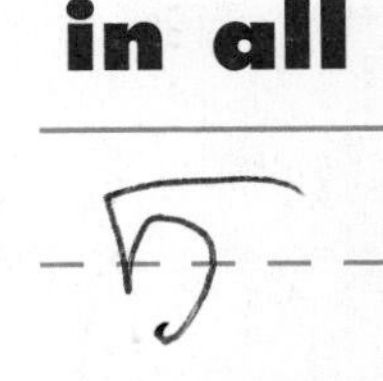

in all

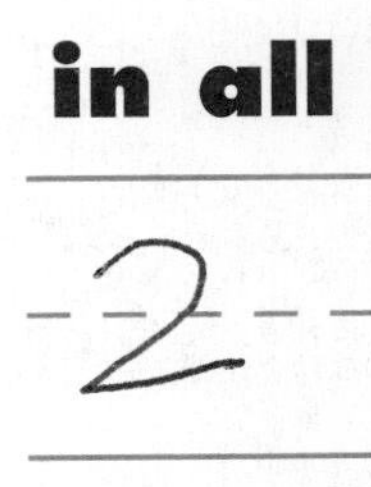

How many in all? Circle the answer.

4 5

ADDITION

Blowing in the Wind

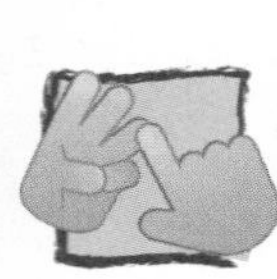
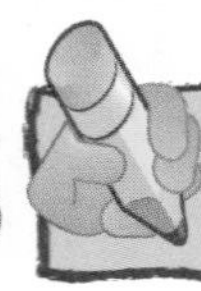

Count. Write how many in all.

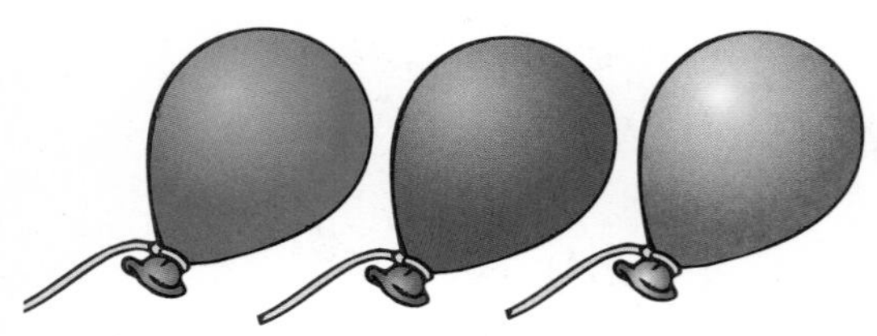

in all

in all

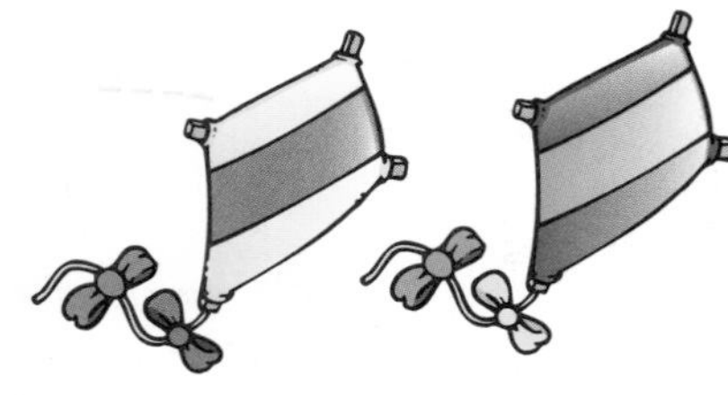

in all

in all

How many in all? Circle the answer.

3 5

Counting on to find how many in all

Falling Leaves

3 2

5 in all

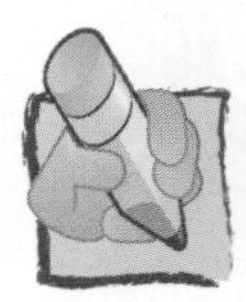

Write how many.

ADDITION

in all

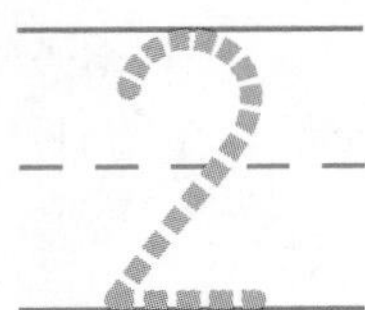
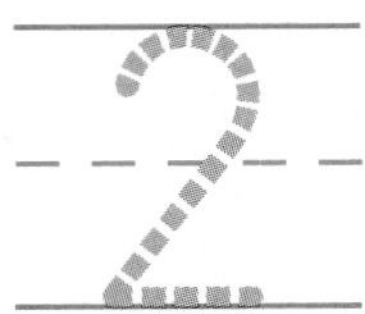
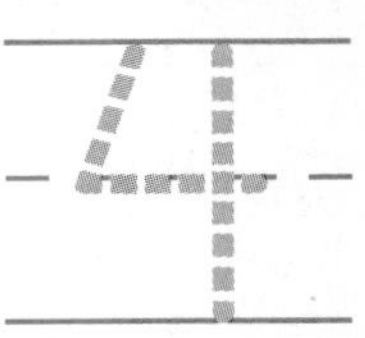

in all

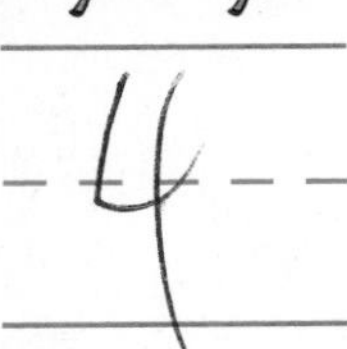
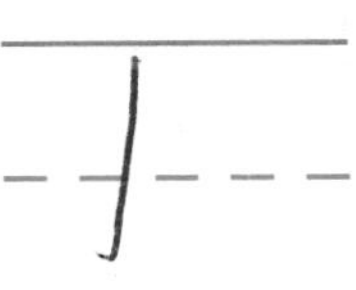
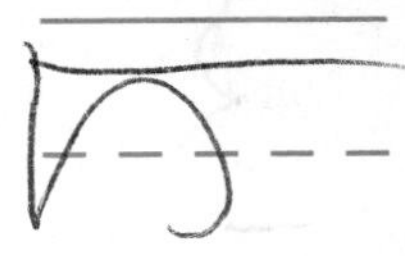

in all

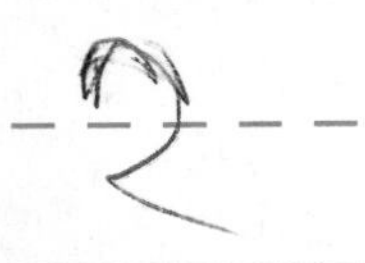
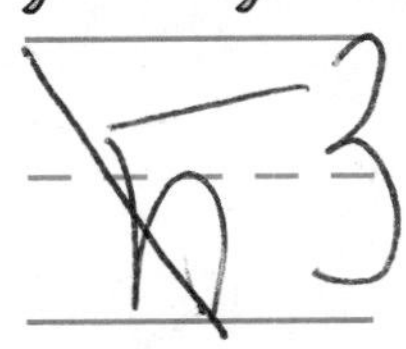
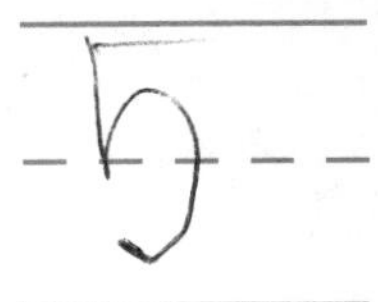

in all

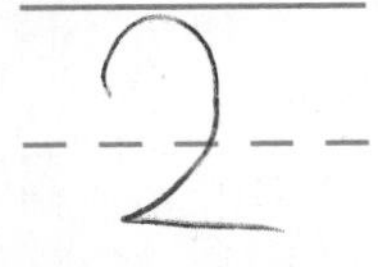
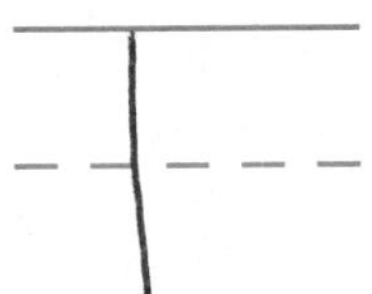
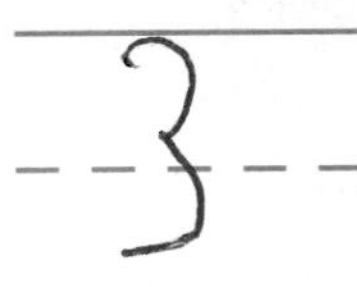

Very Nutty

5
0
5 in all

1
3
4 in all

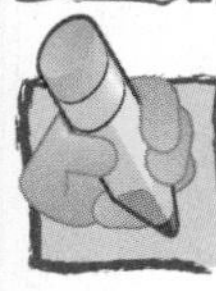

Write how many.

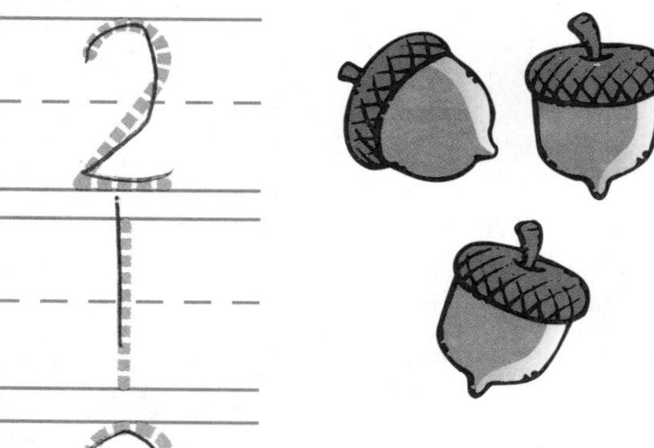

in all

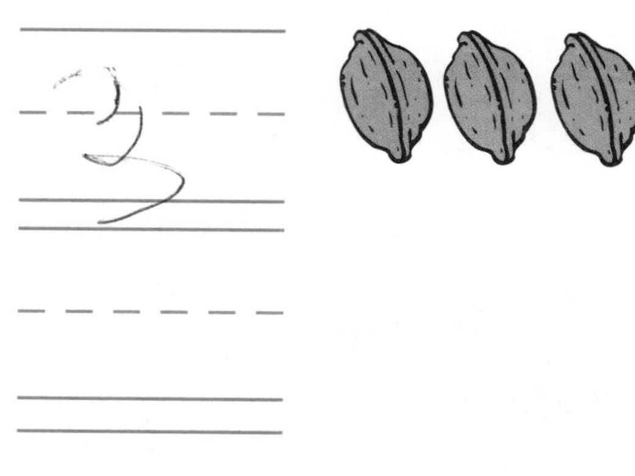

in all

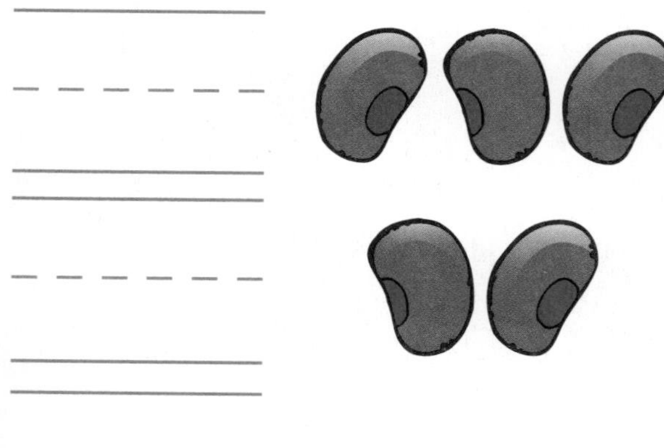

in all

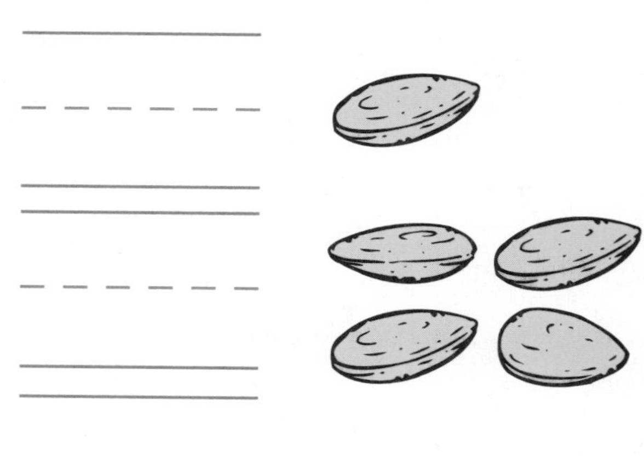

in all

In Bloom

in all

1 + 2 = 3

Write how many.

in all

 + 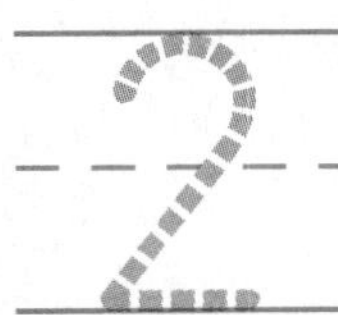 = 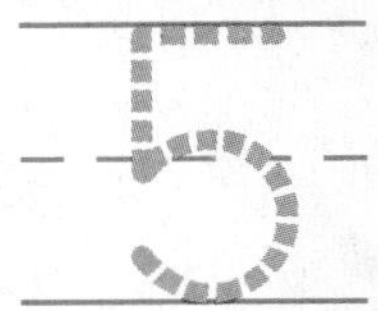

in all

___ + ___ = ___

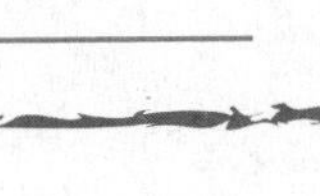  

in all

___ + ___ = ___

in all

___ + ___ = ___

Save It

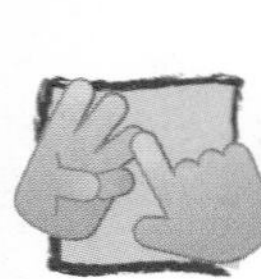 

Add. Write the sum.

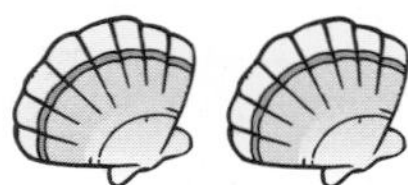

0 + 4 = 4

2 + 1 = ____

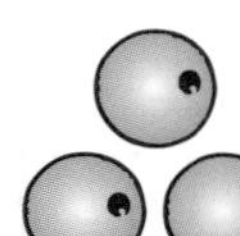

2 + 3 = ____

2 + 2 = ____

3
+ 2
____

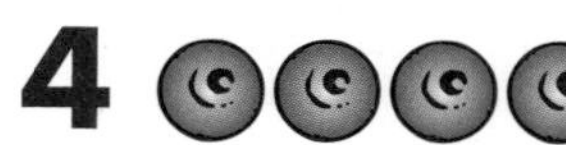

4
+ 1
____

1
+ 2
____

1
+ 3
____

3
+ 1
____

0
+ 5
____

On Wheels

4 1 4 + 1 = 5

Circle the correct number sentence.

2 + 1 = 3
2 + 2 = 4

1 + 1 = 2
2 + 2 = 4

4 + 1 = 5
3 + 2 = 5

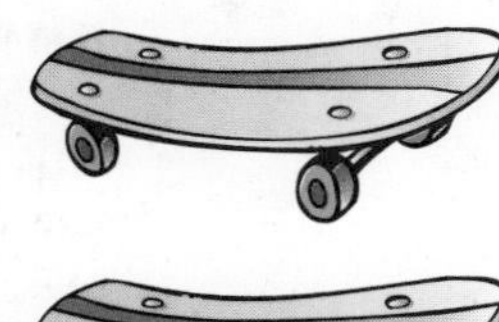

4 + 0 = 4
2 + 2 = 4

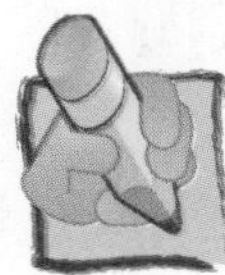

Write the answer.

How many wheels? ______

Hippety Hop

Add. Write how many in all.

in all

1 + 2 = 3

in all

1 + 4 = ____

in all

2 + 2 = ____

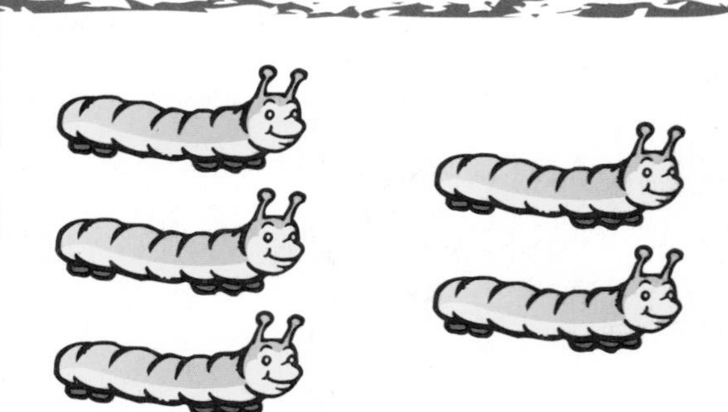

in all

3 + 2 = ____

Matching groups of objects to number sentences; finding sums to 5

Pet Show

4 + 2 = 6 in all

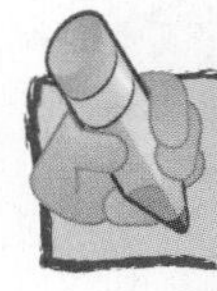

Write how many.

 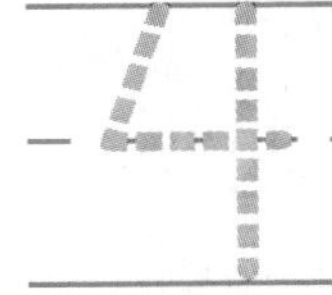

   ___ in all

2 + 4 = ___

___ + ___ = ___ in all

___ + ___ = ___ in all

Circle the answer.

6  s in all.
How many are hiding?

2

4

Sweet Shop

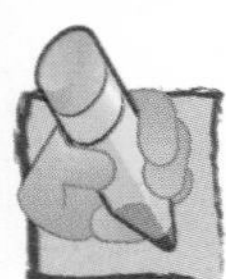

Write how many.

$$\begin{array}{r} 3 \\ +\ 3 \\ \hline 6 \end{array}$$ in all

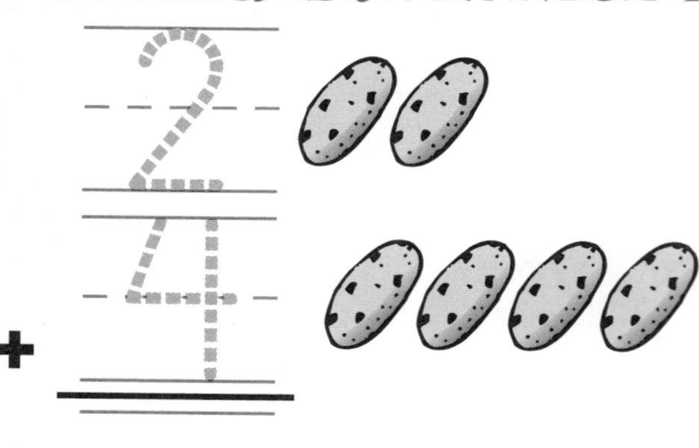

+

____ in all

+

____ in all

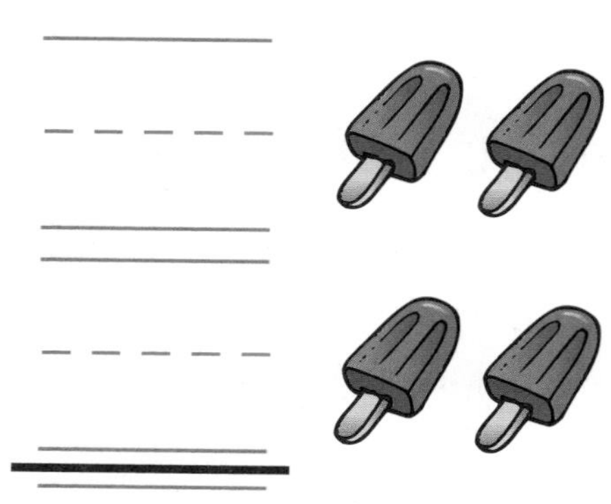

+

____ in all

+

____ in all

Circle the answer.

6 s in all.
How many are in the bag?

1 2

Lunch Time

4 + 2 = 6

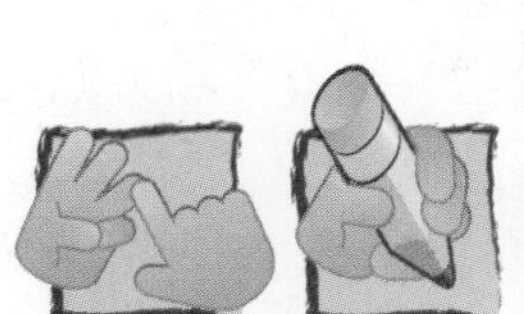

Add. Write the sum.

3 + 1 = 4

3 + 3 = ___

5 + 1 = ___

1 + 2 = ___

2 + 2 = ___

2 + 4 = ___

0 + 5 = ___

2 + 3 = ___

4 + 1 = ___

0 + 6 = ___

Put It Away

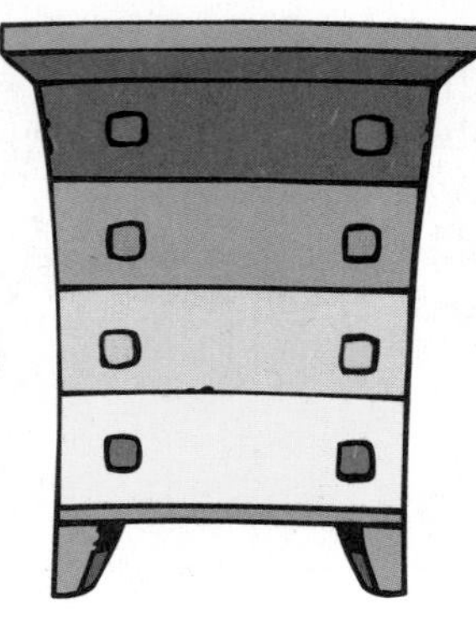

$$\begin{array}{r} 1 \\ +\ 5 \\ \hline 6 \end{array}$$

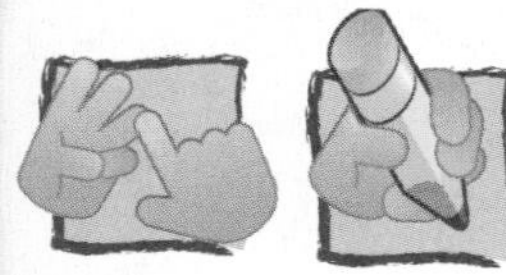

Add. Write the sum.

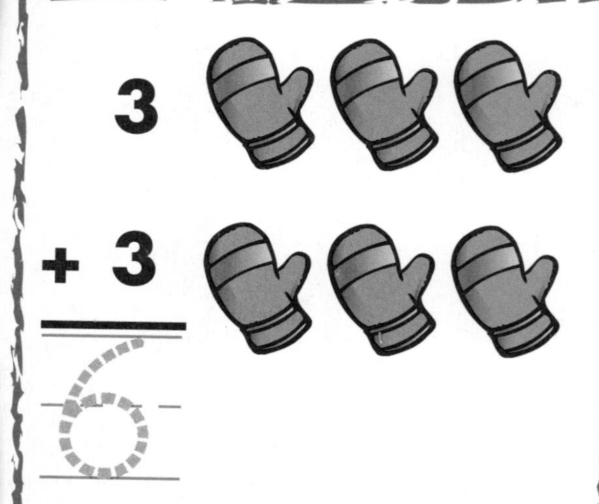

$$\begin{array}{r} 3 \\ +\ 3 \\ \hline 6 \end{array}$$

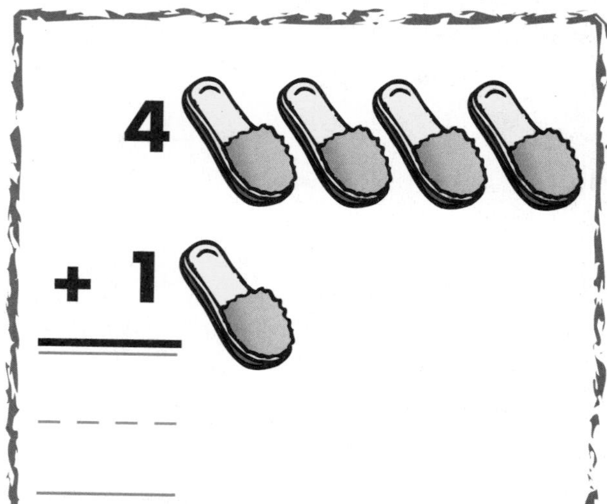

$$\begin{array}{r} 4 \\ +\ 1 \\ \hline \end{array}$$

$$\begin{array}{r} 0 \\ +\ 6 \\ \hline \end{array} \qquad \begin{array}{r} 3 \\ +\ 2 \\ \hline \end{array} \qquad \begin{array}{r} 5 \\ +\ 1 \\ \hline \end{array}$$

$$\begin{array}{r} 2 \\ +\ 2 \\ \hline \end{array} \qquad \begin{array}{r} 2 \\ +\ 4 \\ \hline \end{array} \qquad \begin{array}{r} 1 \\ +\ 3 \\ \hline \end{array}$$

Animal Stories

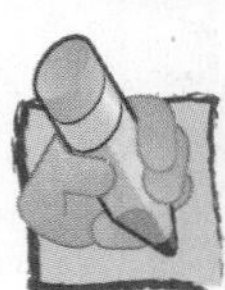

Write the numbers to finish each story.

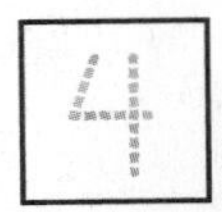

bugs + 

more bugs = ☐ **bugs in all.**

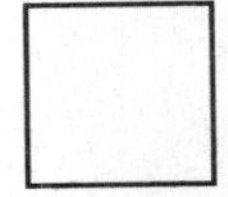 **little dogs +** 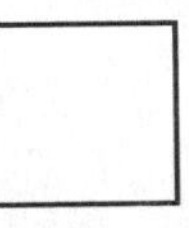 **big dogs =** ☐ **dogs in all.**

 **cats +** 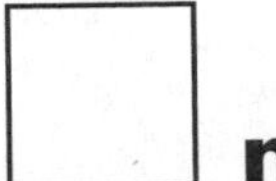 **more cat =** ☐ **cats in all.**

   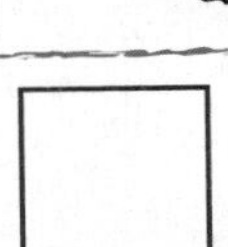

 **blue fish +** ☐ **red fish =** ☐ **fish in all.**

Solving problems with sums to 6

ADDITION

Winter Fun

5 + 3 = 8 in all

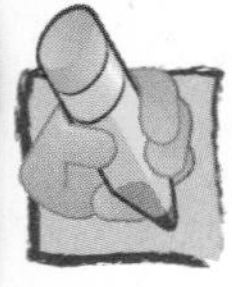

Write how many.

4 + 4 = ____ in all

____ + ____ = ____ in all

____ + ____ = ____ in all

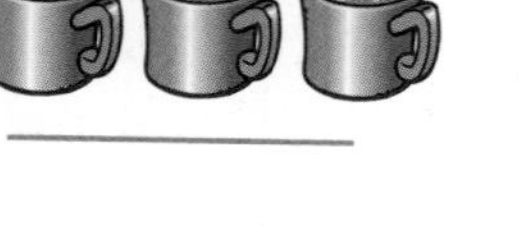

____ + ____ = ____ in all

Very Buggy

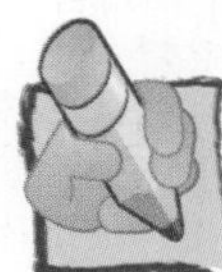

Write the numbers.

☐ + ☐ = ☐

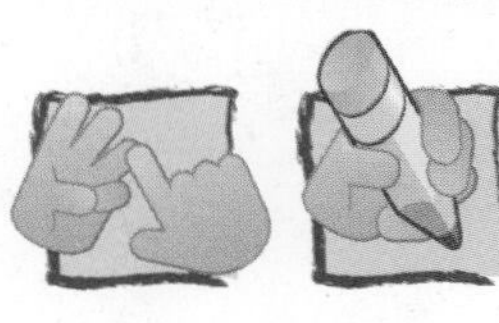

Add. Write the sum.

4 + 4 = 8

1 + 7 = ____

2 + 4 = ____

8 + 0 = ____

6 + 1 = ____

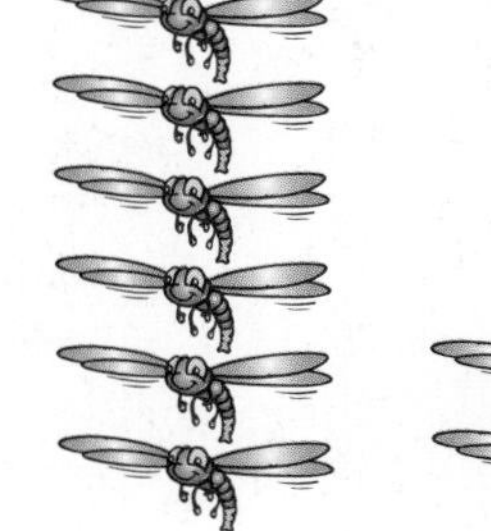

6 + 2 = ____

Finding sums to 8

Breakfast Time

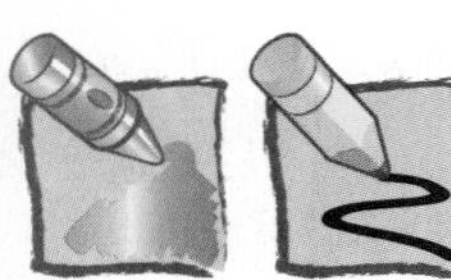

How many s?

Color to show the numbers.

Draw how many in all.

$$\begin{array}{r} 6 \\ +\ 2 \\ \hline 8 \end{array}$$

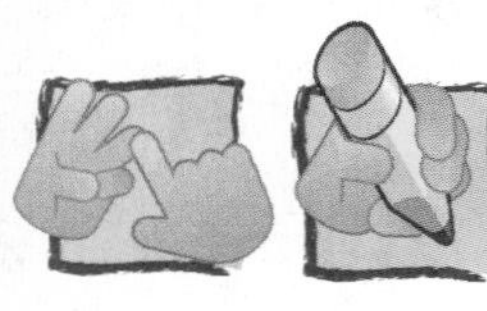

Add. Write the sum.

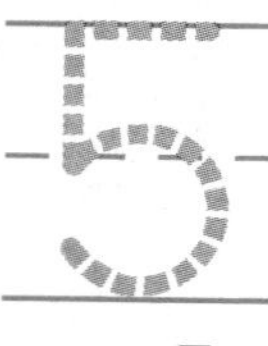

$$\begin{array}{r} 3 \\ +\ 2 \\ \hline 5 \end{array}$$

$$\begin{array}{r} 5 \\ +\ 3 \\ \hline \end{array}$$

$$\begin{array}{r} 6 \\ +\ 2 \\ \hline \end{array}$$

$$\begin{array}{r} 3 \\ +\ 3 \\ \hline \end{array}$$

$$\begin{array}{r} 4 \\ +\ 0 \\ \hline \end{array}$$

$$\begin{array}{r} 0 \\ +\ 6 \\ \hline \end{array}$$

$$\begin{array}{r} 7 \\ +\ 1 \\ \hline \end{array}$$

$$\begin{array}{r} 4 \\ +\ 3 \\ \hline \end{array}$$

Review

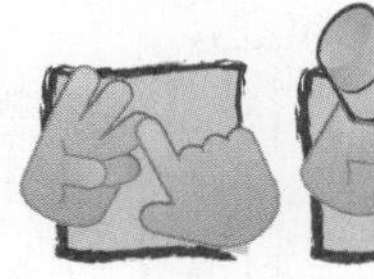

Add. Write the sum.

$$\begin{array}{r} 2 \\ +\ 2 \\ \hline \end{array} \qquad \begin{array}{r} 3 \\ +\ 2 \\ \hline \end{array} \qquad \begin{array}{r} 6 \\ +\ 2 \\ \hline \end{array}$$

$$\begin{array}{r} 6 \\ +\ 1 \\ \hline \end{array} \qquad \begin{array}{r} 4 \\ +\ 2 \\ \hline \end{array} \qquad \begin{array}{r} 3 \\ +\ 4 \\ \hline \end{array}$$

$$\begin{array}{r} 5 \\ +\ 2 \\ \hline \end{array} \qquad \begin{array}{r} 8 \\ +\ 0 \\ \hline \end{array}$$

Get Ready

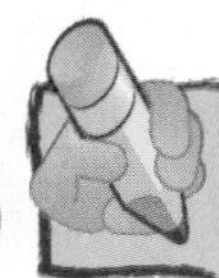

Count how many are left. Write the numbers.

How many are left?

How many are left? ______

How many are left? ______

How many are left? ______

Sail Away

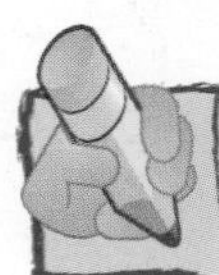

Write how many are left.

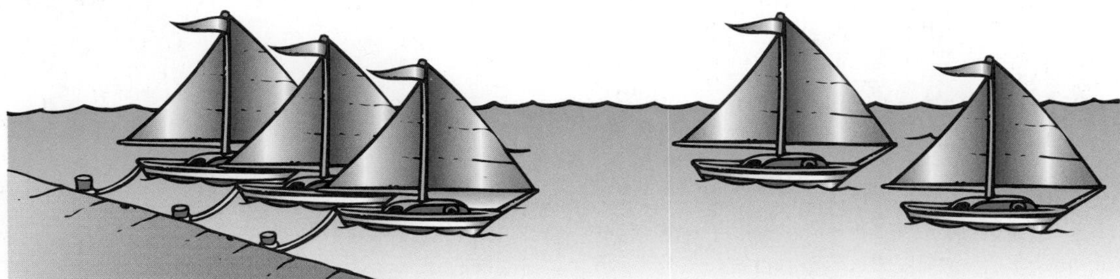

How many are left? 5 − 2 = 3

How many are left? 3 − 2 = ____

How many are left? 3 − 0 = ____

How many are left? 4 − 2 = ____

SUBTRACTION

SUBTRACTION

Bye-Bye!

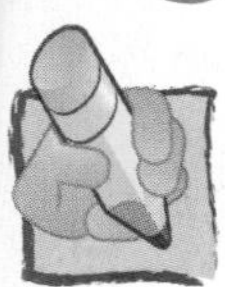

Write how many are left.

5 s. 3 say, "Bye-Bye." How many are left? 2

4 s. 1 says, "Bye-Bye." How many are left?

5 s. 5 say, "Bye-Bye." How many are left?

4 s. 2 say, "Bye-Bye." How many are left?

Get Rolling

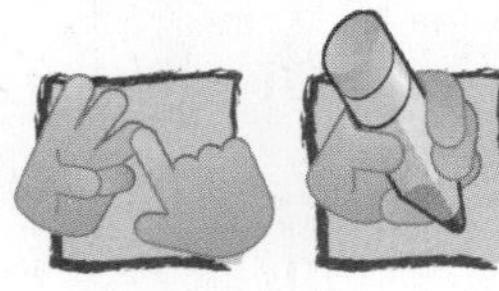

Subtract. Write how many are left.

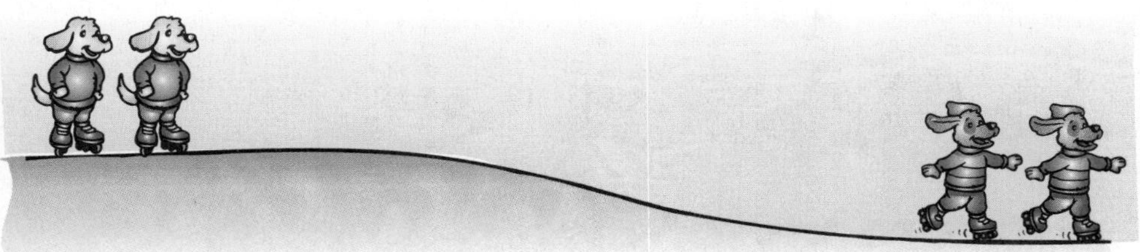

How many are left? 4 – 2 = 2

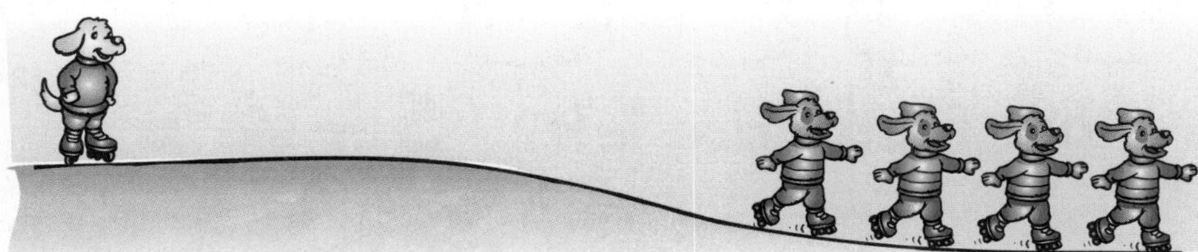

How many are left? 5 – 4 = ____

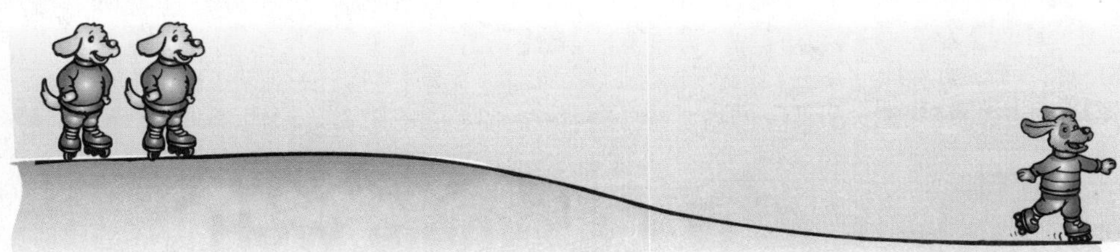

How many are left? 3 – 1 = ____

How many are left? 5 – 3 = ____

SUBTRACTION

Hats Off!

Subtract. Write how many are left.

How many are left? 5 − 3 = 2

How many are left? 5 − 4 = ____

How many are left? 3 − 1 = ____

How many are left? 4 − 3 = ____

Circle the answer. What has a head and a foot, but no body?

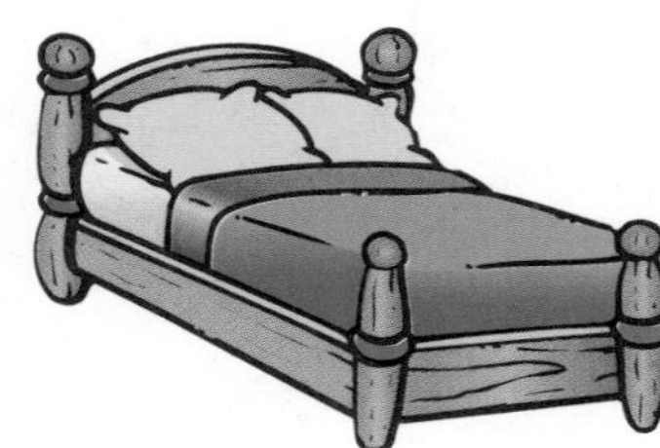

On Your Feet

Subtract. Write how many are left.

X out 1.

How many are left? 4 – 1 = ______

X out 4.

How many are left? 5 – 4 = ______

X out 2.

How many are left? 2 – 2 = ______

X out 3.

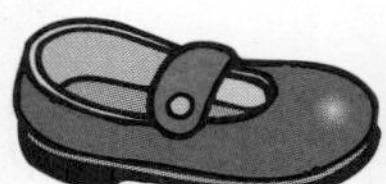 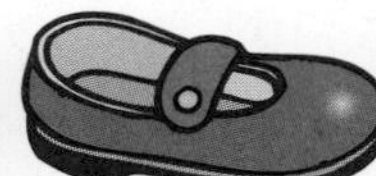  

How many are left? 4 – 3 = ______

Circle the answer. What has 2 hands but no feet?

SUBTRACTION

Away They Go

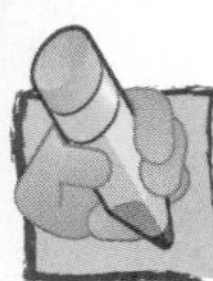

Write how many are left.

7 – 3 = 4

6 – 4 = ____

8 – 5 = ____

7 – 5 = ____

8 – 4 = ____

Take Off

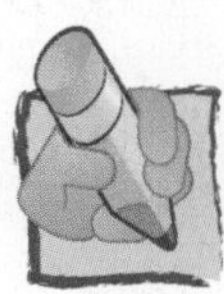

Write how many are left.

How many are left? 8 − 1 = 7

8 − 2 =

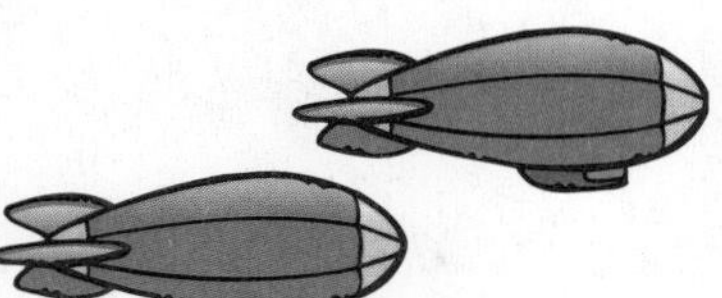

7 − 2 =

8 − 7 =

Circle the answer.

6 ✈ **s way up high.**

4 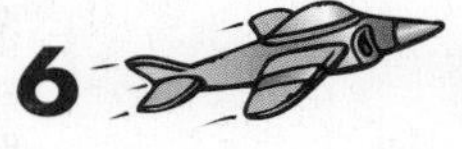 **s land.**

How many are left in the sky?

2 4

SUBTRACTION

In the Kitchen

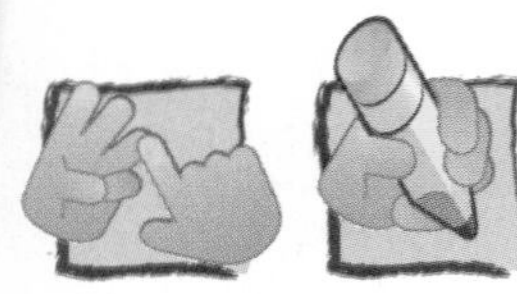

Subtract. Write the answers.

How many are left? 8 – 4 = 4

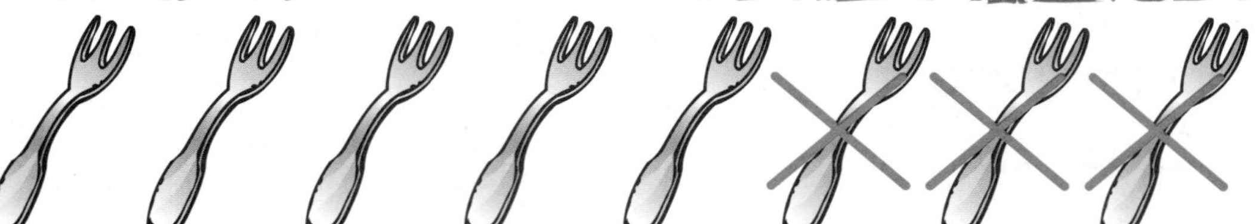

How many are left? 8 – 3 = ____

How many are left? 7 – 6 = ____

How many are left? 7 – 2 = ____

Circle the answer.

7 glasses of milk.

Oops! 5 glasses spill.

How many glasses are left?

3 2

Keys, Please

Cross out and subtract. Write the answers.

X out 6.

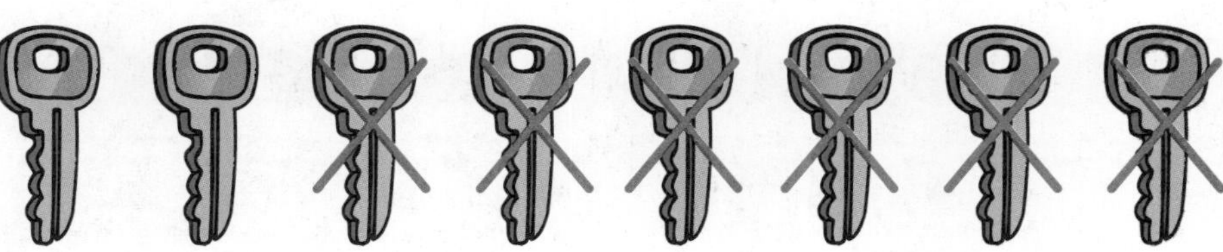

How many are left? 8 – 6 = 2

X out 5.

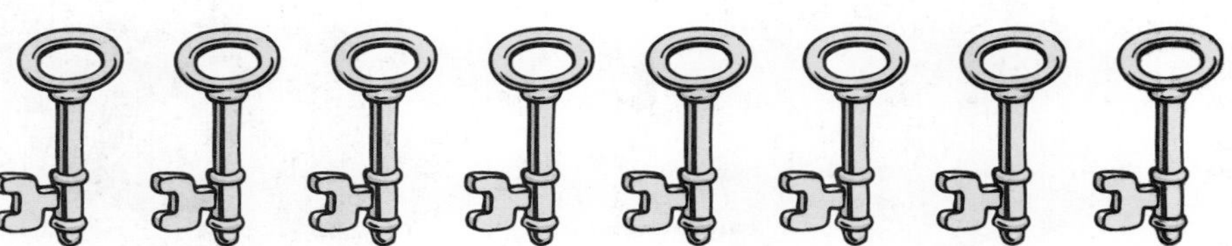

How many are left? 8 – 5 = ____

X out 3.

How many are left? 7 – 3 = ____

X out 6.

How many are left? 7 – 6 = ____

X out 2.

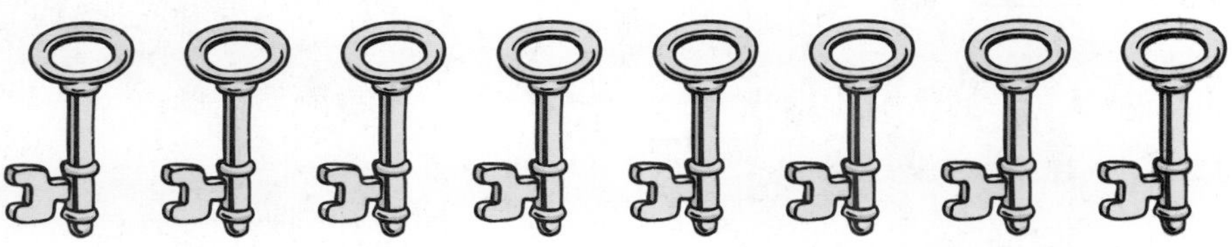

How many are left? 8 – 2 = ____

SUBTRACTION

Top to Bottom

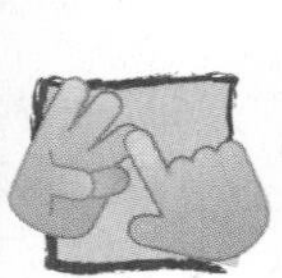

Subtract. Write the answers.

8
− 5

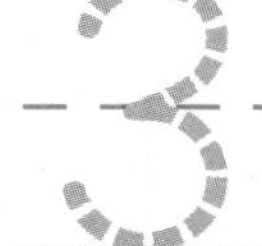

How many are left? ____

8
− 7

How many are left? ____

8
− 6

How many are left? ____

7
− 5

How many are left? ____

7
− 4

How many are left? ____

8
− 4

How many are left? ____

7
− 3

How many are left? ____

Wind It Up

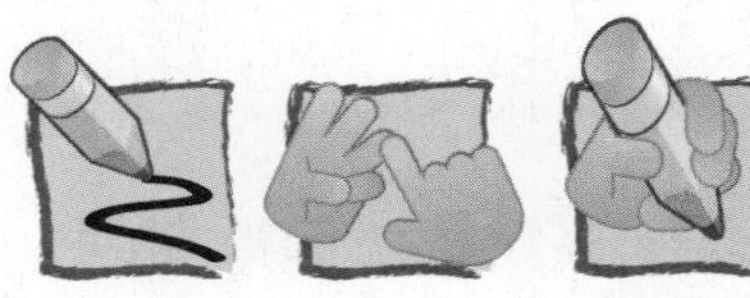

**Cross out and subtract.
Write the answers.**

$$\begin{array}{r} 6 \\ -\ 5 \\ \hline \end{array}$$

How many are left? ____

$$\begin{array}{r} 8 \\ -\ 3 \\ \hline \end{array}$$

How many are left? ____

$$\begin{array}{r} 7 \\ -\ 6 \\ \hline \end{array}$$

How many are left? ____

$$\begin{array}{r} 6 \\ -\ 6 \\ \hline \end{array}$$

How many are left? ____

$$\begin{array}{r} 8 \\ -\ 4 \\ \hline \end{array}$$

How many are left? ____

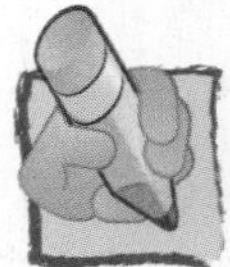

Write the answer.

$$\begin{array}{r} 8 \\ -\ 5 \\ \hline \end{array}$$

How many are left? ____

Review

2= 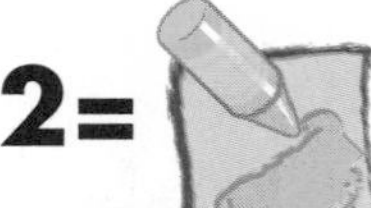 3= 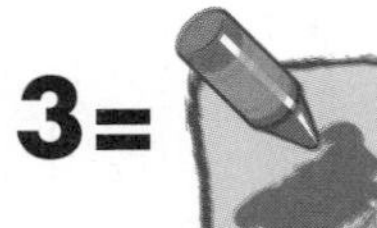 4= 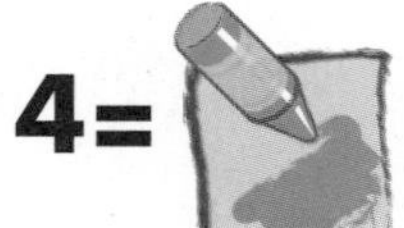 5= 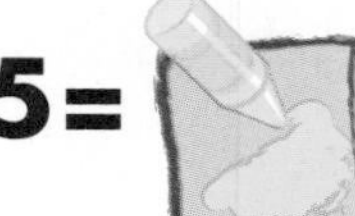

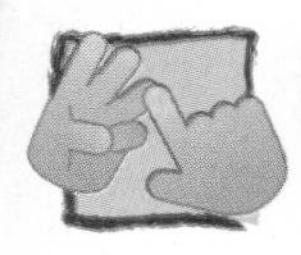 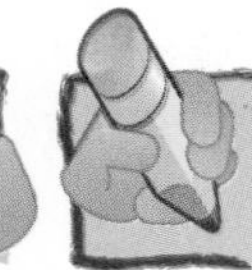

Subtract and write each answer. Color the spaces to match the answers in the color key.

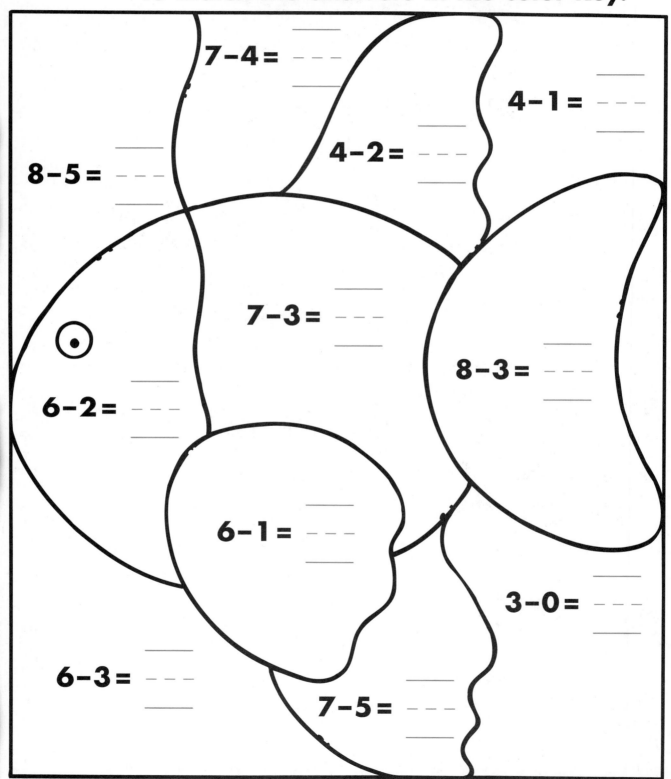

7–4 = ___

4–1 = ___

4–2 = ___

8–5 = ___

7–3 = ___

8–3 = ___

6–2 = ___

6–1 = ___

3–0 = ___

6–3 = ___

7–5 = ___

Hands-on activities to help your child in school!

ADDITION WITH SUMS THROUGH 10

Adding 0-10: pages 67-72, 74-75, 76-82
Continuing Number Patterns: page 73
Linking Math to Literature: pages 77-80

In Month 2, the concepts of addition and subtraction were introduced. Here in Month 3, your child will refine his or her skills by working on addition facts through 10 and learning about the relationship between addition and subtraction. Extensive practice with basic facts will help the child to commit the sums to memory.

- ❑ Complete the worksheets.
- ❑ Give your child up to 10 buttons and ask him or her to count the buttons and write the number. Then say, "Write as many different combinations of buttons as possible to make the number." For example: 5 buttons and 5 buttons or 3 buttons and 7 buttons. Repeat the activity for several other numbers.
- ❑ Make your own *color-rubbing doubles*. Give your child a piece of paper folded in half. Have him or her unfold the paper and color 4 dots on one side of the fold; then refold it and rub firmly to transfer the colored dots onto the other side of the fold. When the paper is opened, have your child write an addition sentence that describes the picture (e.g., 4 + 4).
- ❑ Play "Turnaround Time." Write an addition fact (e.g., 4 + 5) and its turnaround fact (e.g., 5 + 4) on two sides of a flash card. Once 10 cards have been made, flash them one at a time. Your child must respond with the turnaround fact for the fact you flash.

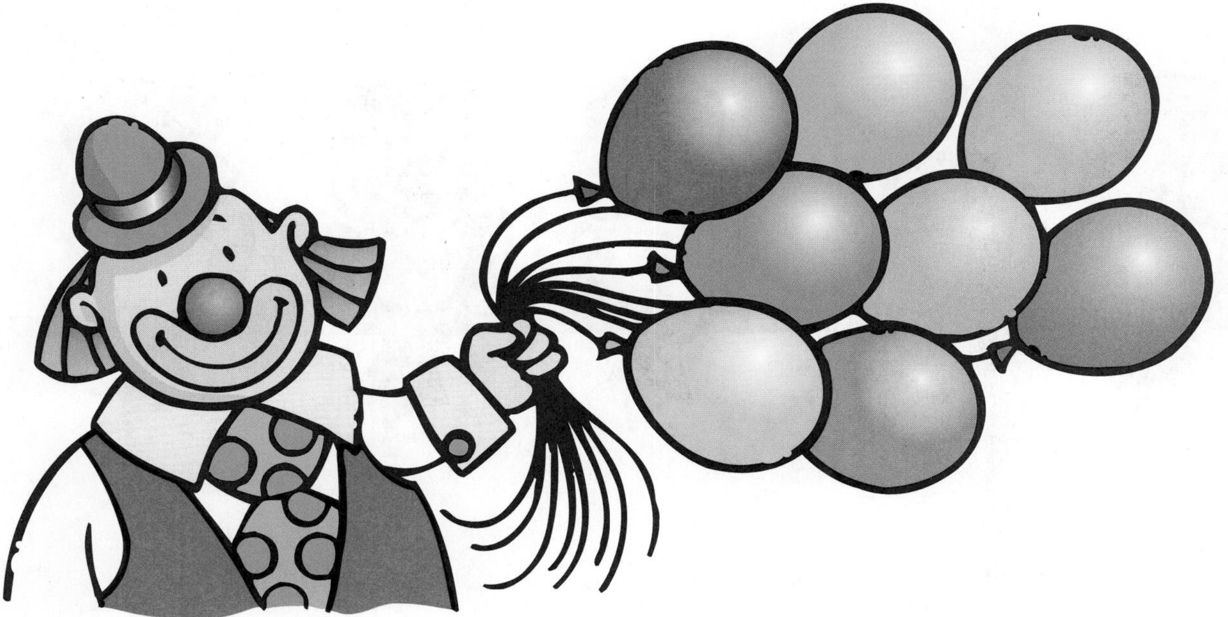

Subtracting 0-10: pages 84-96
Solving Story Problems: pages 83, 92-93
Relate Addition and Subtraction: page 91

In this month, subtraction facts through 10 are presented along with subtraction problem-solving activities. Your child will also learn that addition and subtraction are related because they are inverse operations.

- ❑ Complete the worksheets.
- ❑ Play "Add or Subtract?" Tell a story such as, "3 geese were in a pond. 2 flew away. How many geese were left?" Challenge your child to tell whether the problem could be solved using addition or subtraction. After you tell several stories, challenge your child to tell a story while you provide the operation needed to solve.
- ❑ Make a fact family. Display 6 teaspoons and 4 tablespoons on a table. Have your child write two addition sentences to describe the spoons. Remove the tablespoons and have your child write a subtraction sentence to tell what happened. Replace the tablespoons and repeat, removing the teaspoons. Explain that the four sentences make up a fact family because they all have the same numbers. Repeat the activity for other combinations of 10.

Cowboy Land

5 + 3 = 8 in all

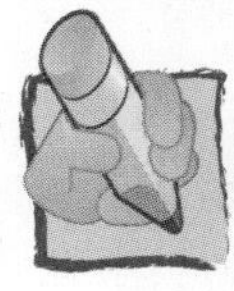

Write how many.

 + 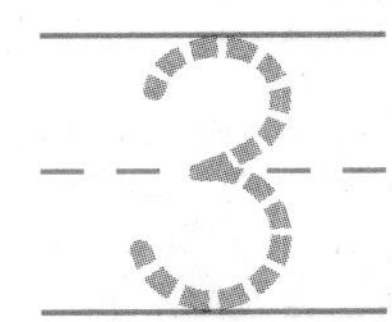 = ____ in all

____ + ____ = ____ in all

____ + ____ = ____ in all

ADDITION

Tennis, Anyone?

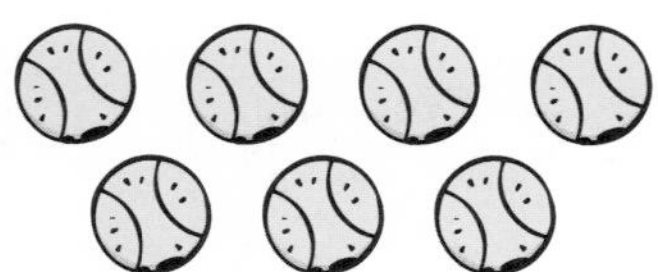

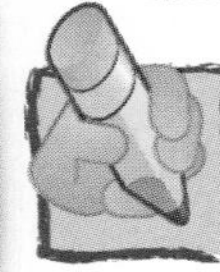

7 + 3 = 10 in all

Write how many.

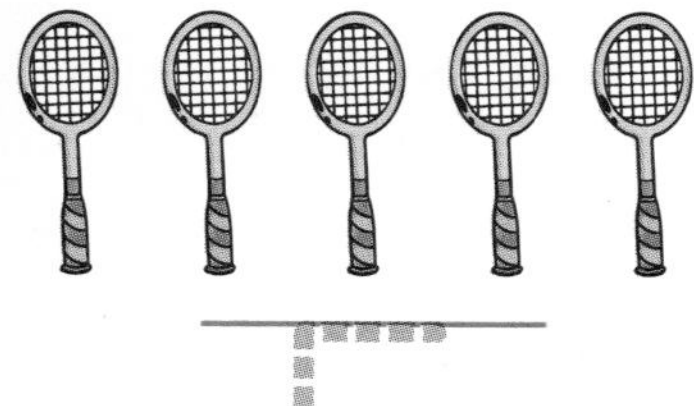

5 + 5 = ____ in all

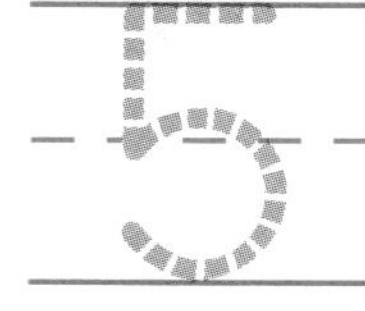

____ + ____ = ____ in all

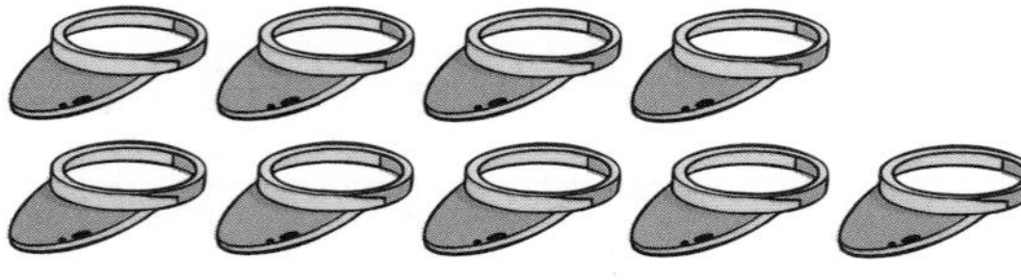

____ + ____ = ____ in all

____ + ____ = ____ in all

Some Fish

3 6

3 + 6 = 9

Circle the correct number sentence.

5 + 4 = 9

5 + 5 = 10

7 + 3 = 10

8 + 2 = 10

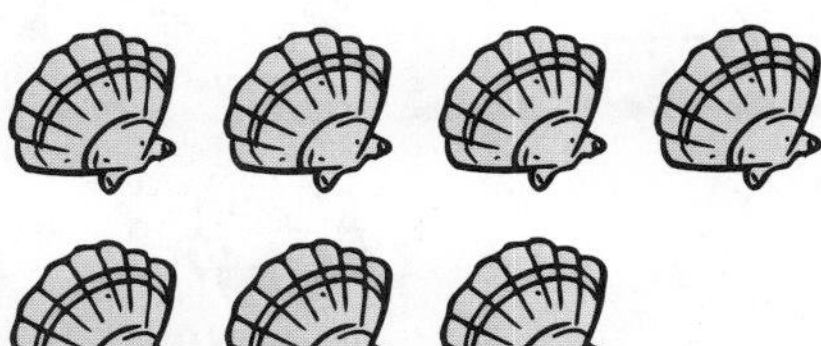

6 + 3 = 9

6 + 2 = 8

0 + 7 = 7

6 + 1 = 7

3 + 6 = 9

3 + 5 = 8

Vegetable Garden

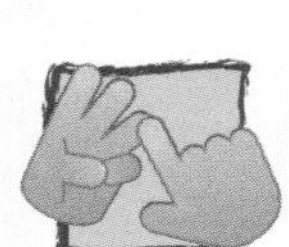

Add to find how many in all. Write the answers.

5 + 5 = ____

4 + 3 = ____

4 + 6 = ____

9 + 1 = ____

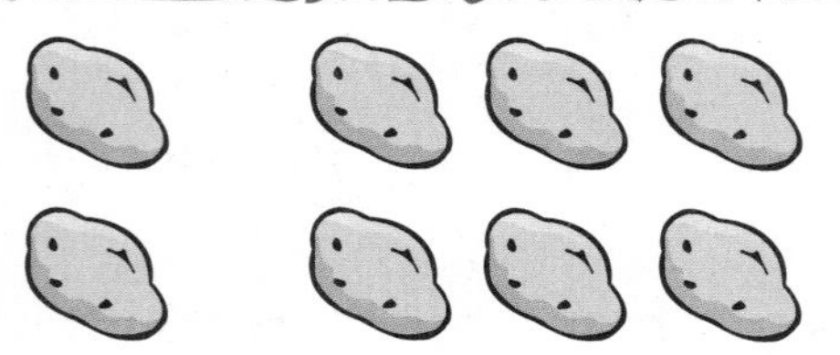

2 + 6 = ____

3 + 3 = ____

Hats Off!

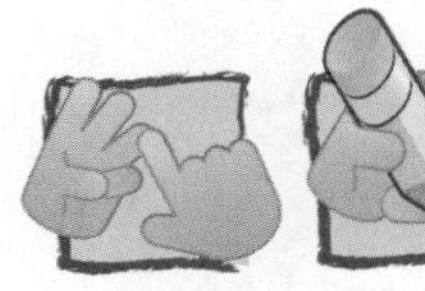

Add. Write the answers.

$$\begin{array}{r} 7 \\ +\ 3 \\ \hline \end{array}$$

$$\begin{array}{r} 5 \\ +\ 4 \\ \hline \end{array}$$

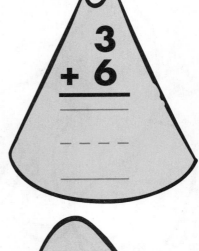

$$\begin{array}{r} 0 \\ +\ 9 \\ \hline \end{array}$$

$$\begin{array}{r} 5 \\ +\ 2 \\ \hline \end{array}$$

$$\begin{array}{r} 3 \\ +\ 6 \\ \hline \end{array}$$

$$\begin{array}{r} 2 \\ +\ 8 \\ \hline \end{array}$$

$$\begin{array}{r} 3 \\ +\ 5 \\ \hline \end{array}$$

$$\begin{array}{r} 6 \\ +\ 1 \\ \hline \end{array}$$

Review

Color the sums according to the code.

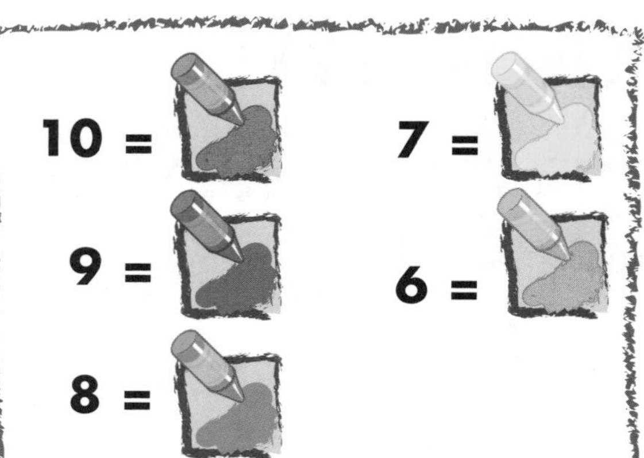

6 + 3

7 + 1

3 + 4

0 + 7

4 + 4

6 +4

4 + 5

5 + 4

1 + 9

5 + 5

8 +2

6 + 0

7 + 3

5 + 1

2 + 4

9 + 1

6 + 2

3 + 3

6 + 1

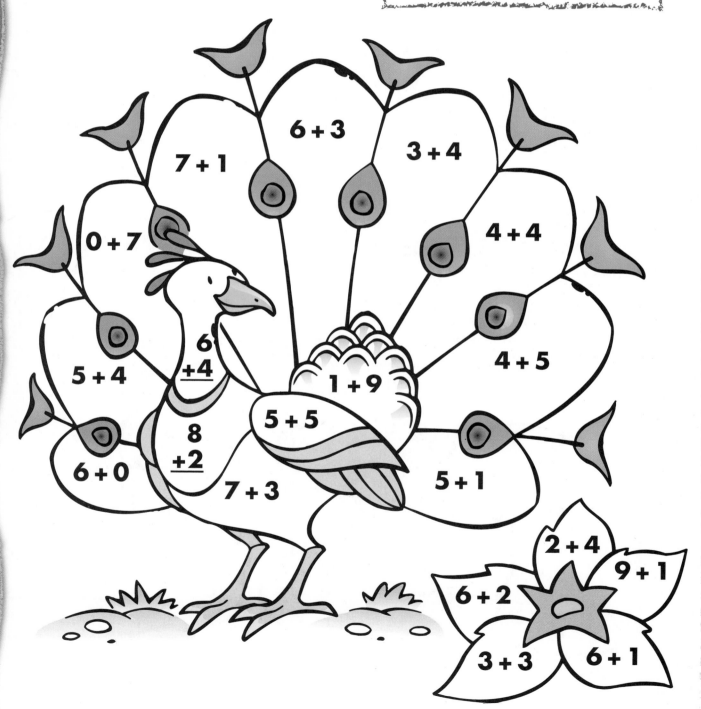

Patterns

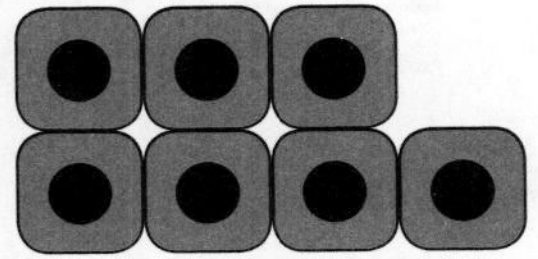

7 + 1 = 8   8 + 1 = 9   9 + 1 = 10

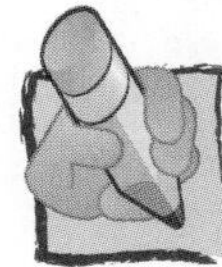

Add 1. Write each number.

0, 1, 2, ___, ___, 5, ___

Add 2. Write each number.

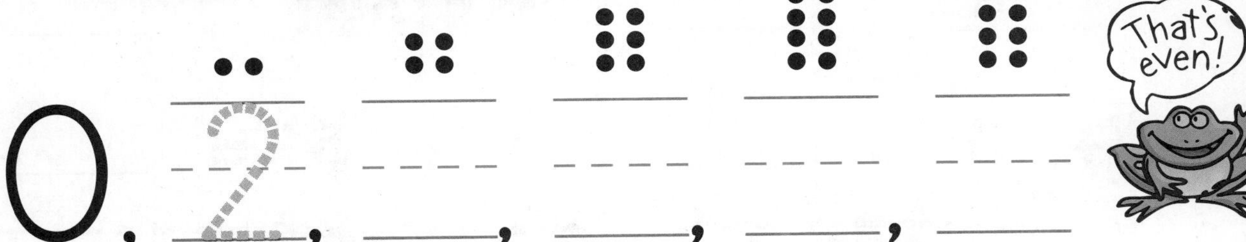

That's even!

Add 2. Write each number.

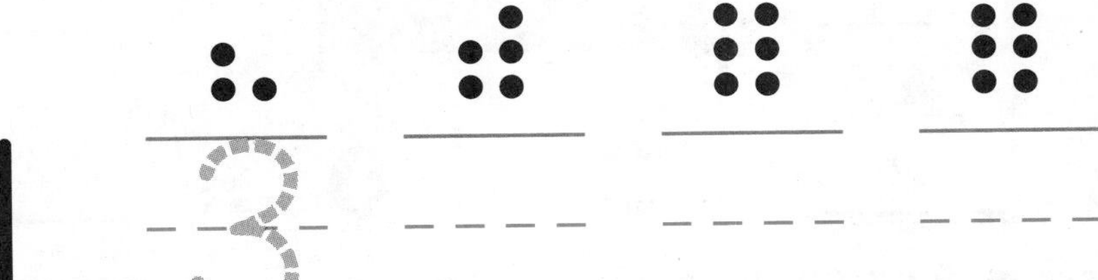

Color even numbers red and odd numbers blue.

1	2	3	4	5
6	7	8	9	10

Recognizing and continuing number patterns

ADDITION

ADDITION

Domino Doubles

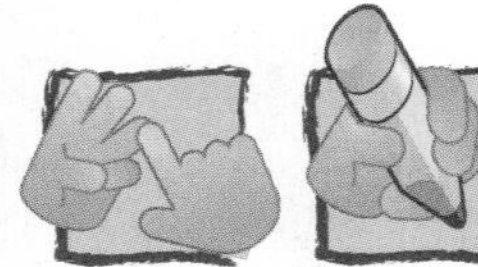

Add. Write the answers.

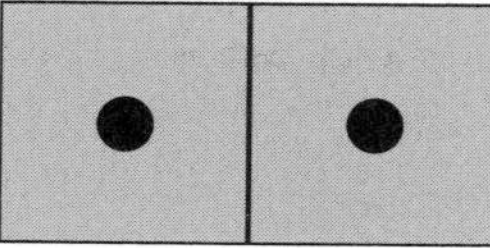

1 + 1 = ____

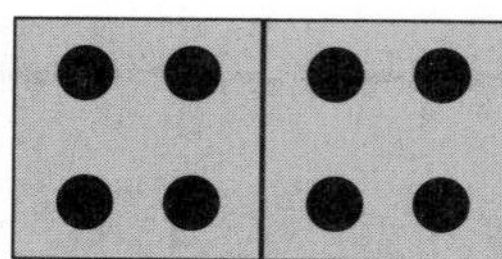

4 + 4 = ____

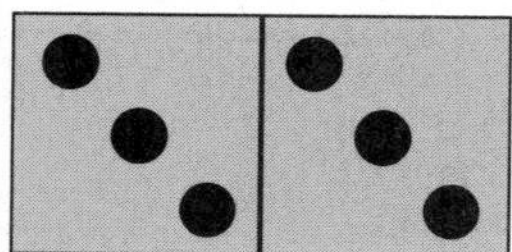

3 + 3 = ____

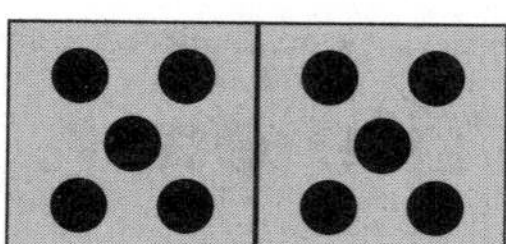

5 + 5 = ____

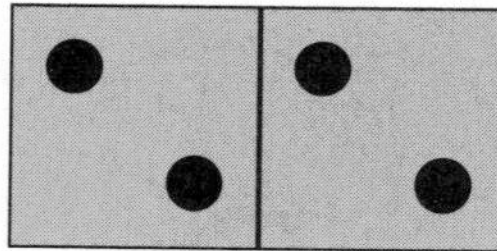

2 + 2 = ____

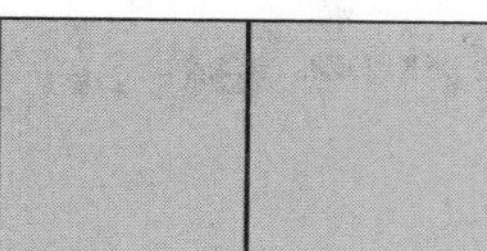

0 + 0 = ____

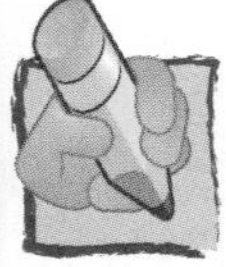

Write the answer.

2  **s. How many**  **s?** ____

Finding sums for doubles

Turn Arounds

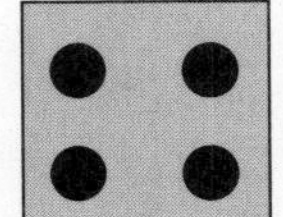

4

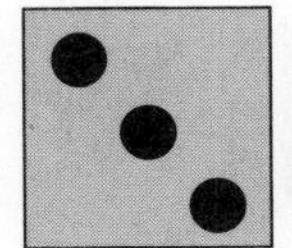

+3

7

3

+4

7

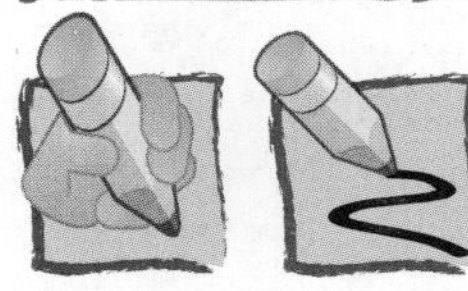

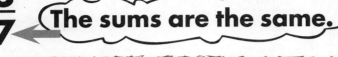

Write the sums. Then, match the same sums.

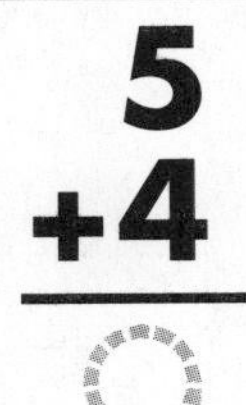

5 + 4 = 9	2 + 6 =	3 + 6 =	4 + 6 =
3 + 7 =	4 + 5 =	5 + 5 =	6 + 3 =
6 + 2 =	7 + 0 =	6 + 4 =	5 + 5 =
0 + 7 =	7 + 3 =		

Using turnaround addition facts to find sums

Wish You Were Here

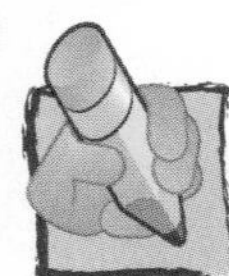

Solve and write the answers.

Rita sent 3  s.

Rob sent 6  s.

How many 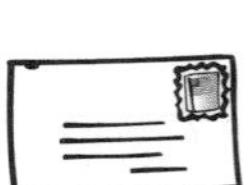 s in all?

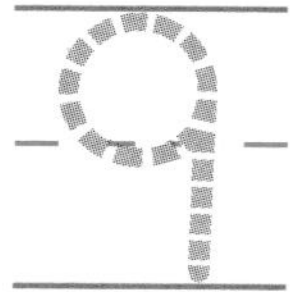

Kate got 6  s.

Ken got 2  s.

How many  s in all?

Liz has 4 s.

Len has 5 s.

How many s in all?

Zack has 7 s.

Matt has 2 s.

How many s in all?

Parents: Remove pages 77-80 from this book. See directions for making mini storybooks on the inside of the front cover.

And guess what happened?

The Lost Mitten

Long ago, in a very cold land, a little boy lost a mitten in the snow.

Into that mitten crawled 1 cold kitten.

Into that mitten hopped 1 tiny flea.

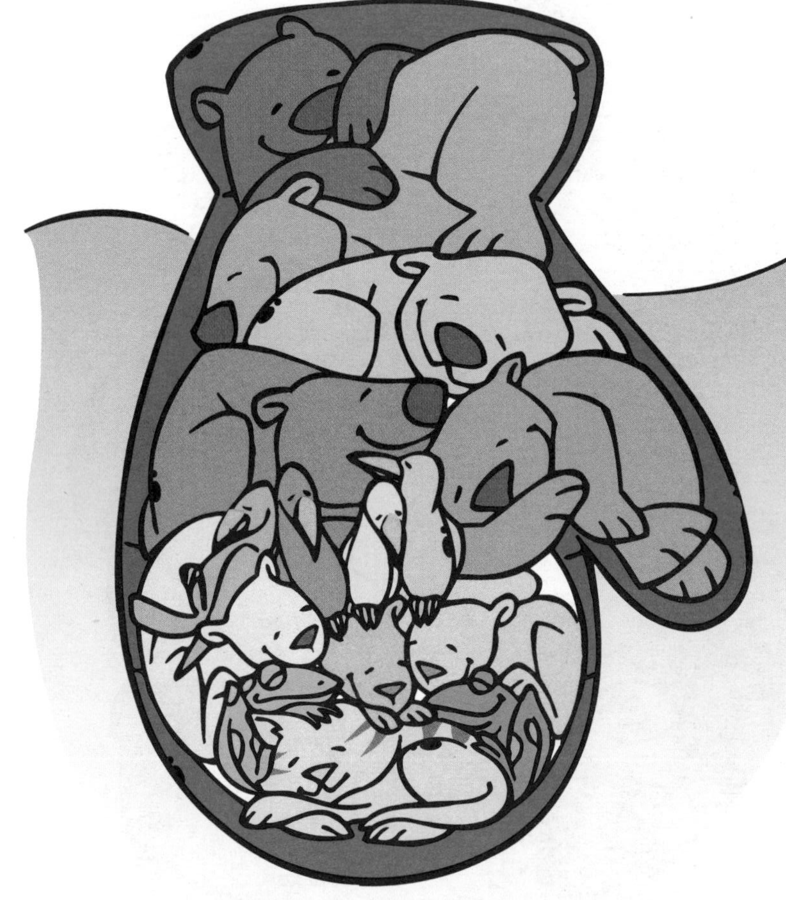

15 + 1 = 16 in all

Into that mitten burst
5 brown bears.

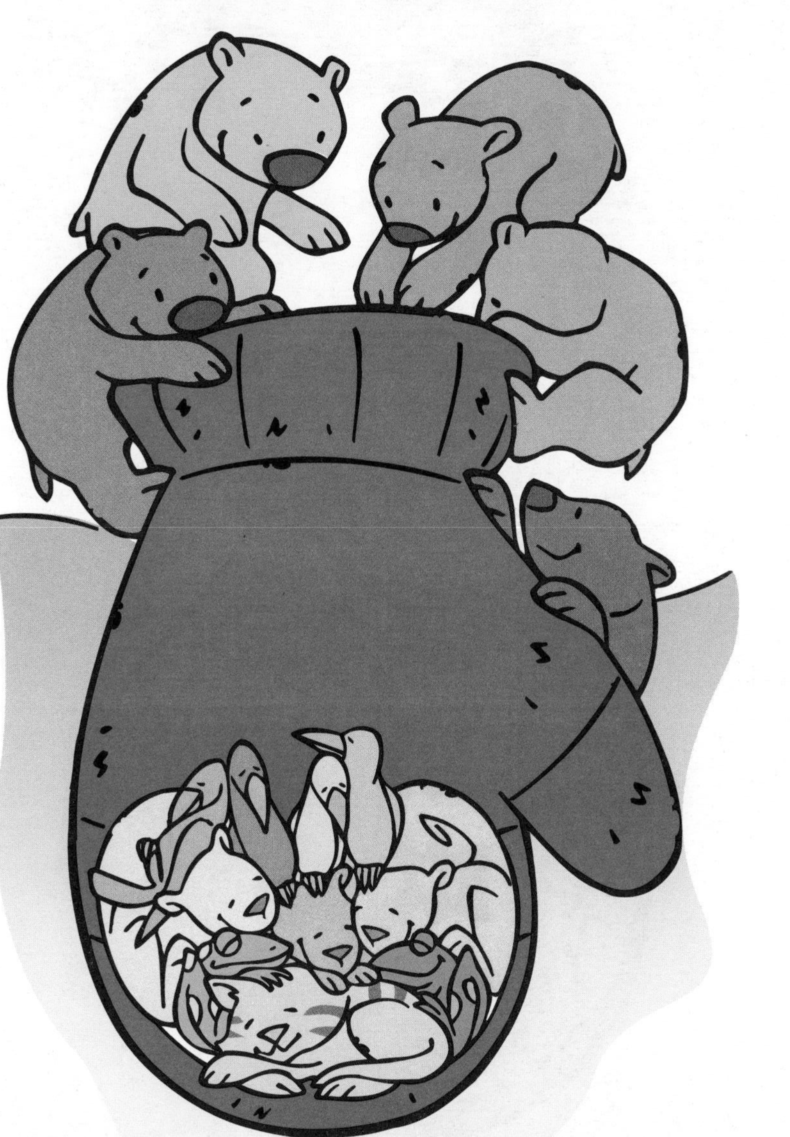

10 + 5 = 15 in all

Into that mitten hopped
2 freezing frogs.

1 + 2 = 3 in all

Into that mitten squeezed
3 squeaky squirrels.

3 + 3 = 6 in all

Into that mitten crowded
4 creaky crows.

6 + 4 = 10 in all

Practice Test

I can add across.

4 + 3 = 7 ○ 6 ● 7 ○ 8

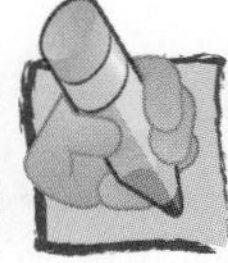

Add. Fill in the circle next to the correct answer.

GREAT JOB!

A. 3 + 4 = ____ ○ 5 ○ 6 ○ 7

E. 1 + 9 = ____ ○ 8 ○ 6 ○ 10

B. 5 + 1 = ____ ○ 6 ○ 7 ○ 8

F. 4 + 4 = ____ ○ 6 ○ 7 ○ 8

C. 0 + 6 = ____ ○ 0 ○ 6 ○ 1

G. 6 + 3 = ____ ○ 9 ○ 10 ○ 11

D. 7 + 2 = ____ ○ 7 ○ 8 ○ 9

H. 3 + 2 = ____ ○ 4 ○ 5 ○ 6

Practice Test

I can add up and down.

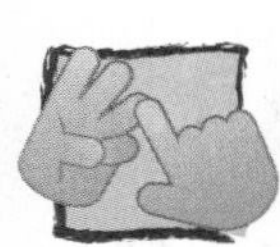
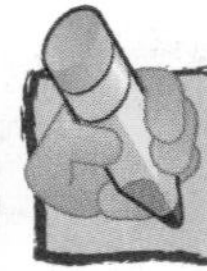

Add. Fill in the circle next to the correct answer.

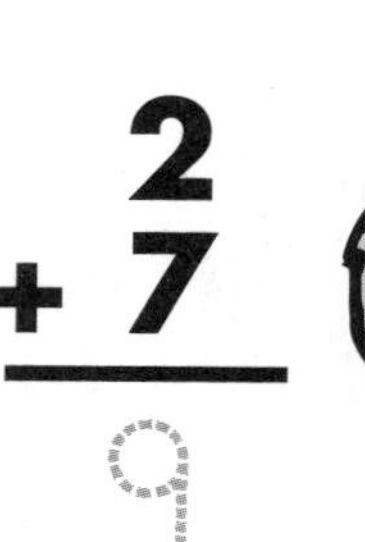

$$\begin{array}{r} 2 \\ +\ 7 \\ \hline 9 \end{array}$$

○ 7
○ 8
● 9

A.

$$\begin{array}{r} 9 \\ +\ 1 \\ \hline \end{array}$$

○ 9
○ 10
○ 11

E.

$$\begin{array}{r} 4 \\ +\ 5 \\ \hline \end{array}$$

○ 8
○ 9
○ 10

B.

$$\begin{array}{r} 5 \\ +\ 3 \\ \hline \end{array}$$

○ 6
○ 7
○ 8

F.

$$\begin{array}{r} 6 \\ +\ 2 \\ \hline \end{array}$$

○ 6
○ 7
○ 8

C.

$$\begin{array}{r} 0 \\ +\ 9 \\ \hline \end{array}$$

○ 8
○ 9
○ 10

G.

$$\begin{array}{r} 2 \\ +\ 6 \\ \hline \end{array}$$

○ 7
○ 8
○ 9

D.

$$\begin{array}{r} 3 \\ +\ 7 \\ \hline \end{array}$$

○ 10
○ 11
○ 12

Toy Stories

Read the story. Write the answer.

4  s on the 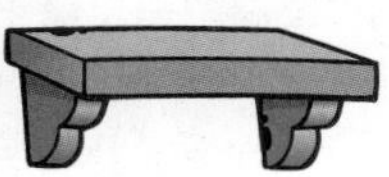

3  s fall off.

How many  s are left?  ______

8  s on the 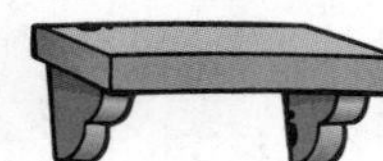 ______

5 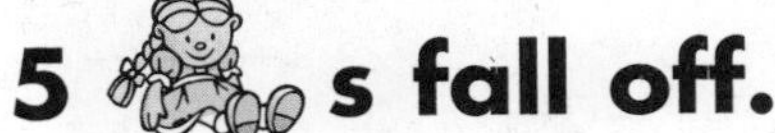 s fall off. ______

How many   s are left? ______

8  s on the 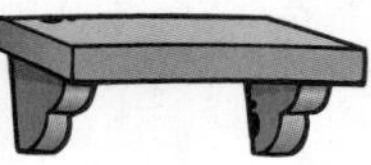 ______

7 s roll off. ______

How many  s are left? ______

6  s on the 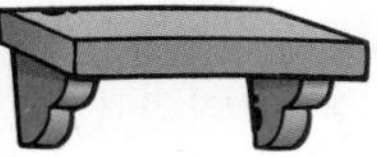 ______

3 s roll off. ______

How many  s are left? ______

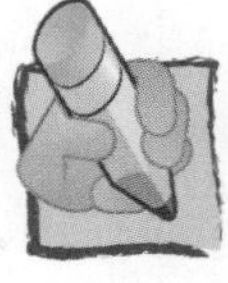

Write the answer.

7 toy cars all in a row. ______

6 can go fast. ______

How many go slow? ______

Fly Away

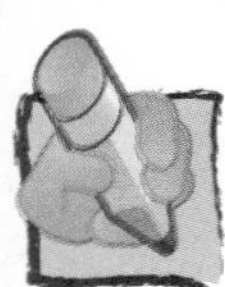

Write how many are left.

10 – 3 = 7

10 – 8 = ____

9 – 6 = ____

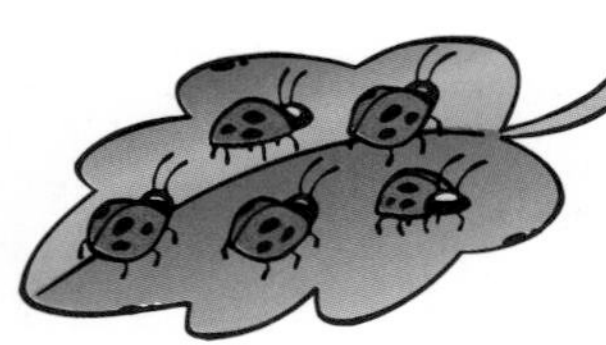

10 – 5 = ____

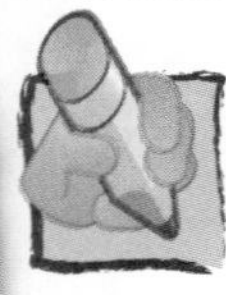

Write the answer.

9  **–** **7**  **=** ____ 

Clown Around

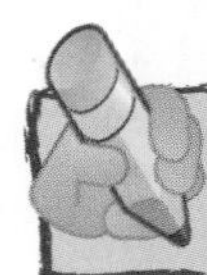

Write how many are left.

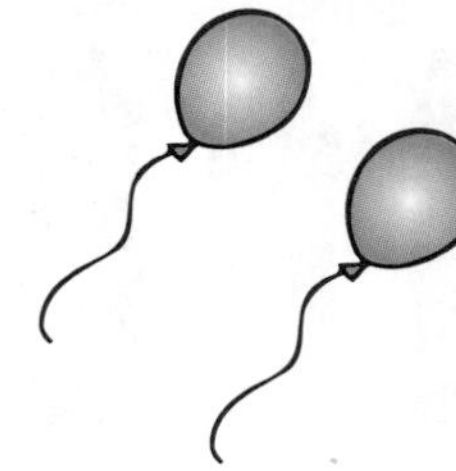

10 – 2 = 8

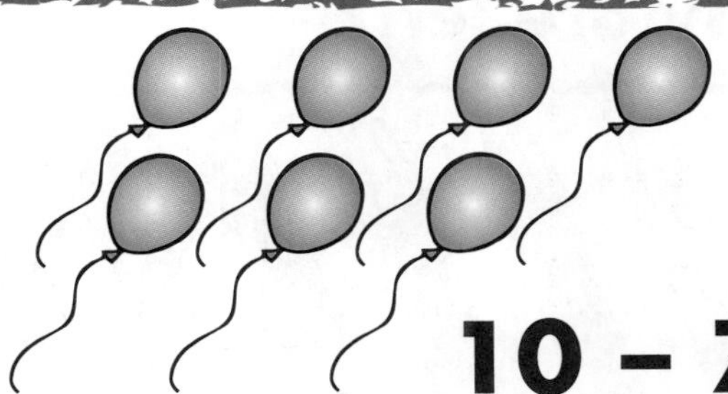

10 – 7 = ____

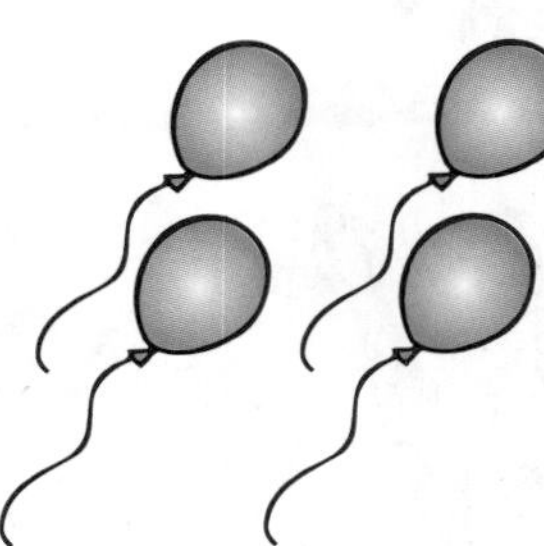

10 – 4 = ____

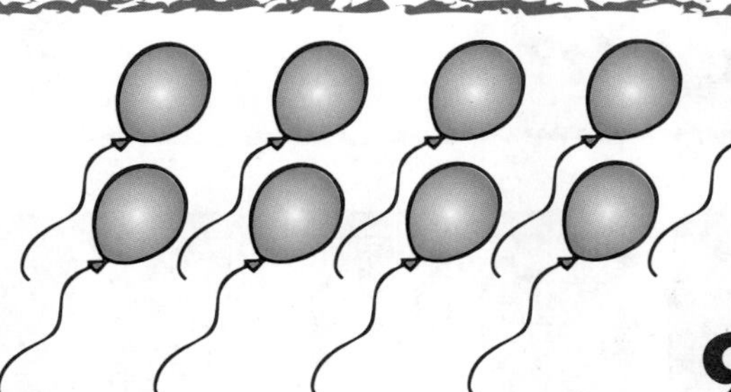

9 – 9 = ____

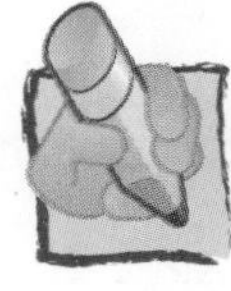

Write the answer.

10  **–** **8**  **=** ____ 

Color Away

Subtract. Write the answers.

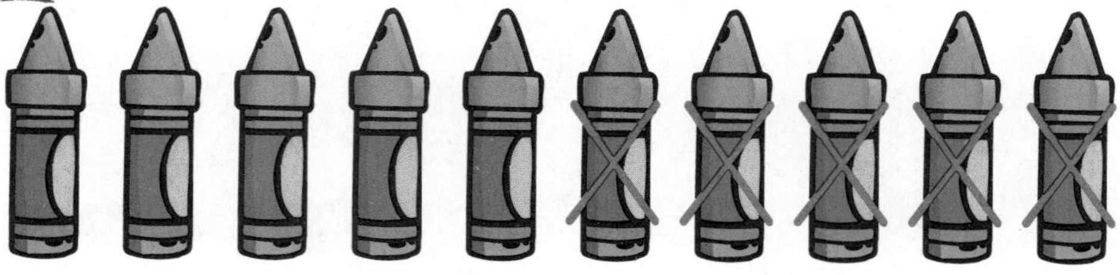

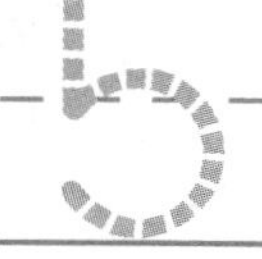

How many are left? **10 – 5 =** 5

How many are left? **10 – 6 =** ____

How many are left? **9 – 5 =** ____

How many are left? **8 – 6 =** ____

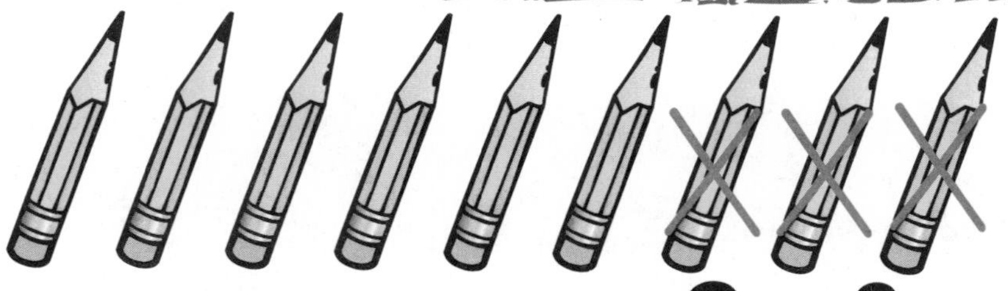

How many are left? **9 – 3 =** ____

Subtracting numbers 0 -10 from numbers to 10

Make Music

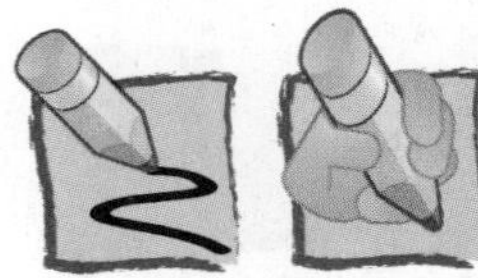

Cross out and subtract.
Write the answers.

X out 7.

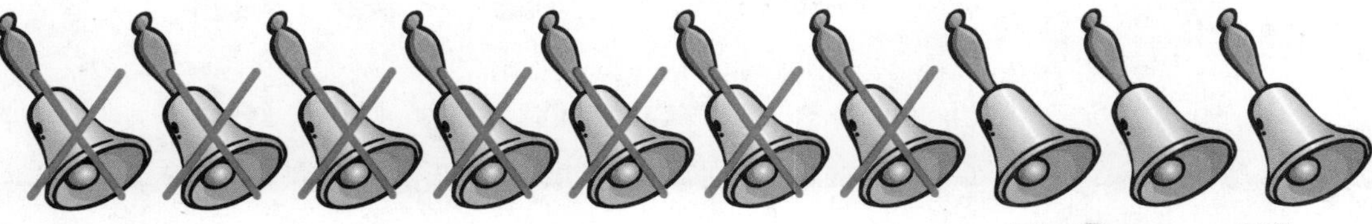

How many are left? **10 – 7 =** 3

X out 7.

How many are left? **9 – 7 =** ____

X out 8.

How many are left? **8 – 8 =** ____

X out 5.

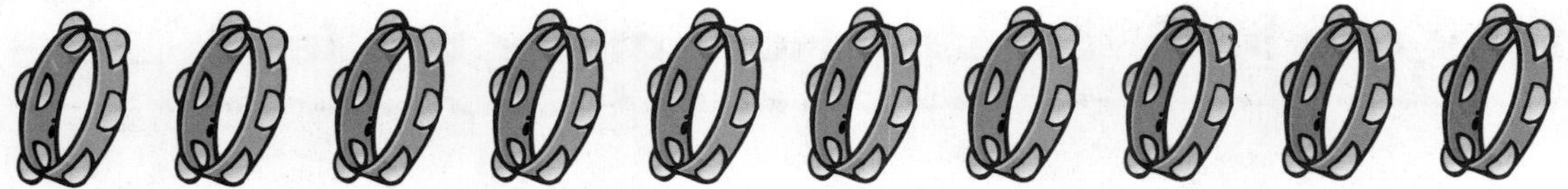

How many are left? **10 – 5 =** ____

Write the answer.

10 small bells rang so fine.
1 bell fell. **Now there are ____ .**

SUBTRACTION

Good and Fruity

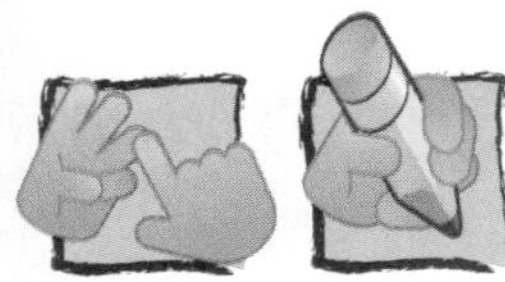

Subtract. Write the answers.

$$\begin{array}{r} 10 \\ -\ 4 \\ \hline \end{array}$$

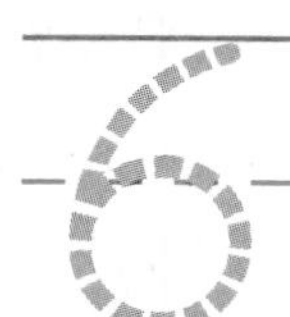

How many are left? ______

$$\begin{array}{r} 9 \\ -\ 6 \\ \hline \end{array}$$

How many are left? ______

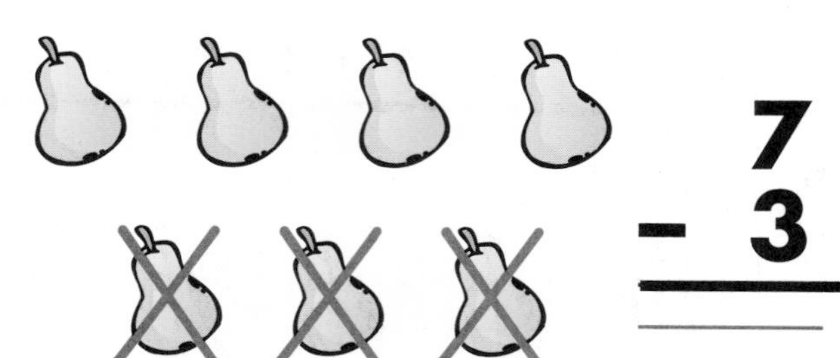

$$\begin{array}{r} 7 \\ -\ 3 \\ \hline \end{array}$$

How many are left? ______

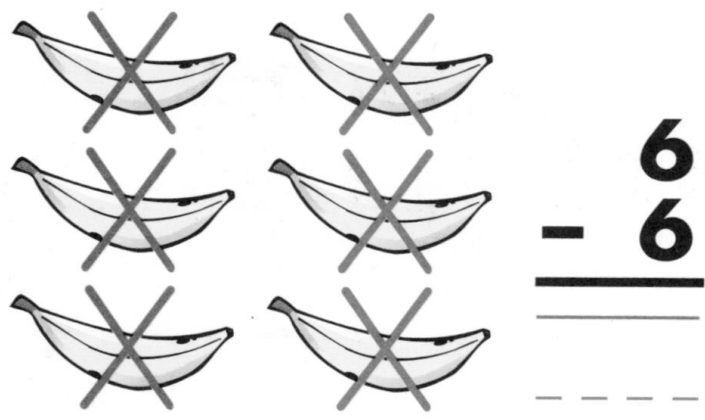

$$\begin{array}{r} 6 \\ -\ 6 \\ \hline \end{array}$$

How many are left? ______

$$\begin{array}{r} 10 \\ -\ 2 \\ \hline \end{array}$$

How many are left? ______

Circle the answer.

What has a mouth but cannot talk?

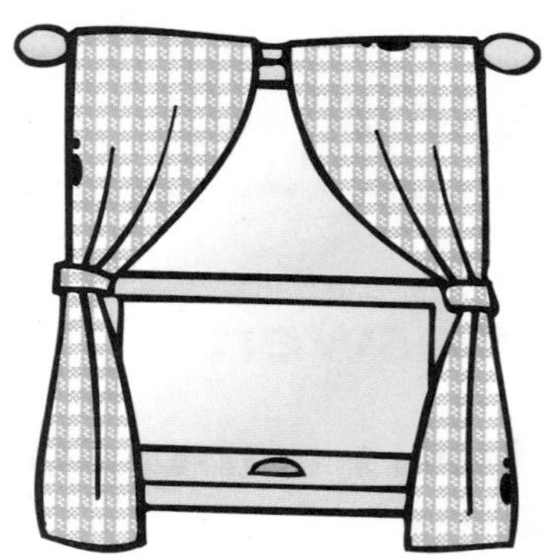

Go Fish

Cross out and subtract.
Write the answers.

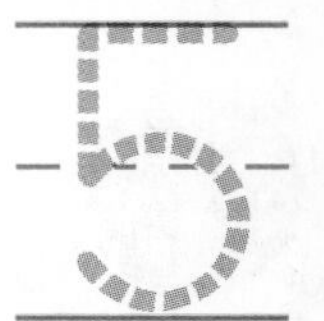

$$\begin{array}{r} 9 \\ -\ 4 \\ \hline 5 \end{array}$$

How many are left? ____

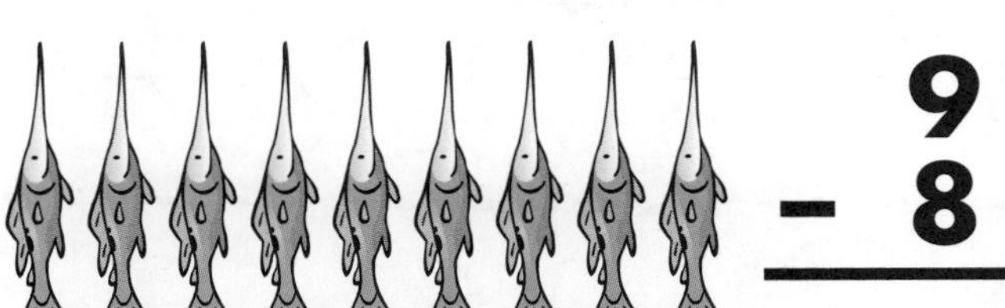

$$\begin{array}{r} 9 \\ -\ 8 \\ \hline \end{array}$$

How many are left? ____

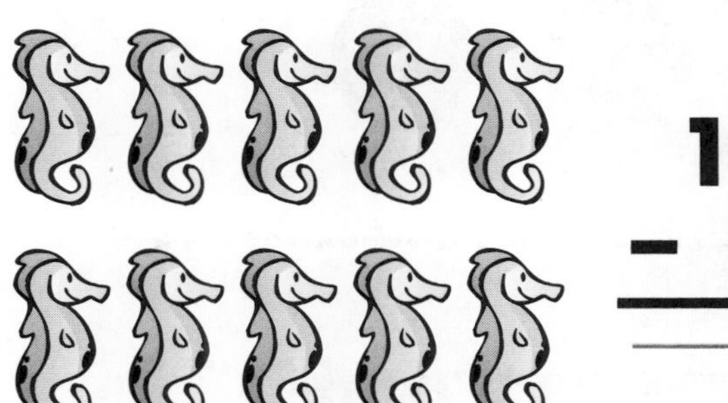

$$\begin{array}{r} 10 \\ -\ 6 \\ \hline \end{array}$$

How many are left? ____

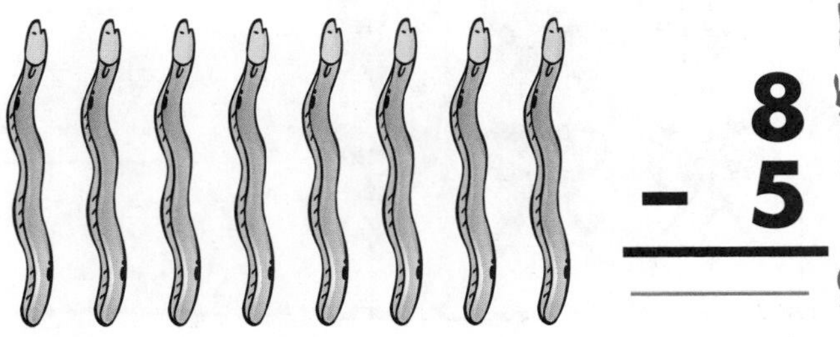

$$\begin{array}{r} 8 \\ -\ 5 \\ \hline \end{array}$$

How many are left? ____

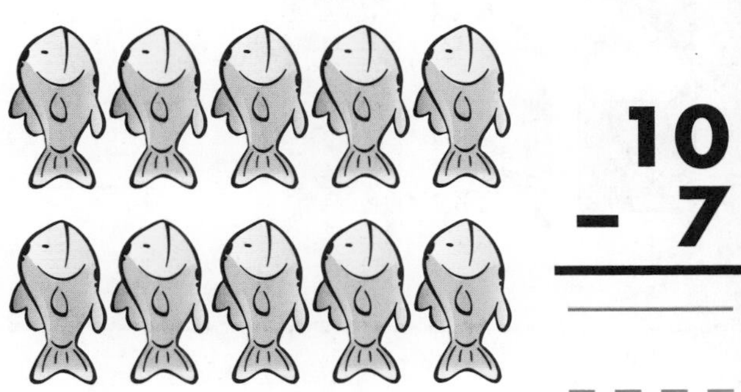

$$\begin{array}{r} 10 \\ -\ 7 \\ \hline \end{array}$$

How many are left? ____

Circle the answer.

What runs but never gets tired?

SUBTRACTION

Shape Up

Subtract. Write the answers.

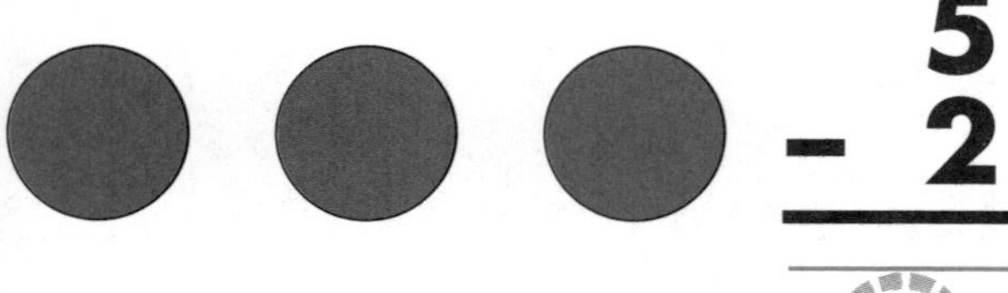

$$\begin{array}{r} 5 \\ -\ 2 \\ \hline 3 \end{array}$$

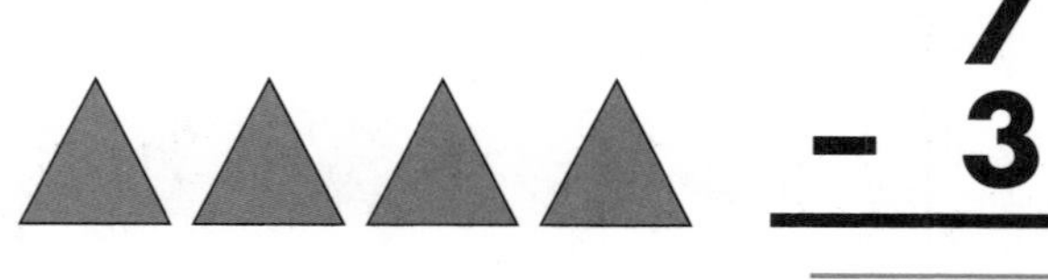

$$\begin{array}{r} 7 \\ -\ 3 \\ \hline \end{array}$$

$$\begin{array}{r} 9 \\ -\ 7 \\ \hline \end{array}$$

$$\begin{array}{r} 10 \\ -\ 5 \\ \hline \end{array}$$

$$\begin{array}{r} 6 \\ -\ 0 \\ \hline \end{array}$$

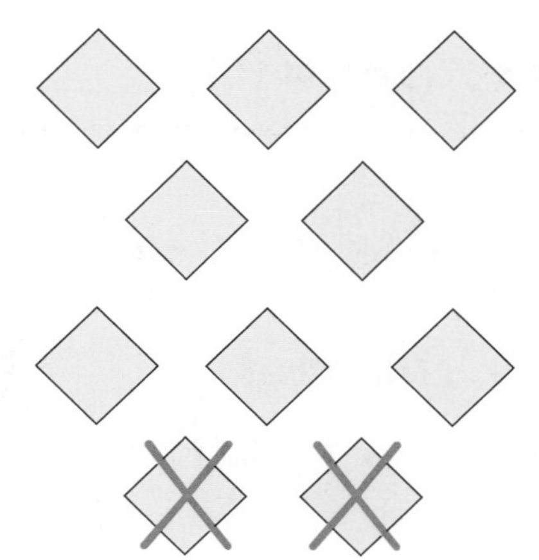

$$\begin{array}{r} 10 \\ -\ 2 \\ \hline \end{array}$$

Check It Out

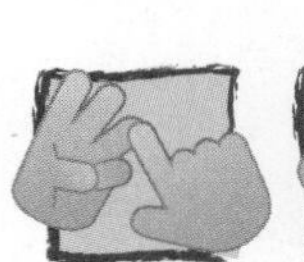

Subtract. Then add to check.
Write each answer.

5 − 3 = 2 ✔ 2 + 3 = 5

9 − 5 = ____ ✔ 4 + 5 = ____

6 − 4 = ____ ✔ 2 + 4 = ____

10 − 3 = ____ ✔ 7 + 3 = ____

9 − 6 = ____ ✔ 3 + 6 = ____

SUBTRACTION

Subtraction Stories

Read each story. Write the answer.

5 

4 run away.

How many are left? **5 – 4 = ____**

9 

3 go out.

How many are left? **9 – 3 = ____**

10 

7 get picked.

How many are left? **10 – 7 = ____**

8 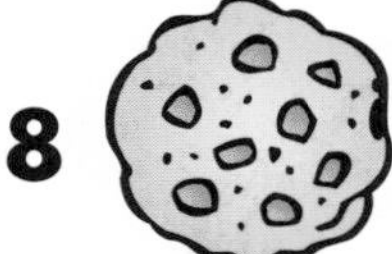

4 are eaten.

How many are left? **8 – 4 = ____**

Many Pennies

 A penny is 1¢.

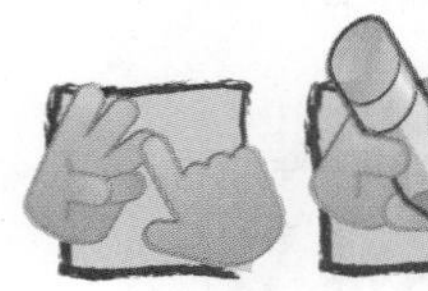 

Subtract pennies.
How much money is left?

I have  ______

I buy 

10¢ – 8¢ = ______ ¢

I have  ______

I buy

9¢ – 5¢ = ______ ¢

I have  ______

I buy 

8¢ – 4¢ = ______ ¢

I have  ______

I buy 

10¢ – 10¢ = ______ ¢

Review

Subtract. Write the answers.

Practice Test

I can subtract across.

7 − 5 = 2 ❍ 4 ❍ 3 ● 2

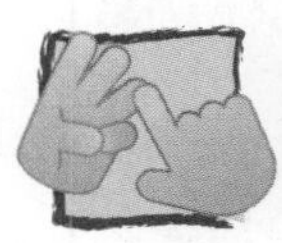

Subtract. Fill in the circle next to the correct answer.

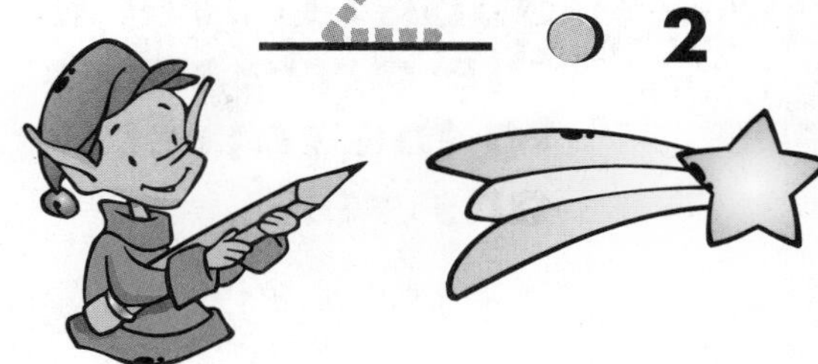

A. 5 − 1 = ____ ❍ 6 ❍ 5 ❍ 4

E. 7 − 3 = ____ ❍ 5 ❍ 4 ❍ 3

B. 10 − 9 = ____ ❍ 3 ❍ 2 ❍ 1

F. 9 − 6 = ____ ❍ 4 ❍ 3 ❍ 2

C. 8 − 4 = ____ ❍ 4 ❍ 3 ❍ 2

G. 10 − 7 = ____ ❍ 3 ❍ 2 ❍ 1

D. 6 − 6 = ____ ❍ 2 ❍ 1 ❍ 0

H. 9 − 4 = ____ ❍ 6 ❍ 5 ❍ 4

SUBTRACTION

Practice Test

I can subtract down.

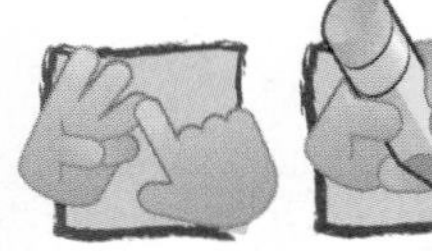

Subtract. Fill in the circle next to the correct answer.

$$\begin{array}{r} 8 \\ -\ 3 \\ \hline 5 \end{array}$$

○ 6
● 5
○ 4

A. $\begin{array}{r} 7 \\ -\ 4 \\ \hline \end{array}$

○ 4
○ 3
○ 2

E. $\begin{array}{r} 9 \\ -\ 5 \\ \hline \end{array}$

○ 5
○ 4
○ 3

B. $\begin{array}{r} 6 \\ -\ 1 \\ \hline \end{array}$

○ 7
○ 6
○ 5

F. $\begin{array}{r} 8 \\ -\ 7 \\ \hline \end{array}$

○ 2
○ 1
○ 0

C. $\begin{array}{r} 10 \\ -\ 6 \\ \hline \end{array}$

○ 6
○ 5
○ 4

G. $\begin{array}{r} 9 \\ -\ 9 \\ \hline \end{array}$

○ 2
○ 1
○ 0

D. $\begin{array}{r} 8 \\ -\ 3 \\ \hline \end{array}$

○ 6
○ 5
○ 4

H. $\begin{array}{r} 10 \\ -\ 5 \\ \hline \end{array}$

○ 4
○ 5
○ 6

Month 4 Checklist

Hands-on activities to help your child in school!

NUMBERS

Counting and Patterns: pages 99-110, 113-115
Ordinal Numbers: pages 111-112, 115

Counting and recognizing number patterns is a prerequisite for all future work in mathematics. The activities this month will help your child: 1) practice recognizing number patterns; 2) learn to skip count by 2's, 5's, and 10's; and 3) become familiar with patterns involving place value. He or she will also learn how to use ordinal numbers to describe location or position.

- ❑ Complete the worksheets.
- ❑ Go on a scavenger hunt with your child, looking for items that can be counted by 2's, 5's, or 10's. Socks may be counted by 2's, for example. Have your child skip count the items to find the total amount.
- ❑ Together, make up a jingle or song that involves skip counting by 2's, 5's, or 10's. Sing the song when you see things to skip count by that number: e.g., "5, 10, 15, 20; How many polka dots are too many?"
- ❑ Play "What's Next?" Begin a number sequence, such as 23, 24, 25. Have your child provide the next three numbers. Then invite your child to switch roles and play again.
- ❑ Have your child arrange a row of crayons, stuffed animals or books on a table. Then ask your child to identify, for example, the color that is fourth or name the position of the red crayon.

GEOMETRY

Shapes: pages 116-128

Geometric shapes and patterns are everywhere—on clothing, inside the home, and in nature. Familiarity with flat and three-dimensional shapes provides words and concepts that help children describe the world around them. Sketching shapes helps them refine their fine motor skills and challenges their artistic ability. Help your child build a firm foundation in geometry with these activities:

- ❑ Complete the worksheets.
- ❑ While completing the pattern worksheets, encourage your child to say the shapes aloud, so that the pattern is seen, spoken, and heard.
- ❑ Have your child trace the flat ends of cans or boxes from your pantry onto paper bags or plain paper. Identify the shapes.
- ❑ Make cut-outs of squares, circles, and triangles. Create a pattern using the shapes. Challenge your child to continue the pattern. Reverse roles and repeat the activity.

Count by 2's

Eight big cats walk through the gate.

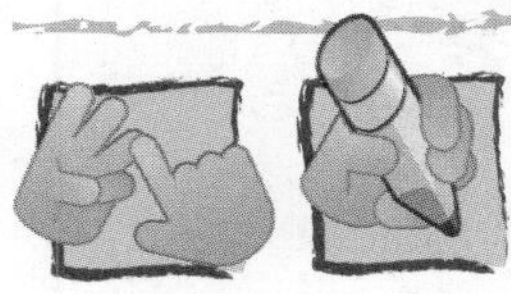

Count by 2's. Write the numbers.

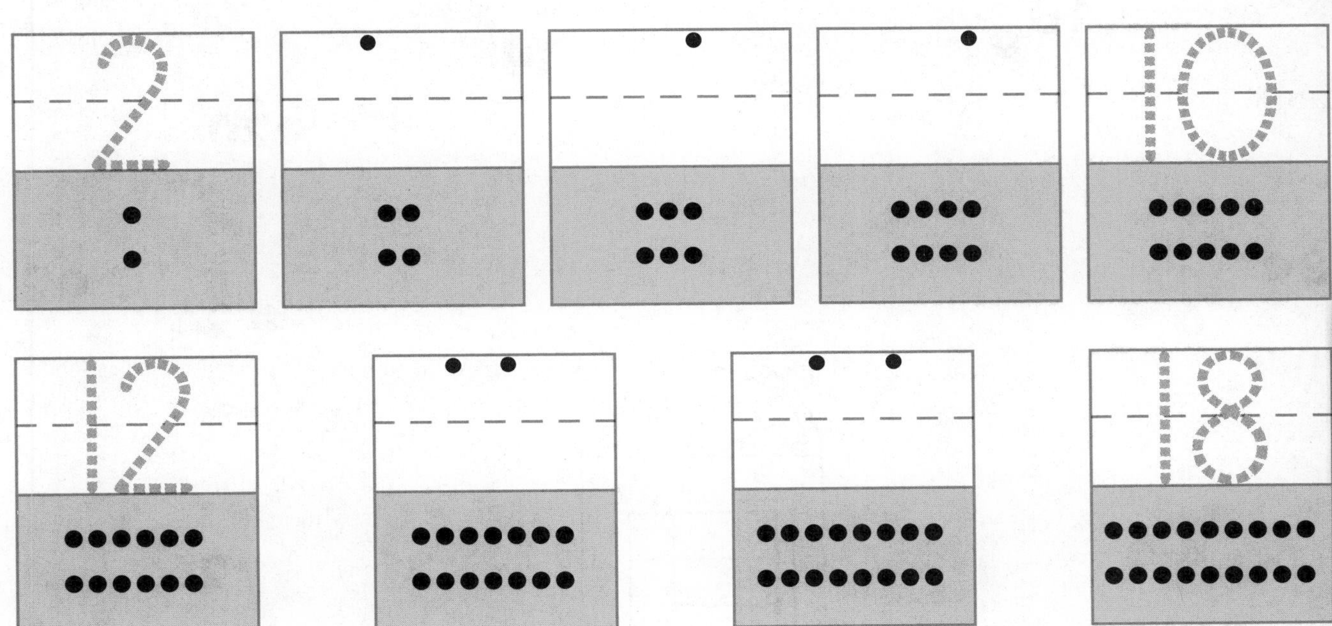

Write the answer.

What kind of trees grow in 2's?

______________________ **trees**

Answer: Pear trees

Dot-Two-Dot

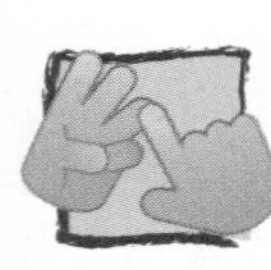

Count by 2's to 30. Connect the dots.

12

16 • •18

10 • • 14

•20

8• •22

6 • • 24

4 • •26

0 30 28

2 • • • •

START

Counting Shoes

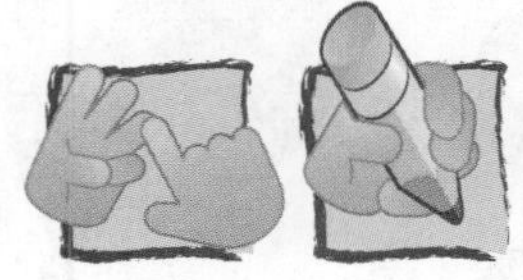

Count by 2's. Write the number.

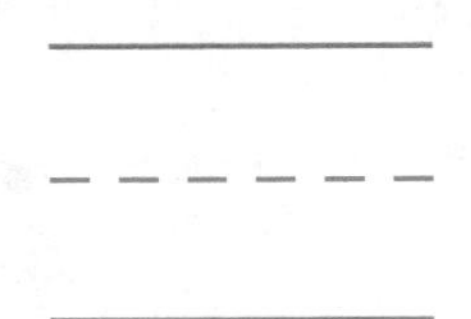

5's Alive

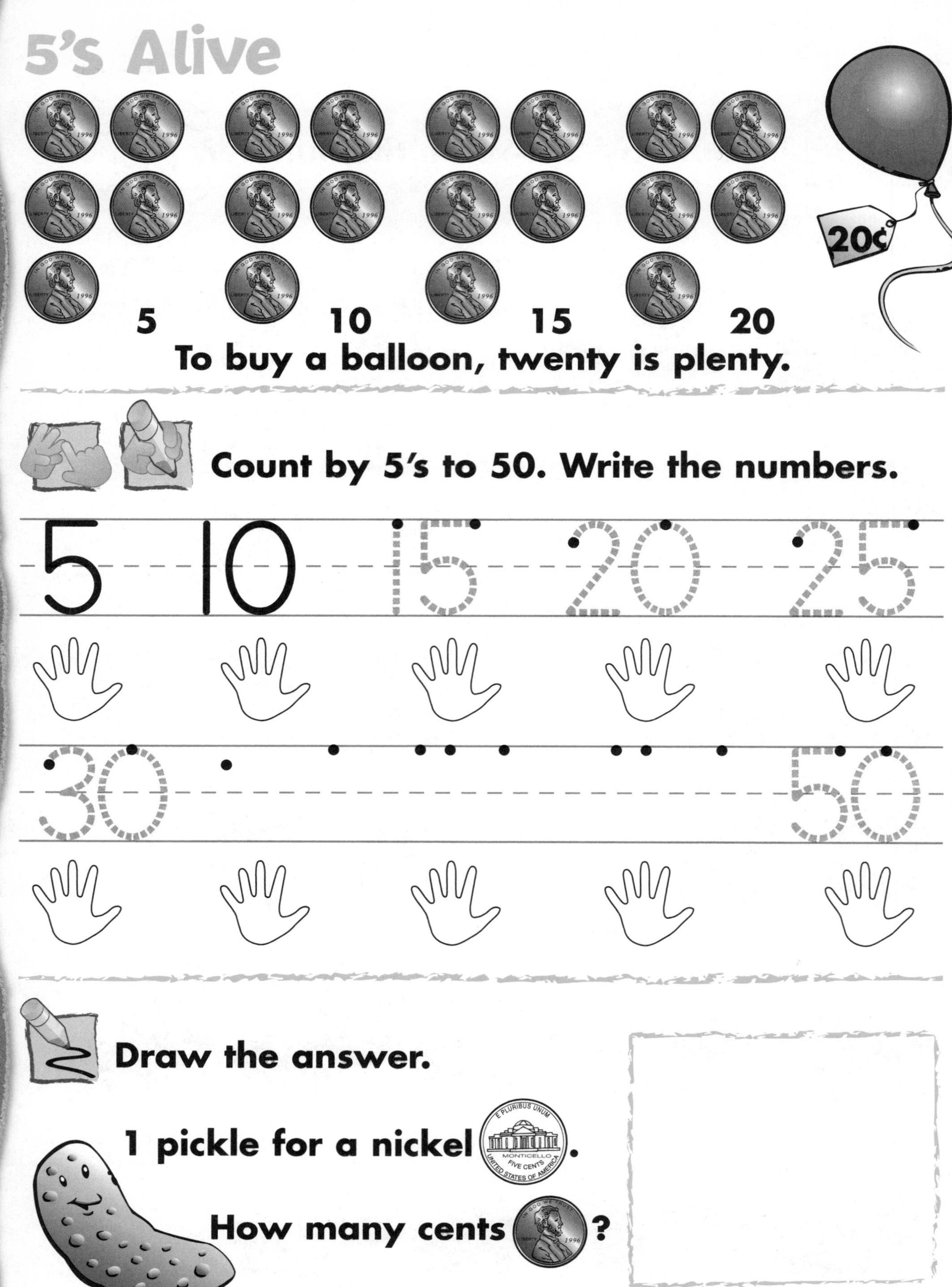

To buy a balloon, twenty is plenty.

Count by 5's to 50. Write the numbers.

Draw the answer.

1 pickle for a nickel.

How many cents?

Golden Path of Fives

Count by 5's to 50. Say the numbers.

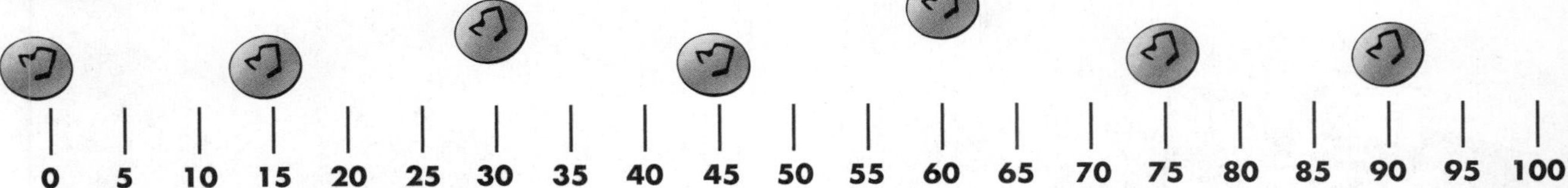

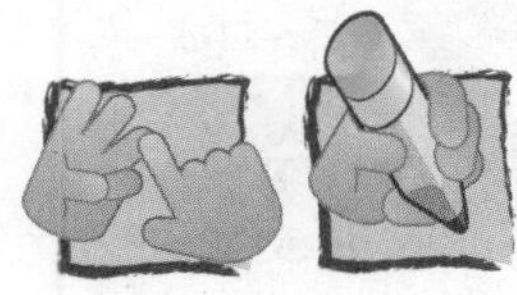

Count by 5's. Write the missing numbers.

5 10 15

A-Mazing Fives

Count by 5's. Draw a path through the maze.

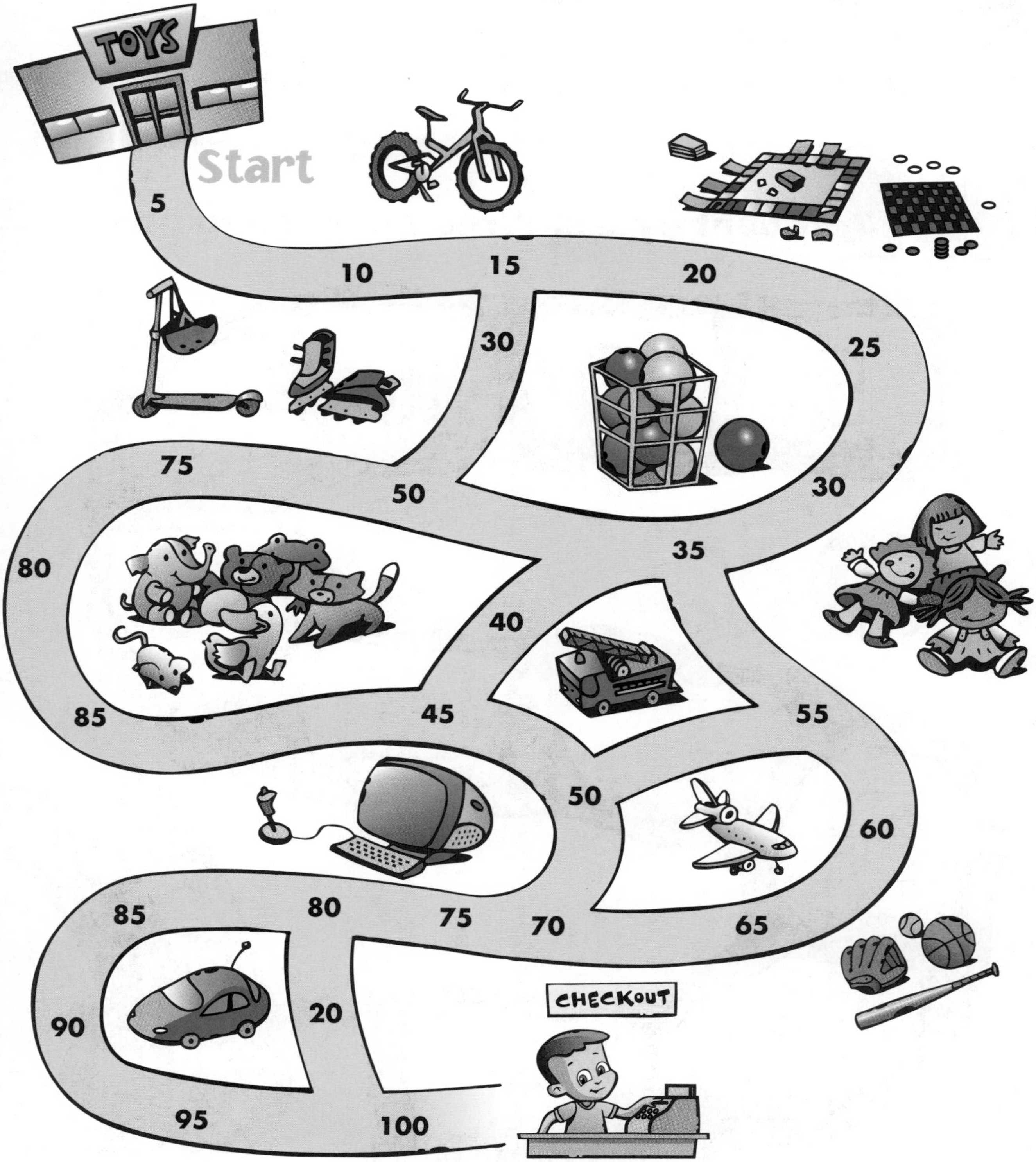

TOYS

Start

5
10
15
20
30
25
75
50
30
80
35
40
85
45
55
50
60
85
80
75
70
65
CHECKOUT
90
20
95
100

Count by 10's

Count by tens for fun. In a flash, you're all done.

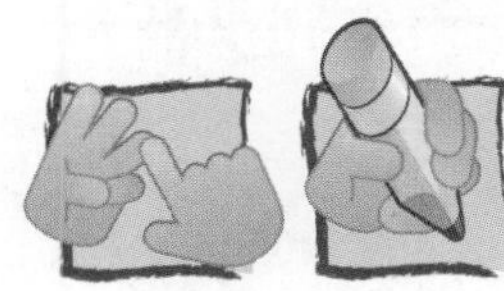

Count by 10's to 100. Write the numbers.

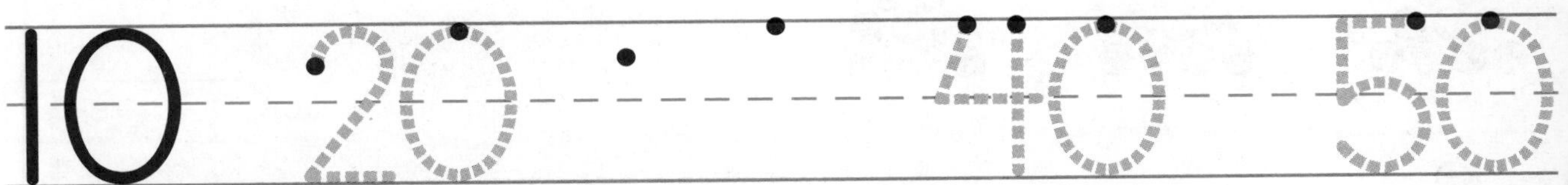

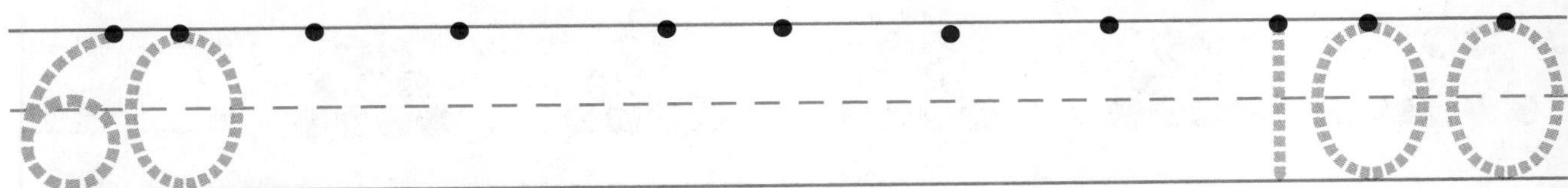

Count 10 pennies at a time, or swap them out for 1 dime.

How many dimes equal these stacks of pennies?

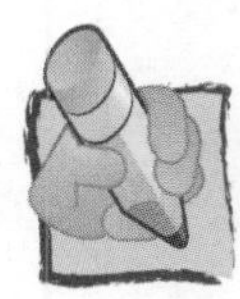

Write the number.

Counting Marbles

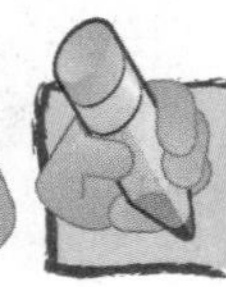

Count by 10's.
Write the number.

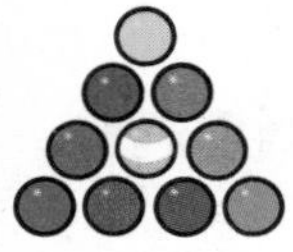
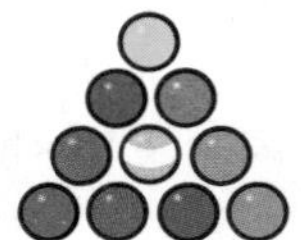
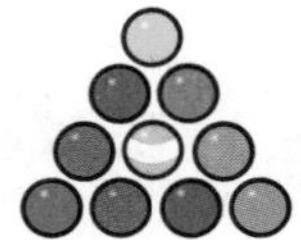
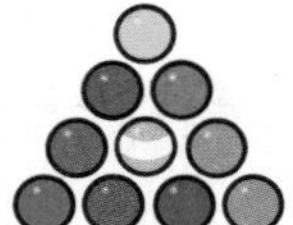

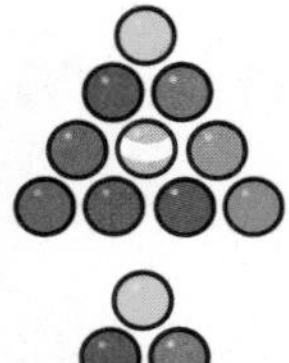
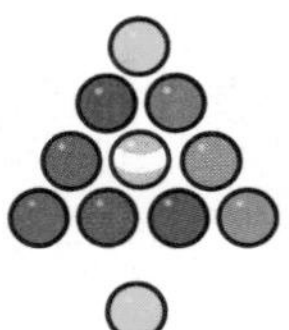
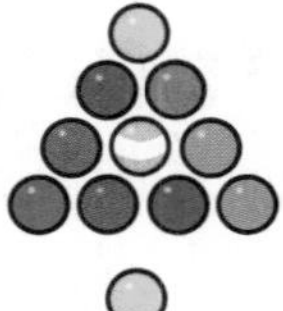
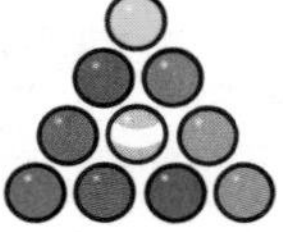

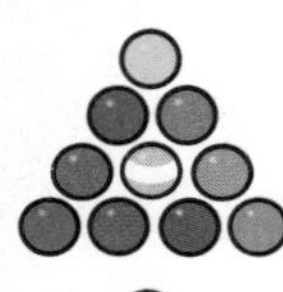
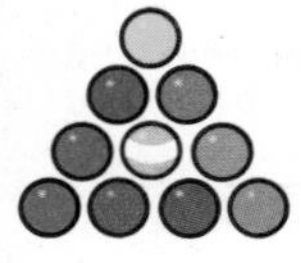
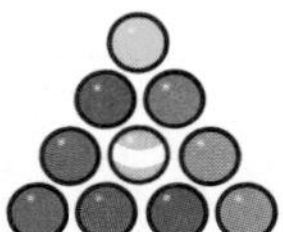
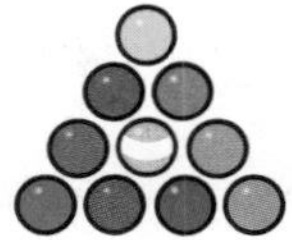
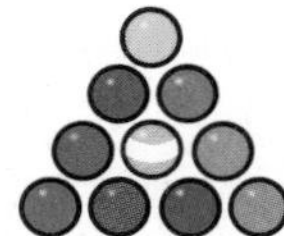

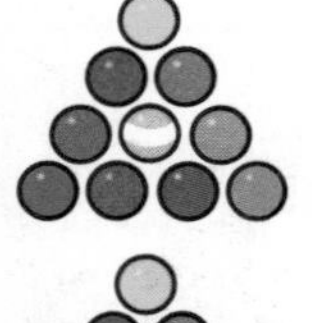
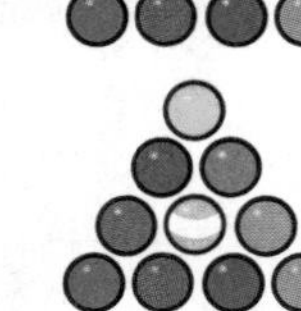
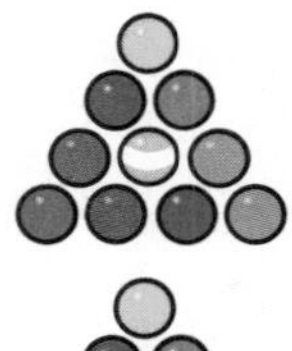
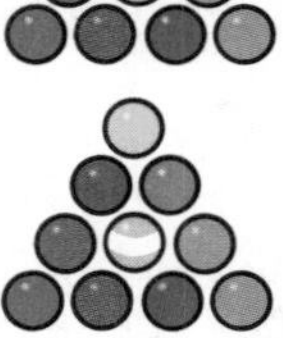
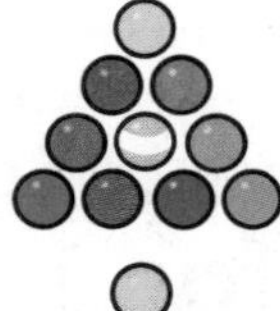
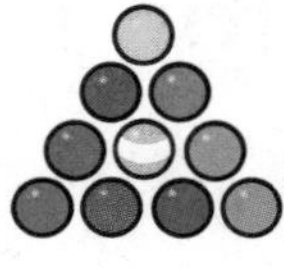

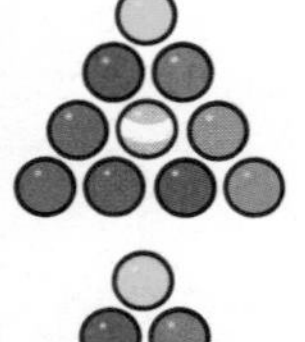
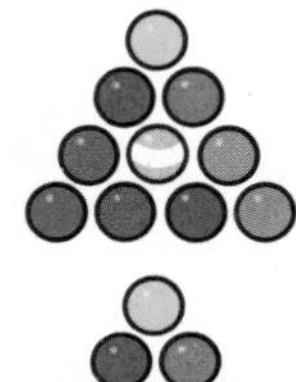
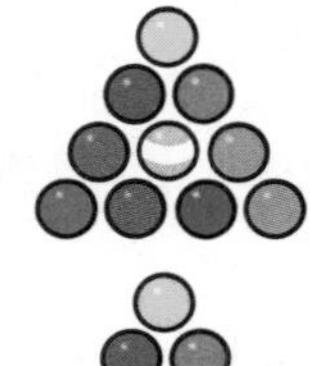
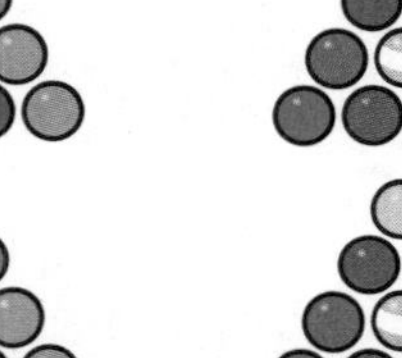
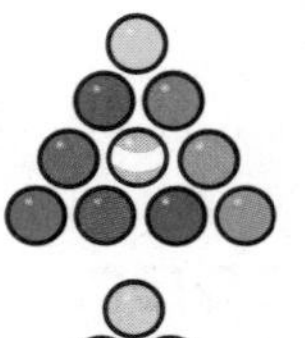
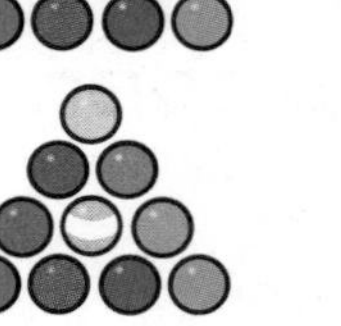
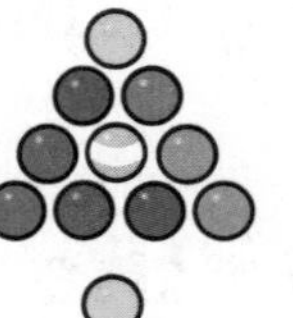
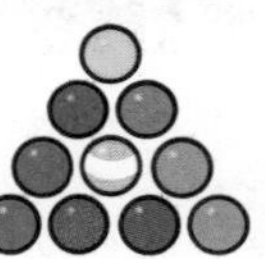

Missing Tens

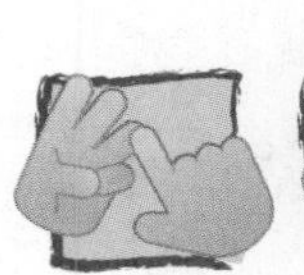
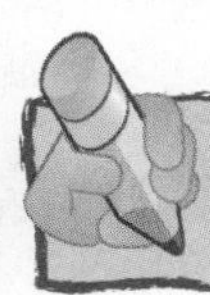

Count by 10's.
Write the missing numbers.

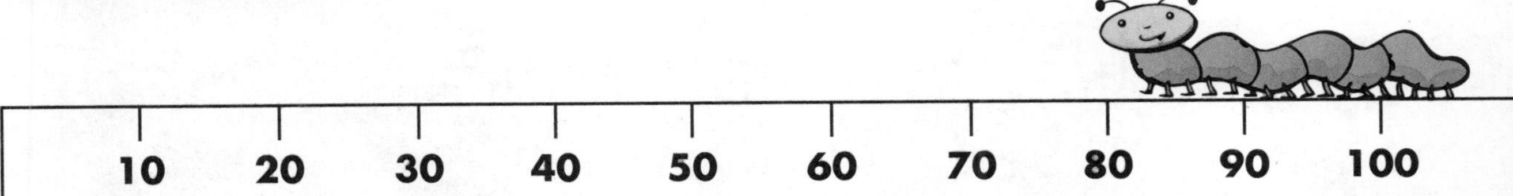

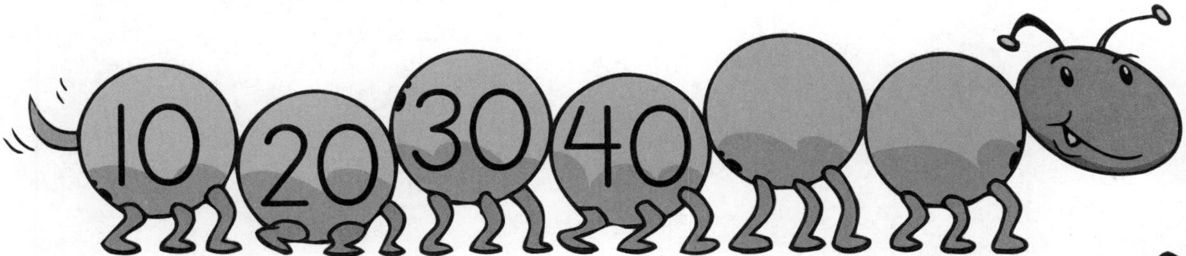

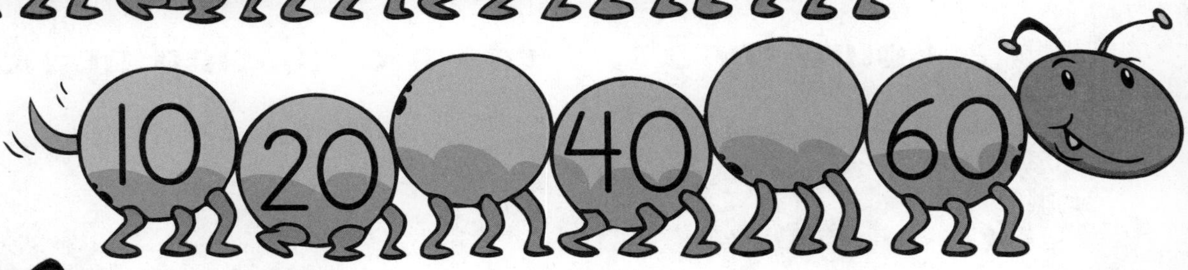

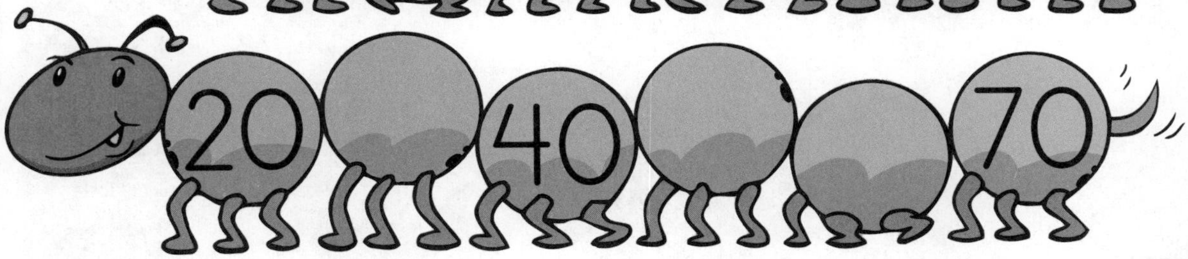

10 20 30 40 ___ ___

10 20 ___ 40 ___ 60

20 ___ 40 ___ ___ 70

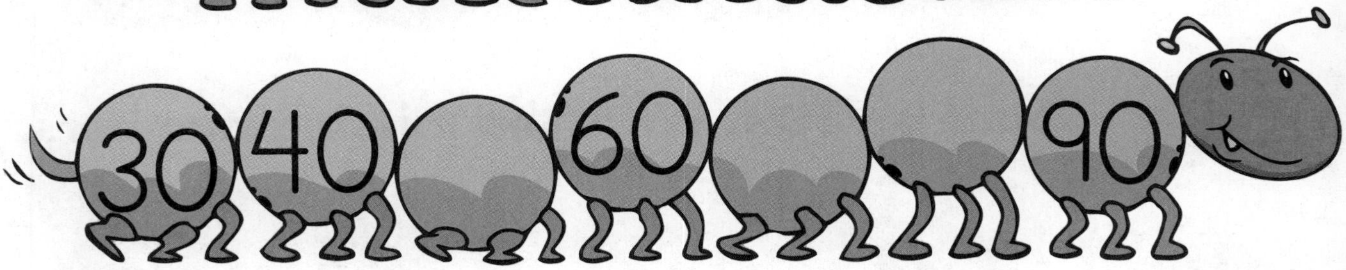

30 40 ___ 60 ___ ___ 90

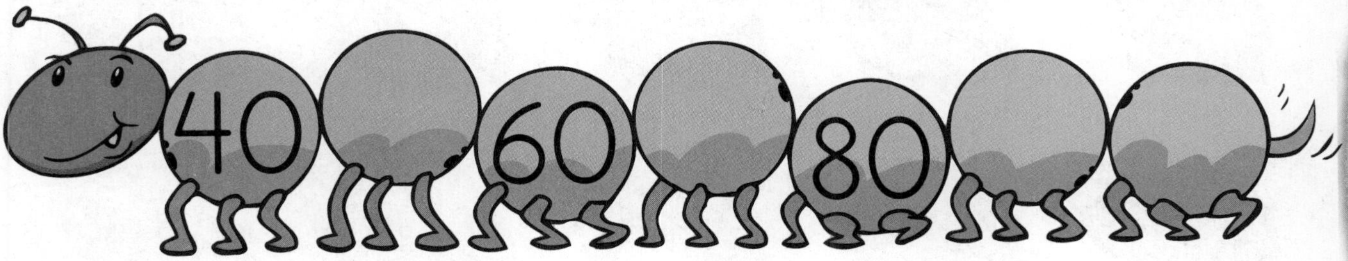

40 ___ 60 ___ 80 ___ ___

Play Ball!

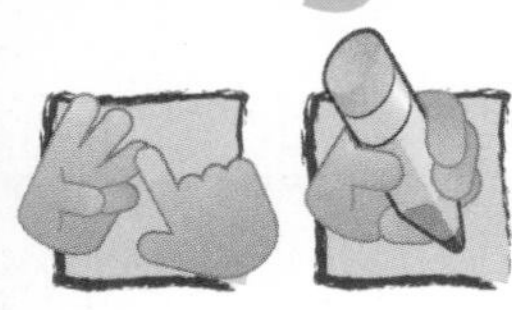

Count by 2's. Write the missing numbers.

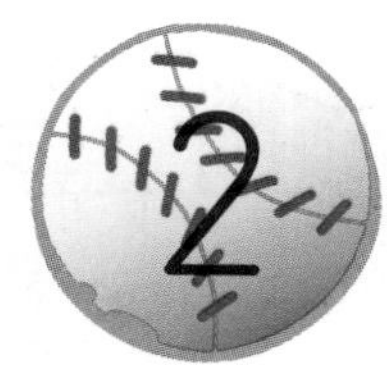

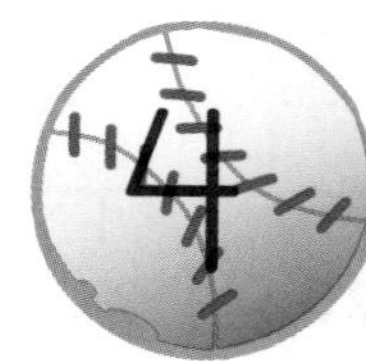

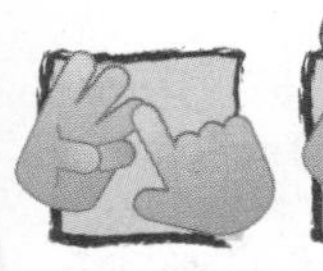
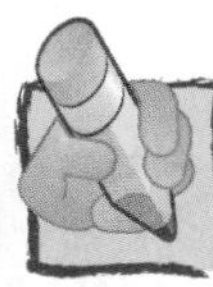

Count by 5's. Write the missing numbers.

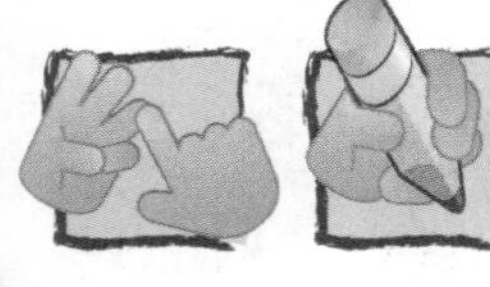

Count by 10's. Write the missing numbers.

Chart Your Way

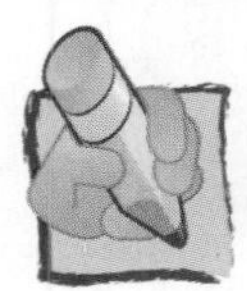

Write the numbers to finish the chart.

1	2			5			8		10
11		13				17		19	20
21			24	25				29	30
31		33			36		38	39	
	42		44			47			50
51				55	56				60
61			64			67		69	
71		73			76				80
	82			85			88		90
91			94		96			99	100

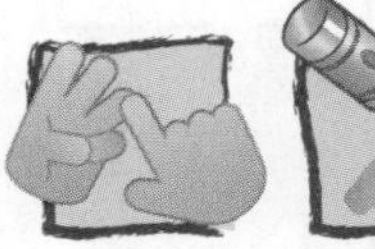

Count by 2's. Color those boxes red. Count by 5's. Circle those boxes with a blue crayon.

Counting and writing numbers from 1 to 100

Zoo Detective

Look at the pictures in the chart. What numbers belong there? Write the number beside each picture below.

1	2	3	4	5	6		8	9	10
11	12	13	14	15		17	18	19	20
21	22		24	25	26	27	28		30
31	32	33	34	35	36		38	39	40
	42	43	44	45	46	47	48	49	50
51	52	53		55	56	57	58	59	
61	62	63	64	65		67	68	69	70
71		73	74	75	76	77	78	79	80
81	82	83	84		86	87	88	89	90
91	92	93	94	95	96		98	99	100

Order in the Store

Read the words and numbers.

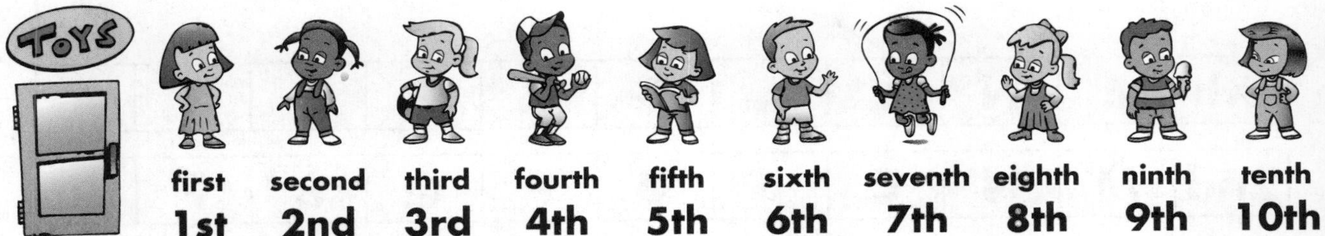

first	second	third	fourth	fifth	sixth	seventh	eighth	ninth	tenth
1st	2nd	3rd	4th	5th	6th	7th	8th	9th	10th

Circle the toy to show the ordinal number.

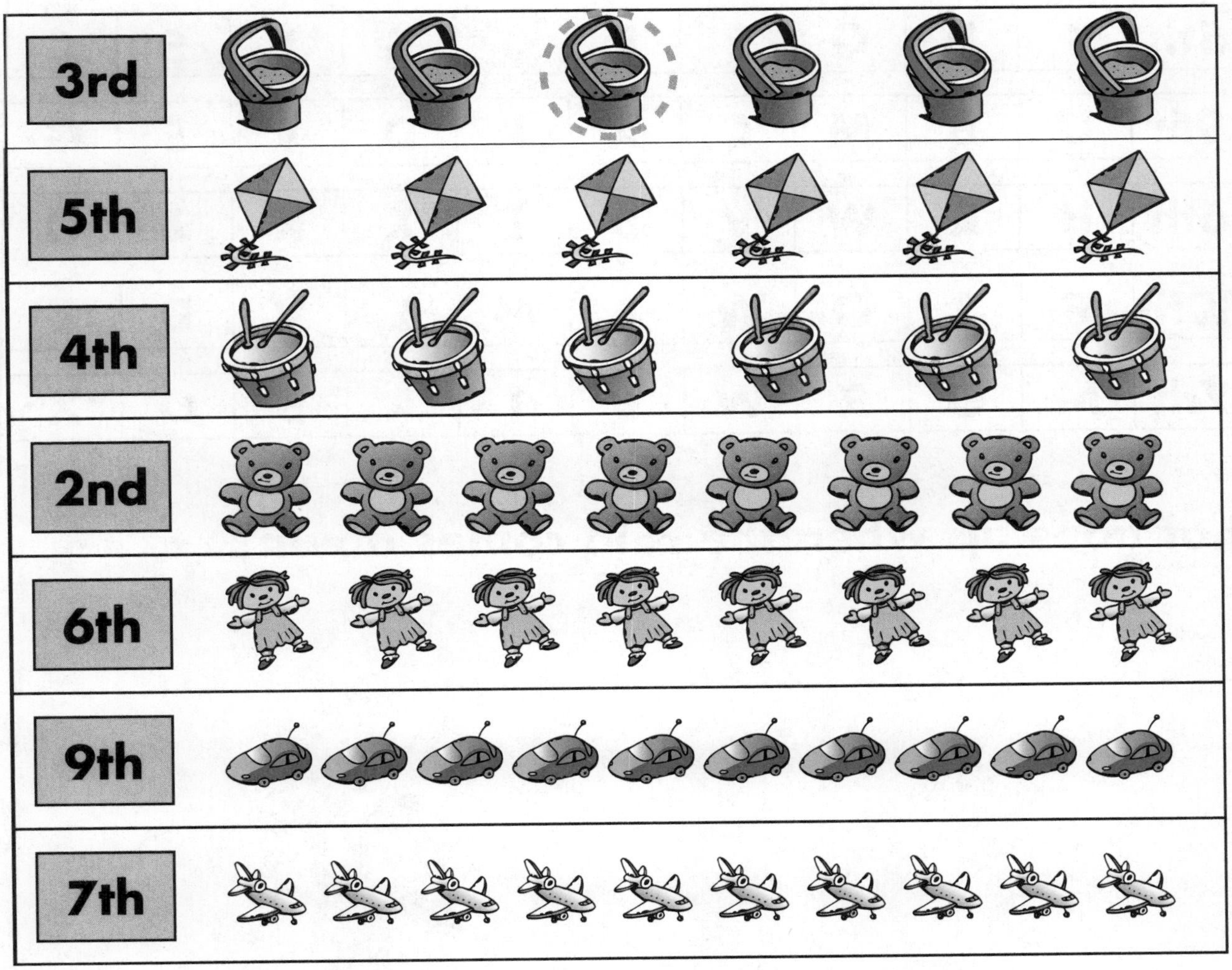

3rd	
5th	
4th	
2nd	
6th	
9th	
7th	

NUMBERS

N U M B E R S

Order Counts!

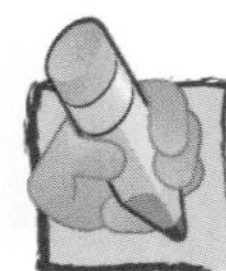

Color the letter box that matches the ordinal number. Write the letters on the lines below.

4th	E	N	Y	A	B	R	P	S	L	T
2nd	M	N	C	F	U	P	Q	B	F	I
8th	I	W	E	K	L	V	X	U	Z	E
3rd	A	S	M	D	F	G	H	J	K	L
1st	B	C	U	P	W	T	G	M	N	X
5th	I	P	Q	E	R	J	B	L	S	C
9th	U	B	M	C	X	P	D	F	E	G
6th	H	R	W	V	B	L	X	K	Z	O
10th	P	I	O	W	A	M	L	V	D	L
7th	M	O	R	W	E	T	A	B	O	X

What goes up when the rain comes down?

___ ___   ___ ___ ___ ___ ___ ___ ___ ___

Answer: An umbrella

Wrap Up a Pattern

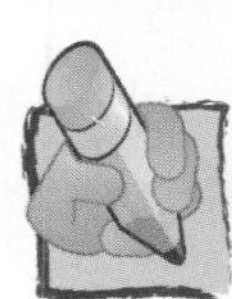

Find the pattern. Write the missing numbers.

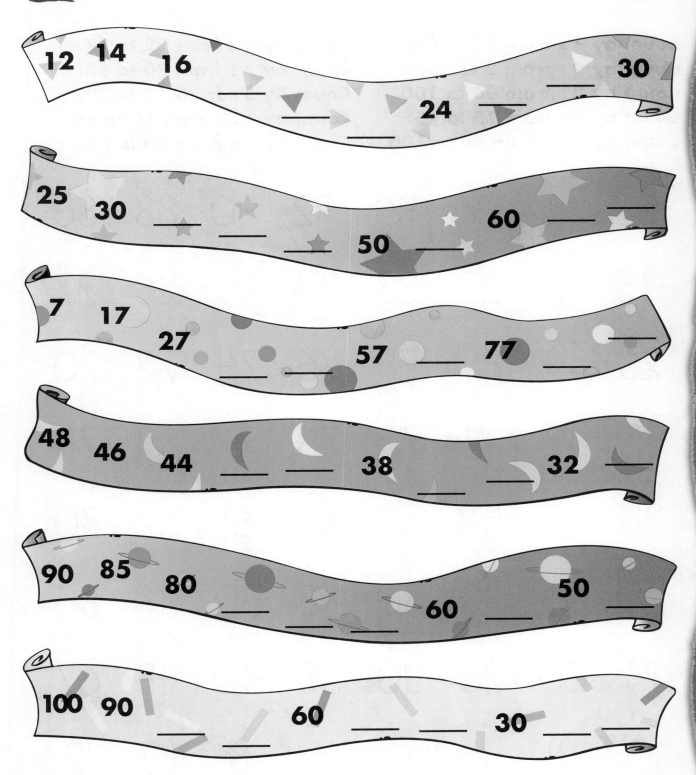

12 14 16 ___ ___ ___ 24 ___ ___ 30

25 30 ___ ___ ___ 50 ___ 60 ___ ___

7 17 27 ___ ___ 57 ___ 77 ___ ___

48 46 44 ___ ___ 38 ___ ___ 32 ___

90 85 80 ___ ___ ___ 60 ___ 50 ___

100 90 ___ ___ 60 ___ ___ 30 ___ ___

N U M B E R S

Pattern Puzzle

Look for the number patterns. Circle them.

Count by 1's from 57 to 62.
Count by 2's from 2 to 12.
Count by 2's from 86 to 100.
Count by 5's from 15 to 45.
Count by 10's from 50 to 100.
Count by 1's from 22 to 27.
Count by 2's from 70 to 80.
Count by 5's from 10 to 30.
Count by 10's from 10 to 50.
Count by 5's from 70 to 85.

100	98	96	94	92	90	88	86
45	90	22	23	24	25	26	27
23	14	80	78	76	74	72	70
30	19	12	70	74	92	89	75
25	57	58	59	60	61	62	80
20	10	20	30	40	50	43	85
15	20	25	30	35	40	45	67
10	91	2	4	6	8	10	12

Review

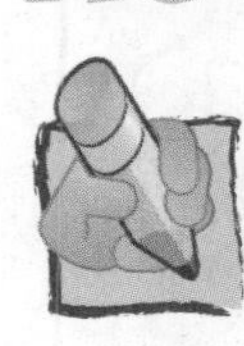

Finish the patterns.
Write the missing numbers.

Draw dots on the ladybugs.

Draw 1 dot on the first ladybug.
Draw 3 dots on the third ladybug.
Draw 6 dots on the sixth ladybug.
Draw 4 dots on the fourth ladybug.

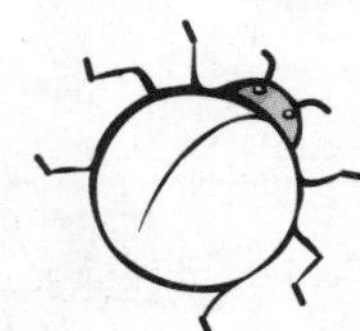    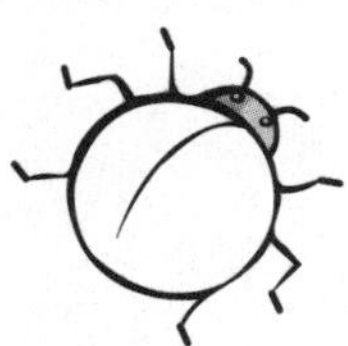 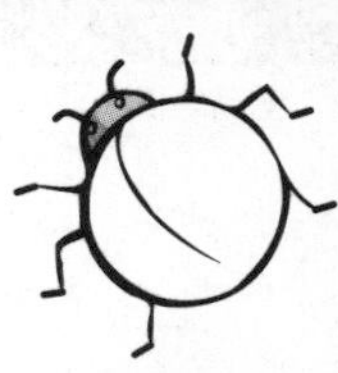

Write the missing numbers from 1 to 40.

1	2			5		7		9	10
		13					18		
21	22		24		26	27		29	30
		33		35	36			39	

Four Shapes

square **circle** **triangle** **rectangle**

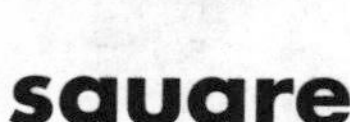

Match each shape to the object that has the same shape.

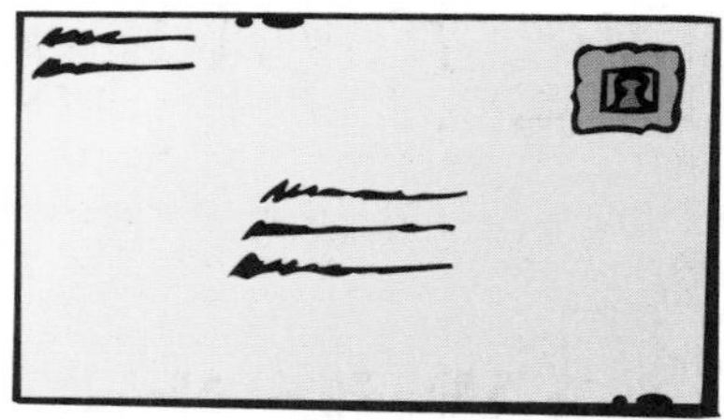

What's the Shape?

Trace each shape.

square **circle** **triangle** **rectangle**

Write S on all the squares.
Write T on all the triangles.

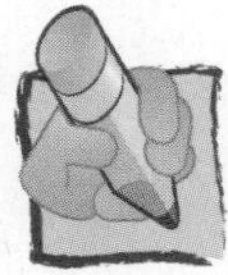

Write C on all the circles.
Write R on all the rectangles.

Shapes to Color

**Find the shapes.
Color the picture
according to the code.**

Color ■ blue.
Color ▲ red.
Color ● yellow.
Color ▬ green.

Count It!

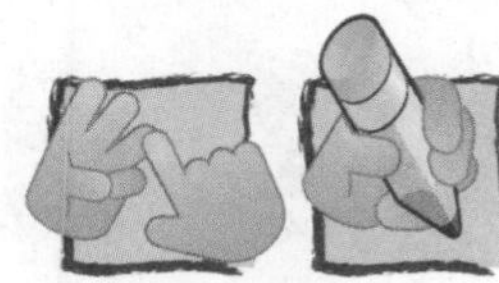

Count the shapes. Write how many.

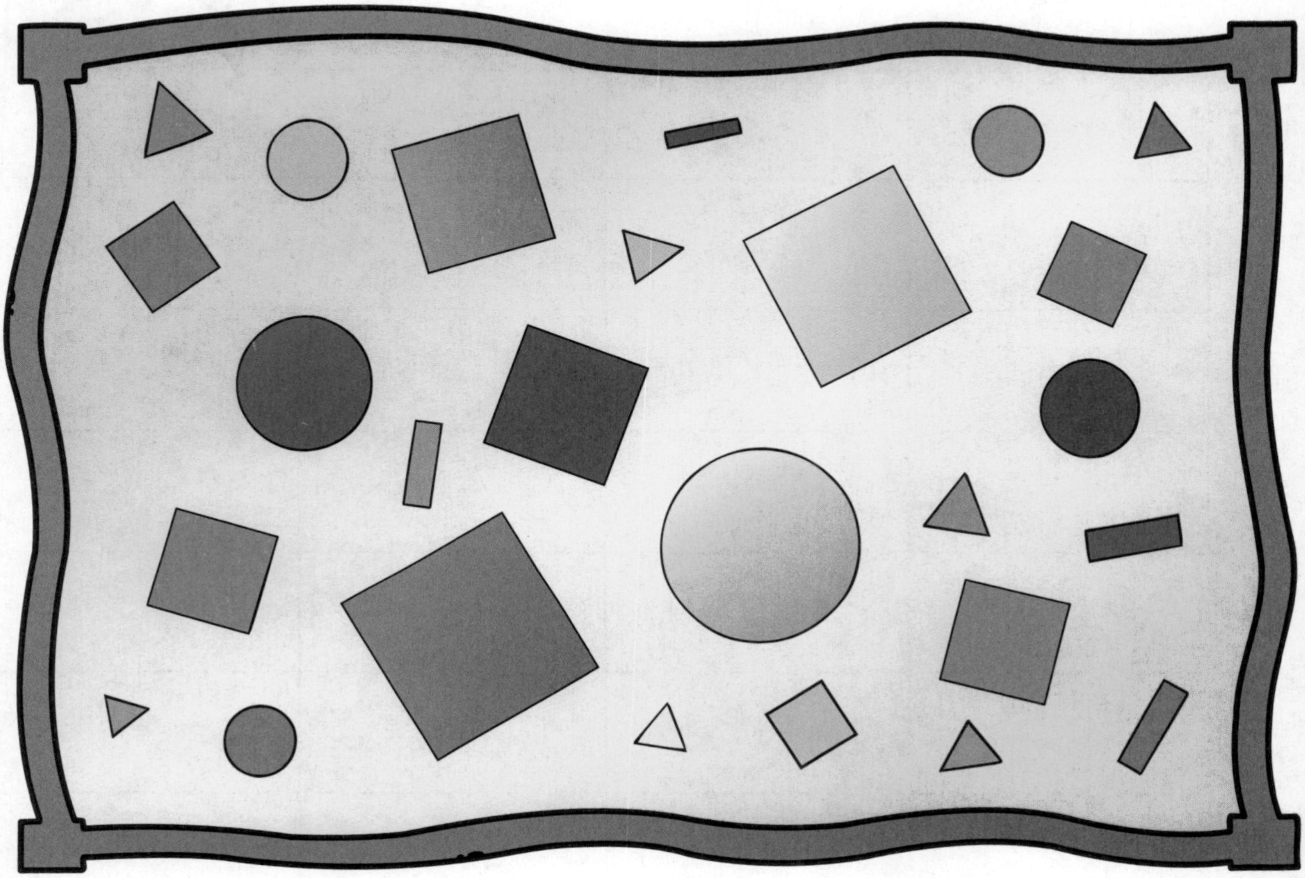

How many □ s? ______

How many △ s? ______

How many ○ s? ______

How many ▭ s? ______

GEOMETRY

Graph It!

Color the graph.
Write how many of each shape you counted on page 119.

10				
9				
8				
7				
6				
5				
4				
3				
2				
1				

What's Next?

Draw and color the shape that comes next.

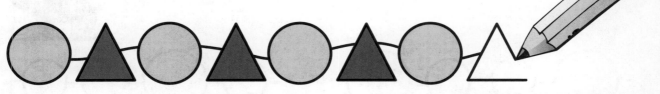

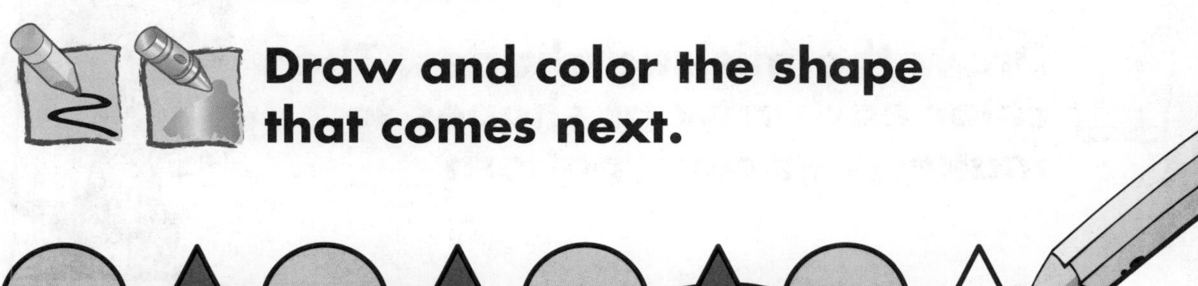

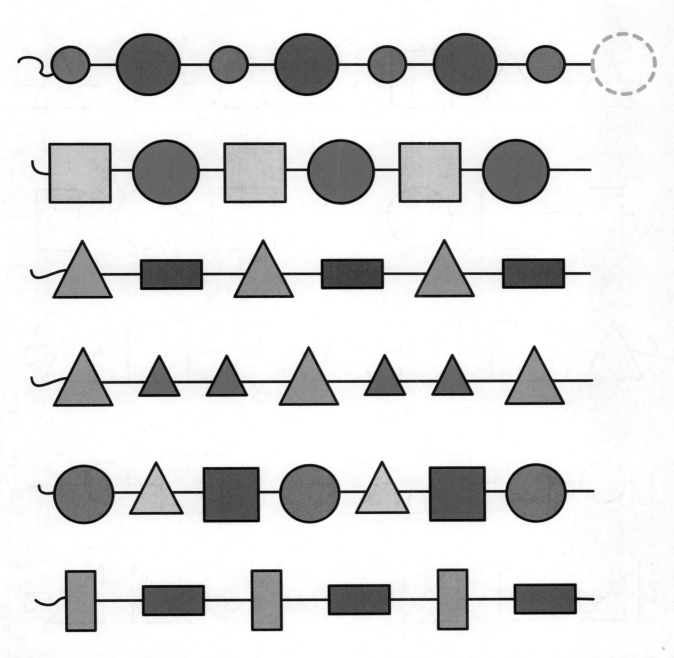

GEOMETRY

What's Missing?

Draw the missing shapes. Then color each row of shapes to make your own pattern.

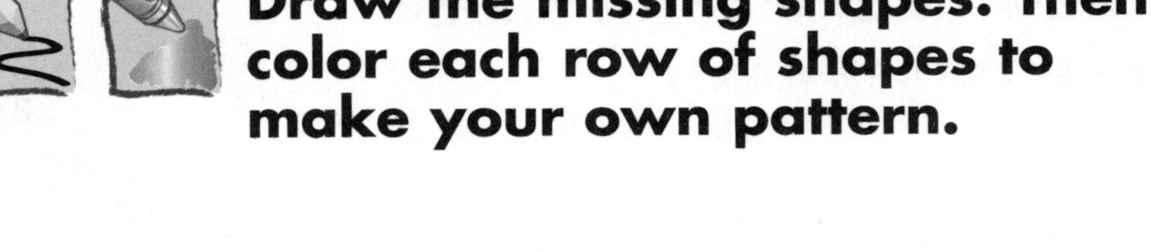

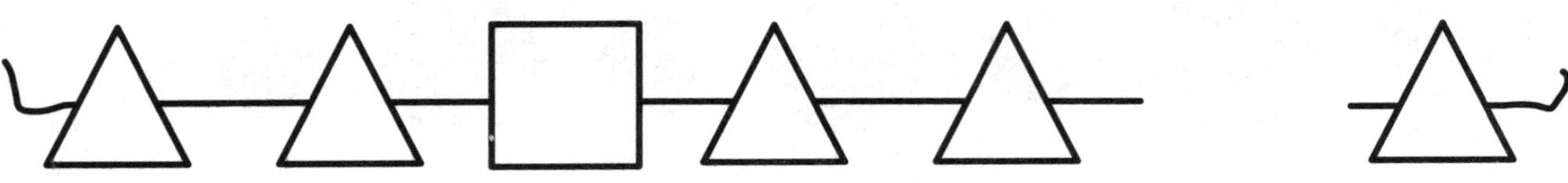

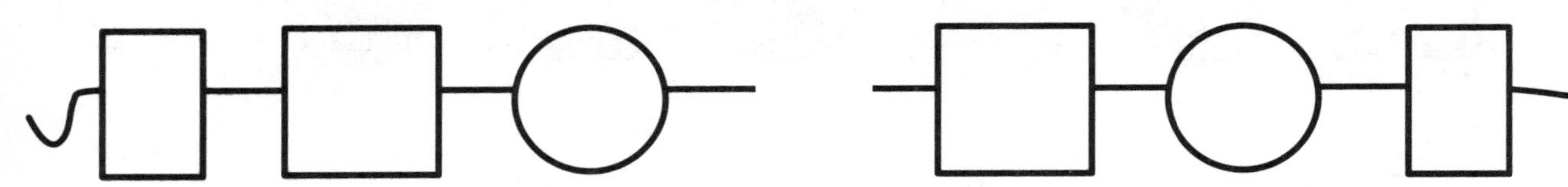

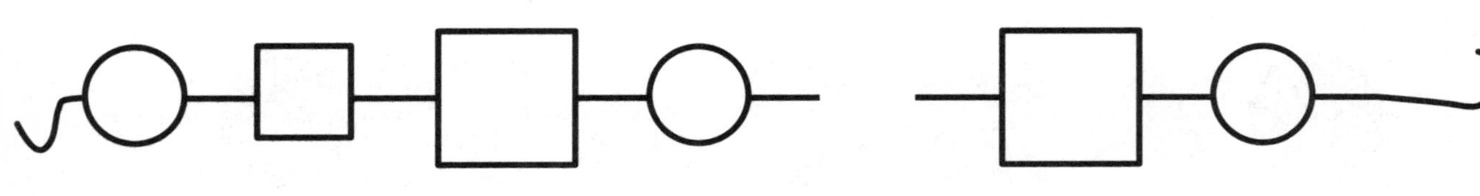

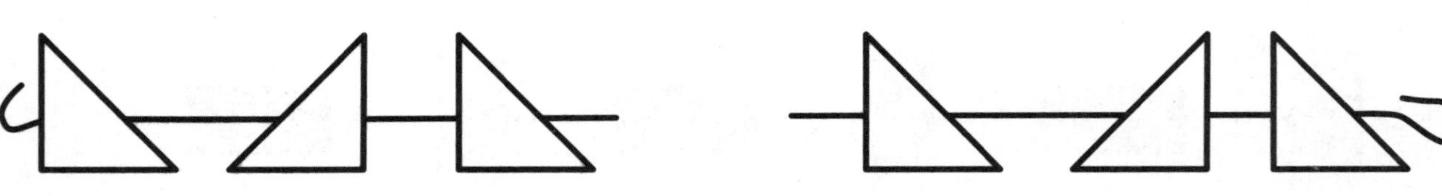

What's the Same?

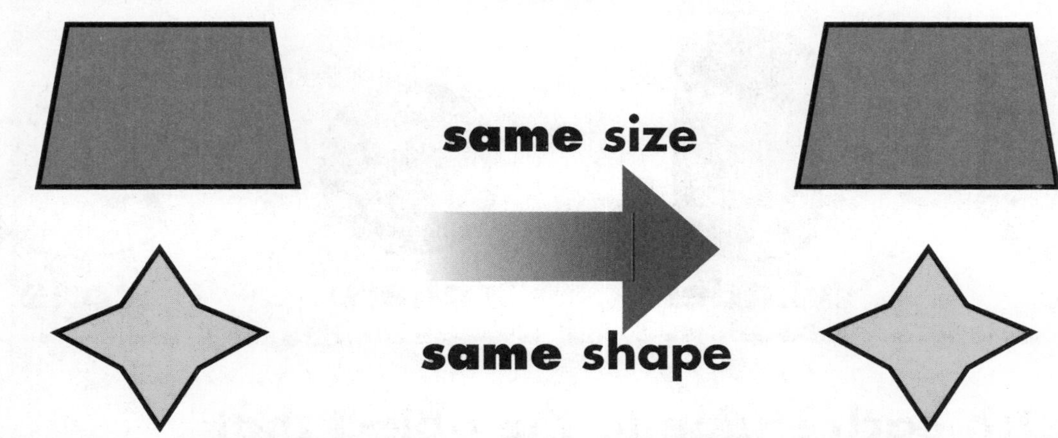

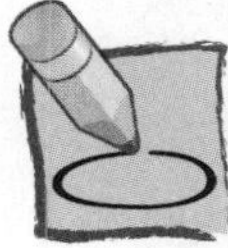

Circle the one that is the same.

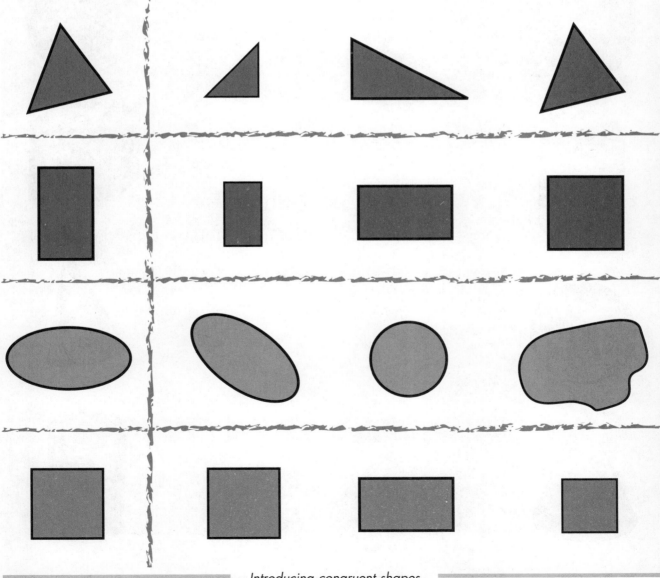

Shape Search

cube

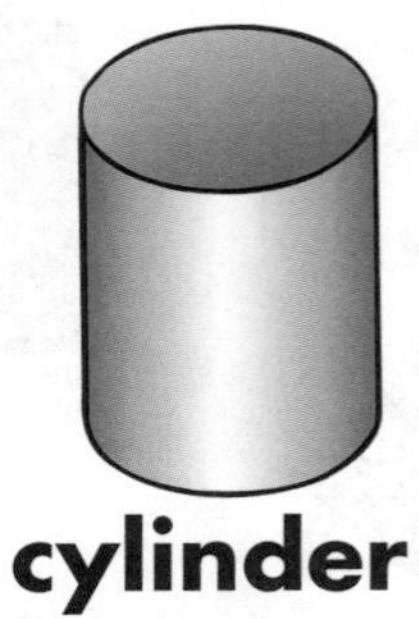
cylinder

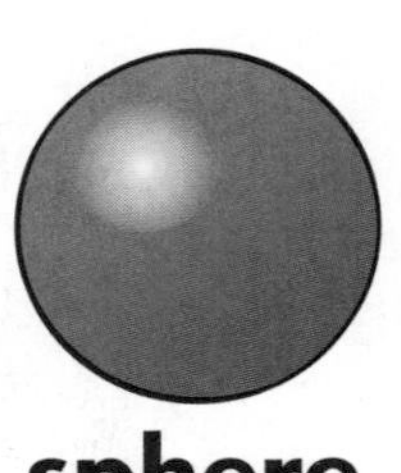
sphere

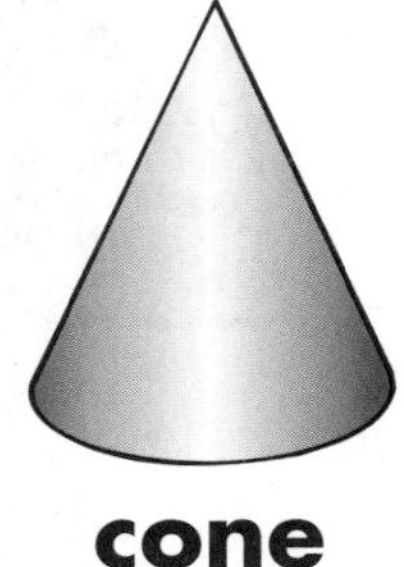
cone

Match each shape to the object that has the same shape.

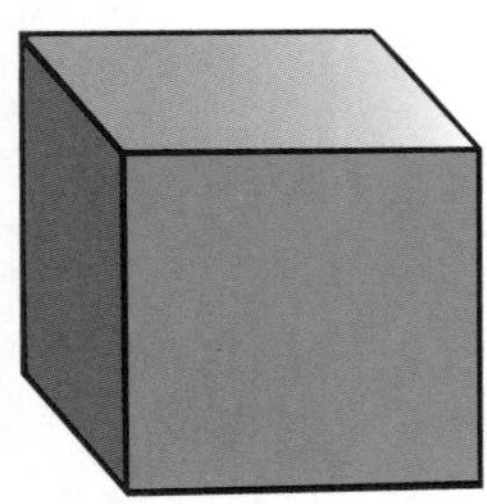

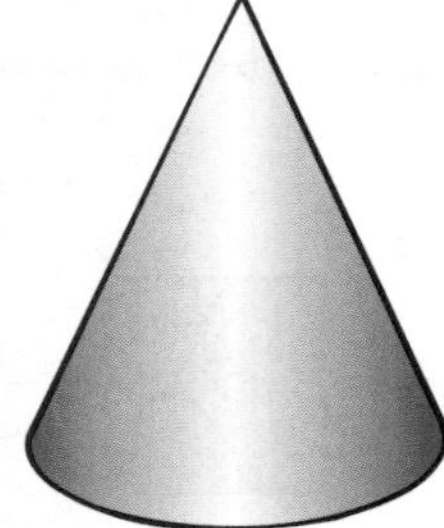

Matching three-dimensional shapes

Tricky Squares

 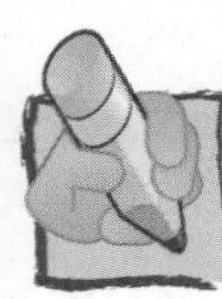

Look closely. How many squares do you see? Write the number.

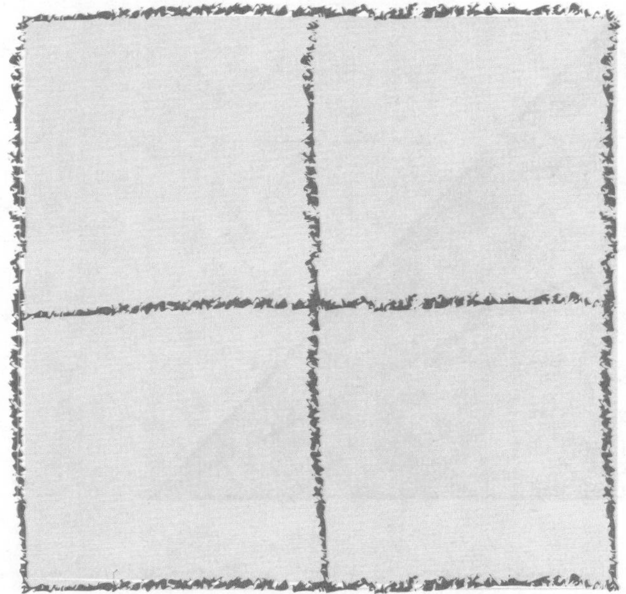

Figure A

Figure B

Some squares are inside other squares!

Answer: Figure A has 5 squares in all. Figure B has 14 squares in all.

More Shape Puzzlers

Look closely. How many triangles do you see? Write the number.

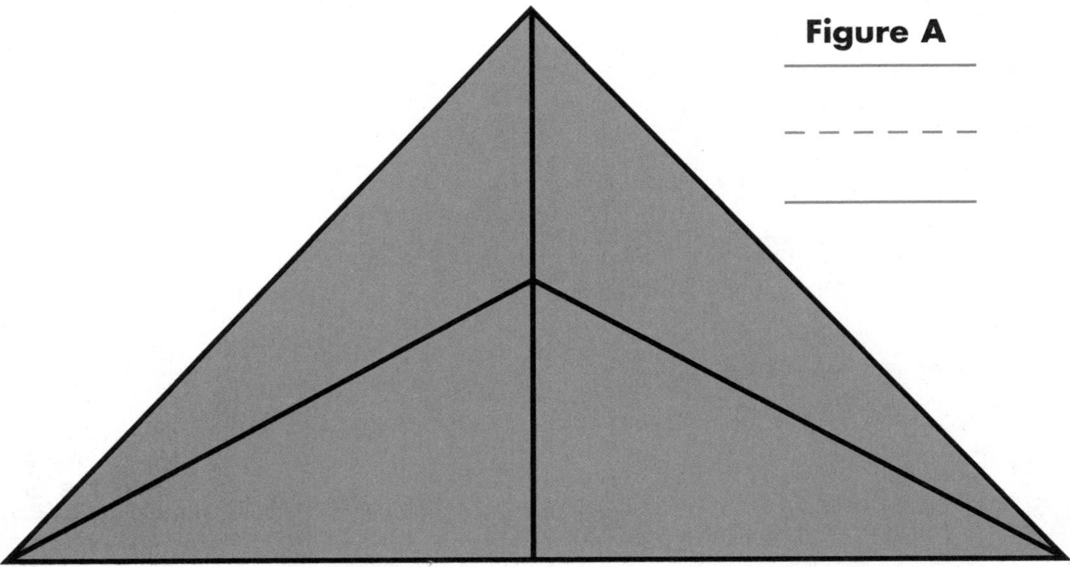

Figure A

Look closely. How many rectangles do you see. Write the number.

Figure B

Answer: Figure A has 8 triangles. Figure B has 11 rectangles.

Using visual discrimination to identify triangles and rectangles

Shapes All Around

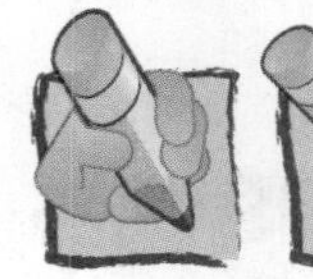

Can you find these shapes? Look in your house and in your neighborhood. Draw or write what you find.

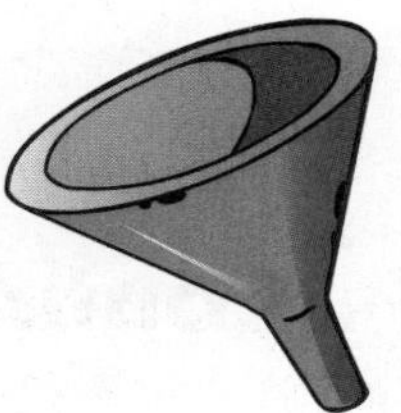

Circle or Sphere	Square or Cube	Triangle or Cone

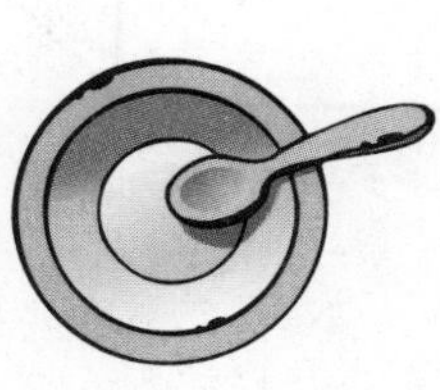

GEOMETRY

Review

Color the circle.

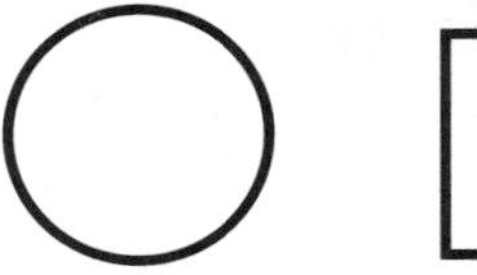

Color the rectangle.

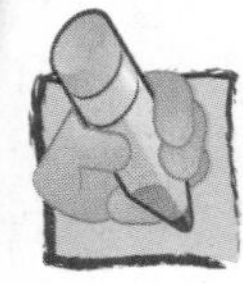

Continue the pattern.

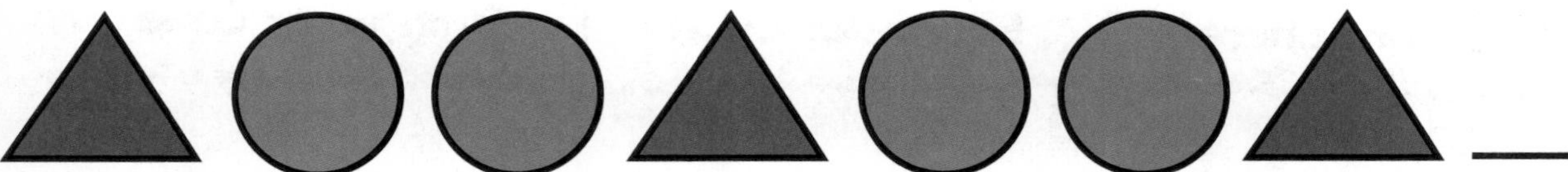

Circle the shape that is the same.

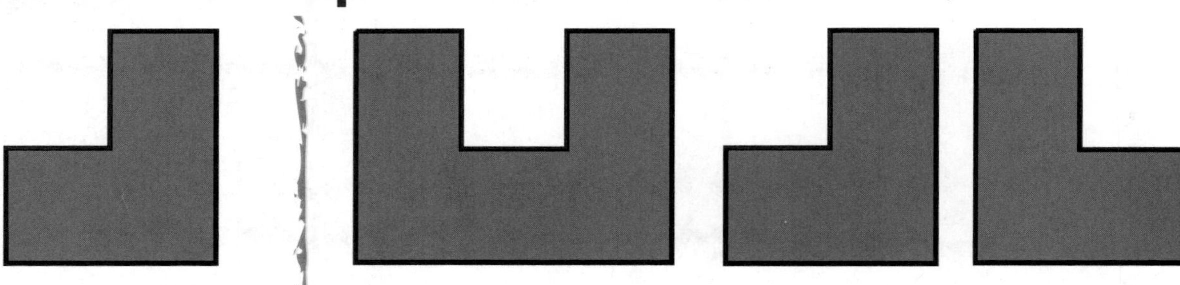

Color the cube.

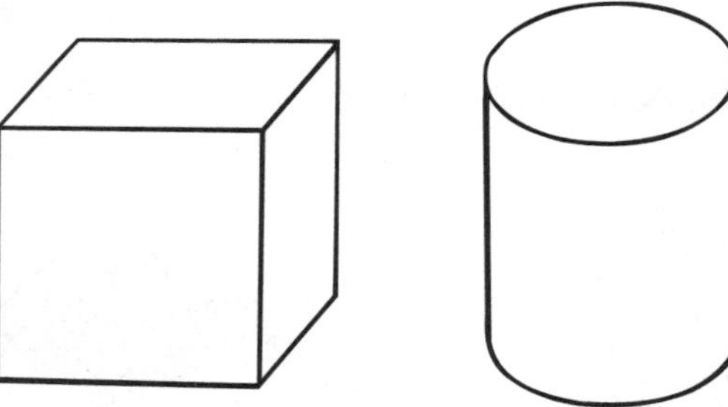

Color the cone.

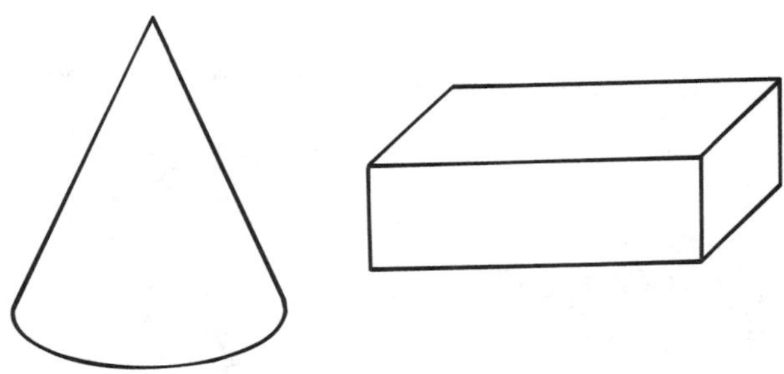

Month 5 Checklist

Hands-on activities to help your child in school!

ADDITION WITH SUMS THROUGH 15

Adding with Sums to 12: pages 131-137, 145
Adding with Sums to 15: pages 138-145

In this month, your child will work on sums through 15. Extensive practice is the best way to help him or her eventually commit the sums to memory.

- ❑ Complete the worksheets.
- ❑ Count out 11 small items, separate them into two groups, and then write a number sentence by recording the number of items in each group: for example, 6 + 5 = 11. Have your child repeat the process independently, challenging him or her to find all 10 number sentences. Then repeat this activity for sums through 15.
- ❑ Have your child choose an addition fact, such as 7 + 8 = 15, and then give him or her materials to draw or paint a picture that illustrates the fact. For example, the child can draw a group of 7 balls and another with 8 balls.
- ❑ Cut an egg carton so that it has only 10 sections. Using an addition sentence such as 8 + 5, have your child place 8 objects in the egg carton, then add 2 more to make 10. With 3 left over, your child finds that 8 + 5 = 10 + 3, or 13. Repeat for several other facts.
- ❑ Make up a song, jingle, or poem with your child to practice a hard-to-learn fact. For example, "When 8 plus 5 birds fly, there are 13 birds way up high."

SUBTRACTION FROM NUMBERS THROUGH 15

Subtracting with Differences to 10: pages 146-148, 160
Subtracting with Differences to 14: pages 149-160

In this month, your child will work on differences through 15:

- ❑ Complete the worksheets.
- ❑ Have your child choose a number between 1 and 9—for example, 3. Challenge your child to find and record as many subtraction facts as possible with a difference of the chosen number: for example, 12 – 9, 11 – 8, and so on.
- ❑ Provide your child with crayons, markers, and plain paper. Challenge your child to create a picture that illustrates a subtraction fact, such as 12 – 7 = 5. For example, 12 balloons, 7 of which are crossed out.
- ❑ Play "Heads and Tails." Count a collection of 14 pennies. Have your child toss the pennies on a table and separate them into "heads-up" and "tails-up" groups. Make two subtraction sentences, *total – heads = tails* and *total – tails = heads* to describe the pennies. Repeat several times to find other subtraction facts with 14.
- ❑ Play "How Many Ways?" Write a subtraction fact, such as 12 – 3, on a piece of paper. Take turns naming the difference and explaining how you figured it out. The difference remains the same; the focus is on the different ways to arrive at the answer. Strategies may include using objects, using a number line, counting back, and using an addition fact.

In the Garden

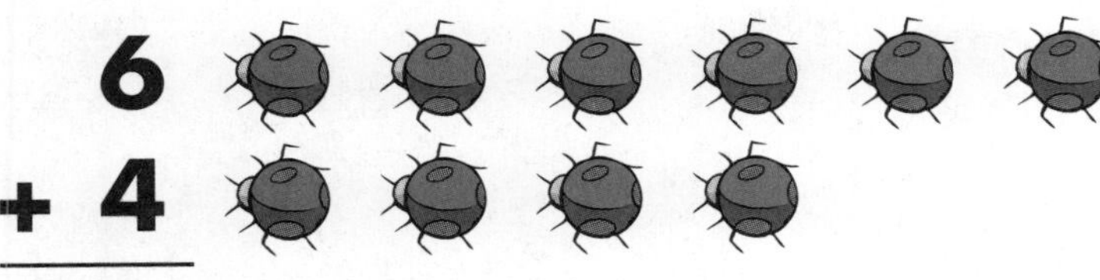

6
+ 4
10 in all

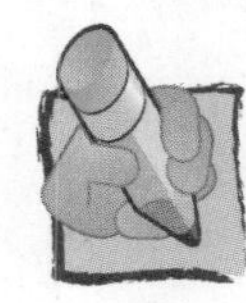

Write how many.

+

in all

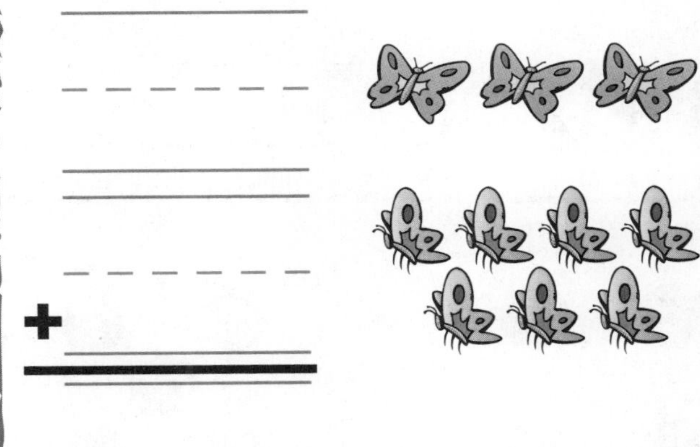

+

in all

+

in all

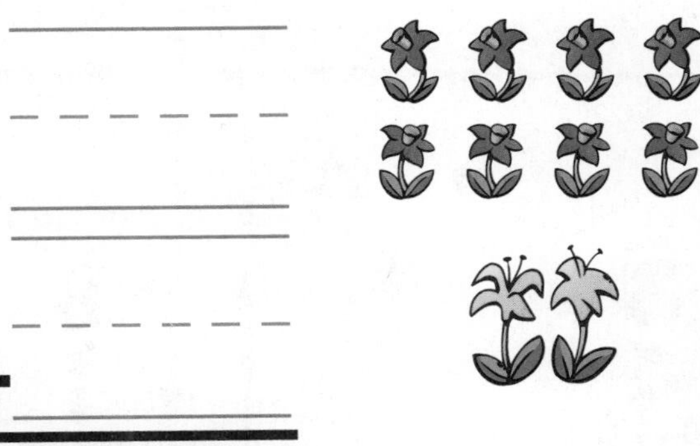

+

in all

Adding Shapes

**Add to find each sum.
Write the answers.**

3 + 7 = 10

6 + 2 = ____

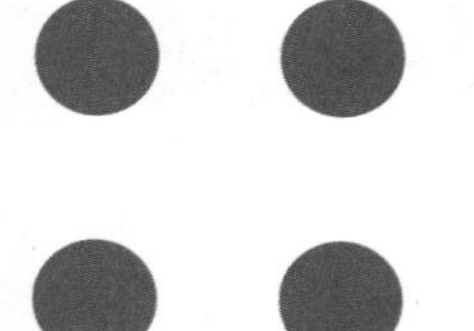 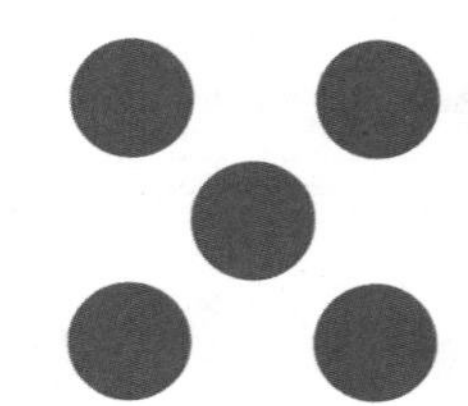

4 + 5 = ____

5 + 5 = ____

$$\begin{array}{r} 3 \\ +\ 4 \\ \hline \end{array}$$

$$\begin{array}{r} 8 \\ +\ 1 \\ \hline \end{array}$$

$$\begin{array}{r} 4 \\ +\ 6 \\ \hline \end{array}$$

Finding sums to 10

Sum Stars

Color the stars with sums of ten.

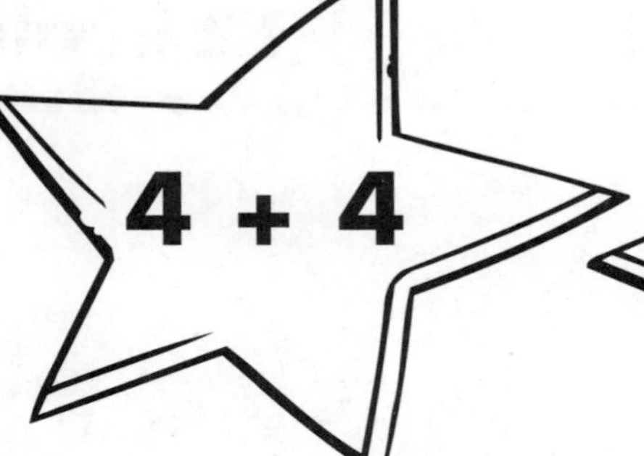

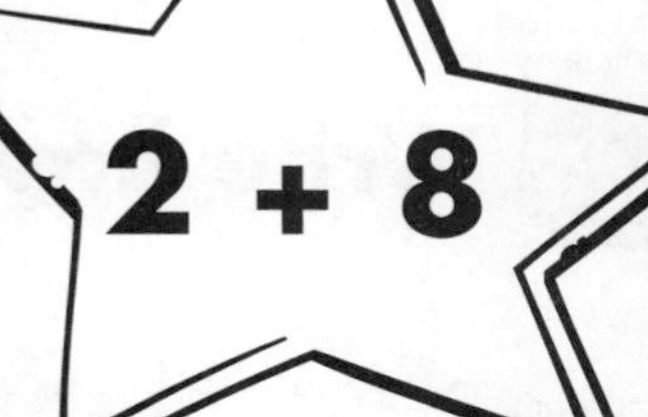

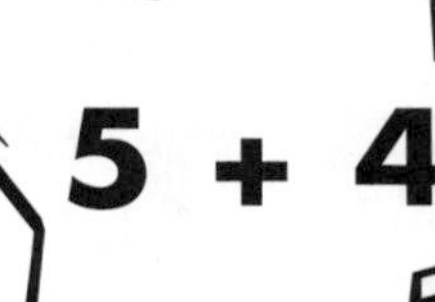

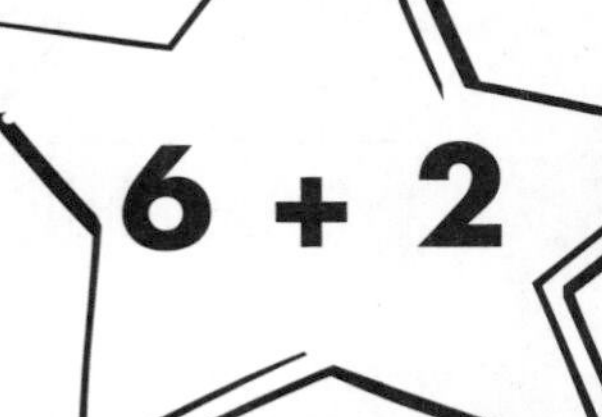

ADDITION

On the Farm

10 + 2 = 12 in all

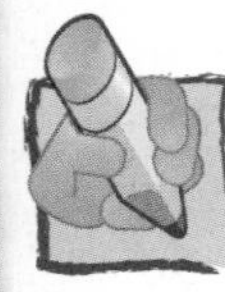

Write how many.

in all

6 + 3 = ____

in all

____ + ____ = ____

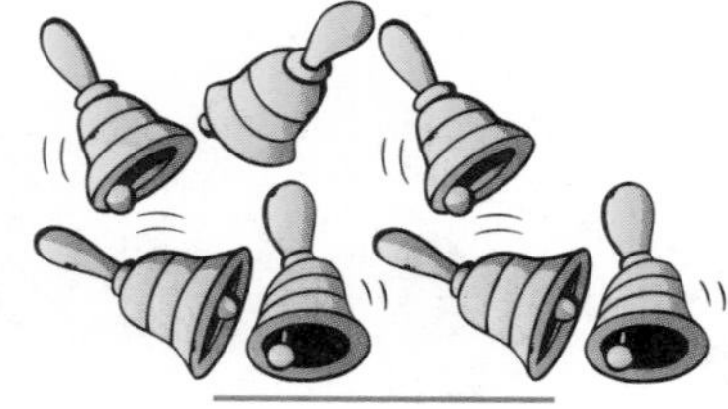

in all

____ + ____ = ____

By the Sea

3
+ 9
12 in all

Write how many.

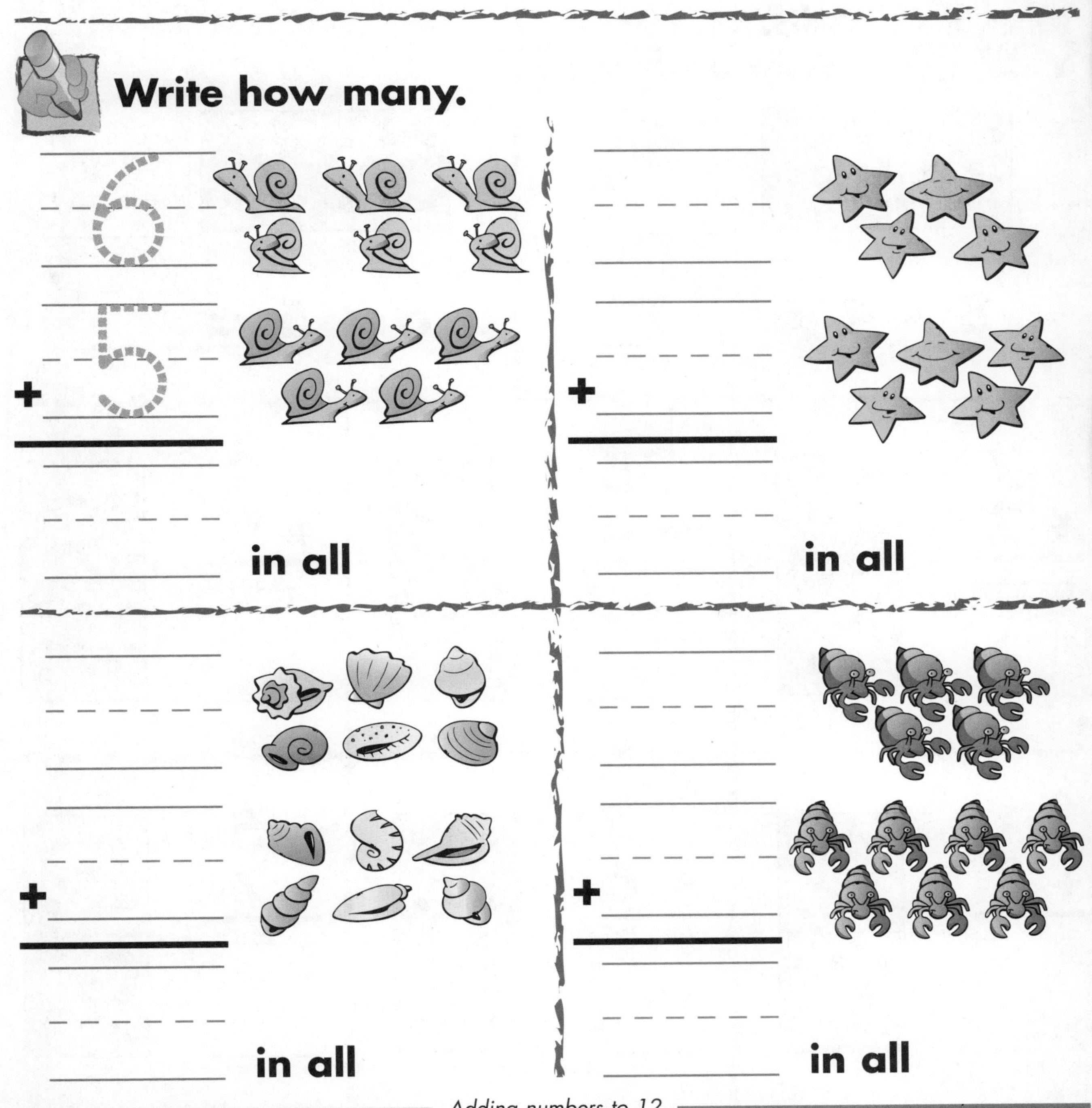

in all

in all

in all

in all

Domino Dots

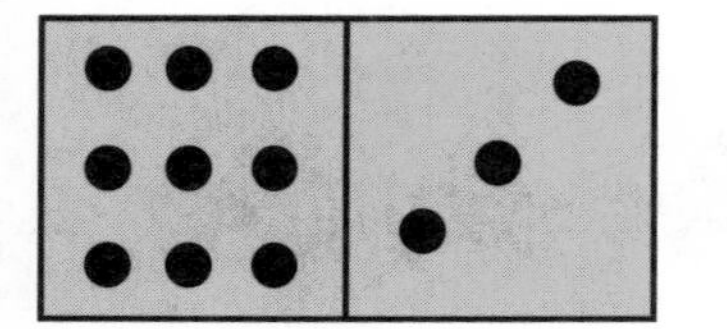

9 + 3 = 12

$$\begin{array}{r} 3 \\ +\ 9 \\ \hline 12 \end{array}$$

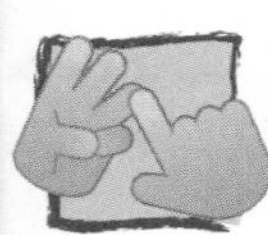

**Add.
Write each sum.**

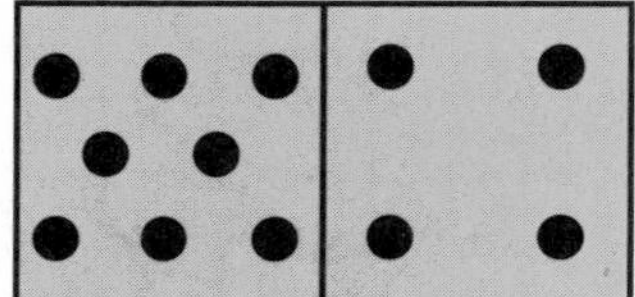

8 + 4 = 12

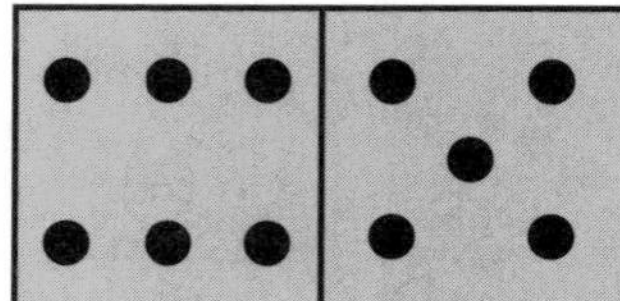

6 + 5 = ____

$$\begin{array}{r} 7 \\ +\ 2 \\ \hline \end{array}$$

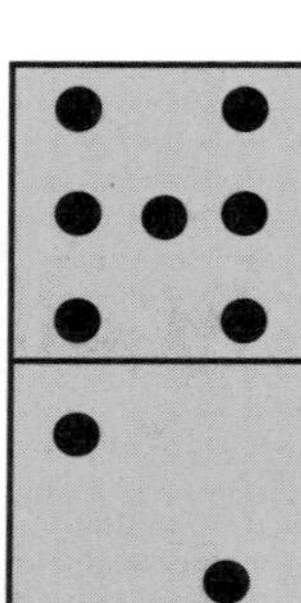

$$\begin{array}{r} 5 \\ +\ 3 \\ \hline \end{array}$$

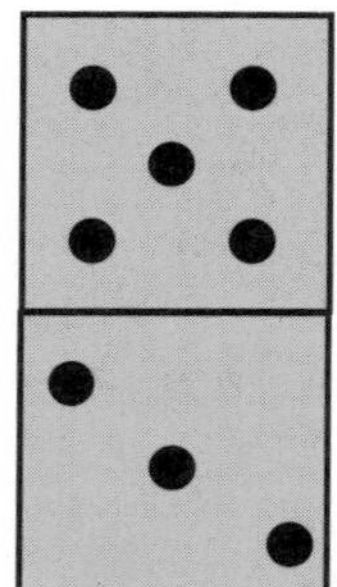

$$\begin{array}{r} 2 \\ +\ 9 \\ \hline \end{array}$$

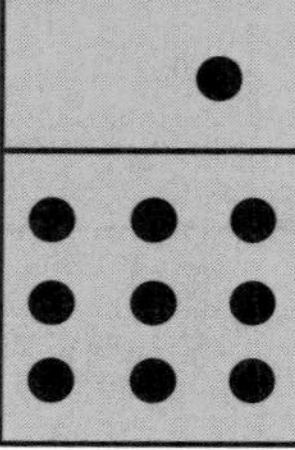

$$\begin{array}{r} 1 \\ +\ 8 \\ \hline \end{array}$$

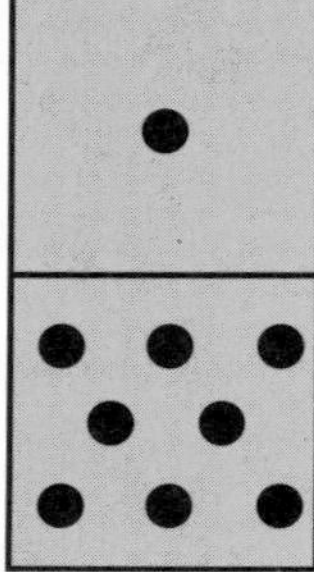

$$\begin{array}{r} 4 \\ +\ 6 \\ \hline \end{array}$$

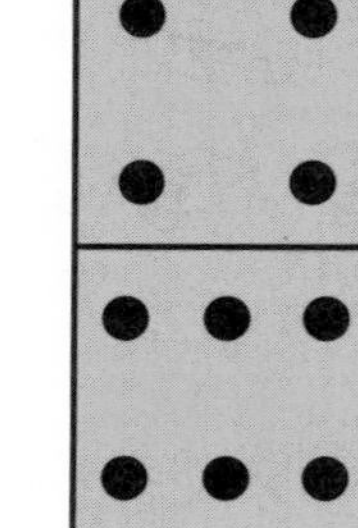

$$\begin{array}{r} 5 \\ +\ 7 \\ \hline \end{array}$$

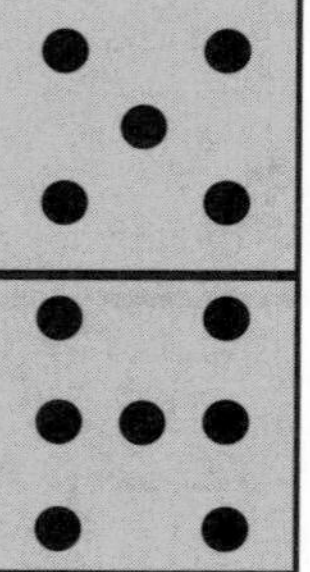

Coloring Fun

Add. Color the sums. According to the code.

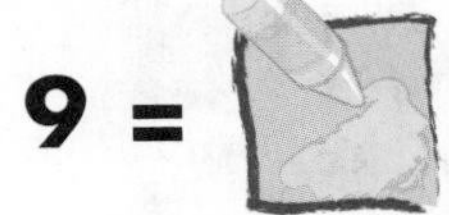

9 =

11 =

10 =

12 =

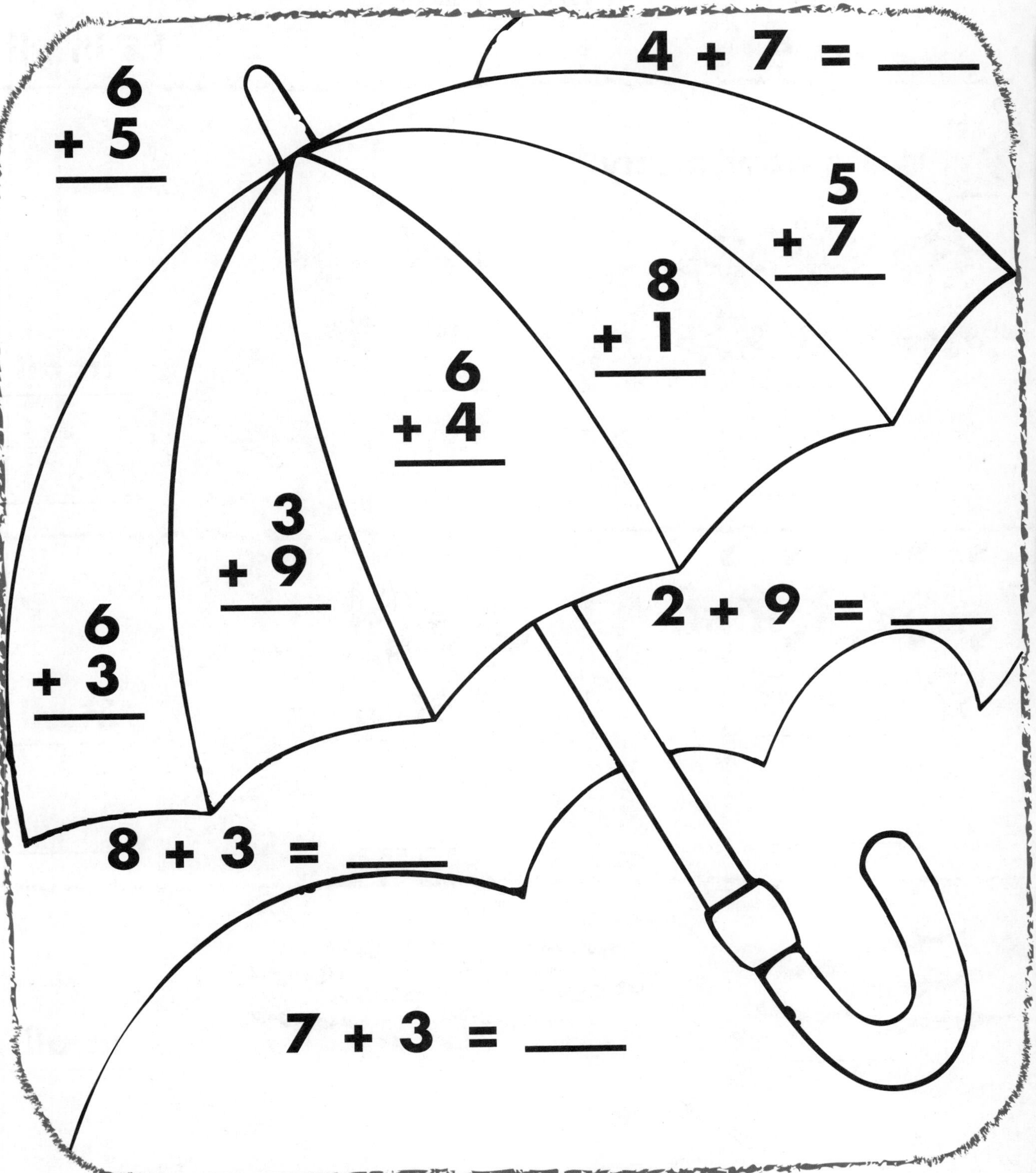

$$\begin{array}{r} 6 \\ +\ 5 \\ \hline \end{array}$$

4 + 7 = ____

$$\begin{array}{r} 5 \\ +\ 7 \\ \hline \end{array}$$

$$\begin{array}{r} 8 \\ +\ 1 \\ \hline \end{array}$$

$$\begin{array}{r} 6 \\ +\ 4 \\ \hline \end{array}$$

$$\begin{array}{r} 3 \\ +\ 9 \\ \hline \end{array}$$

$$\begin{array}{r} 6 \\ +\ 3 \\ \hline \end{array}$$

2 + 9 = ____

8 + 3 = ____

7 + 3 = ____

ADDITION

In the Pond

8 + 7 = 15 in all

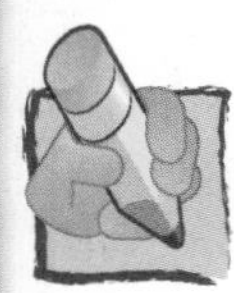

Write how many.

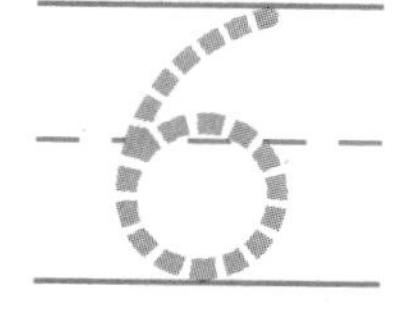

+

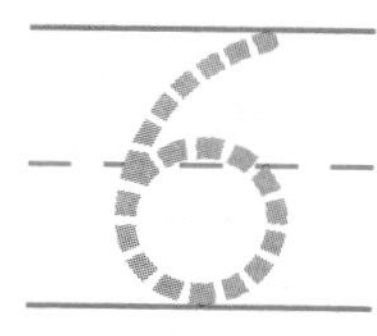

=

in all

\+ =

in all

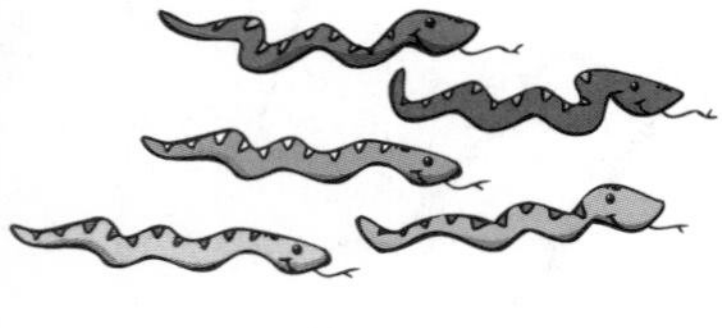

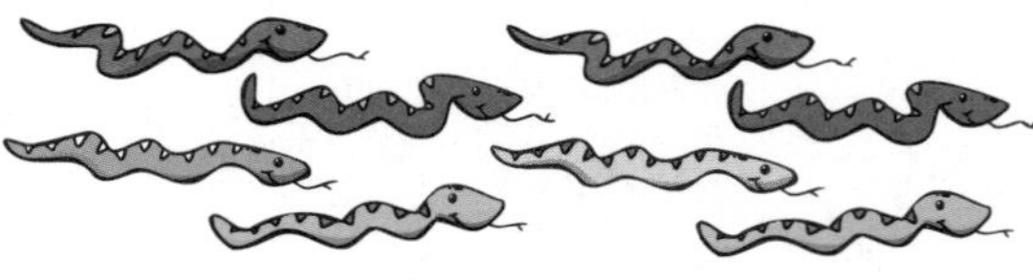

\+ =

in all

Flower Show

9
+ 6
15 in all

7
+ 7
14 in all

Write how many.

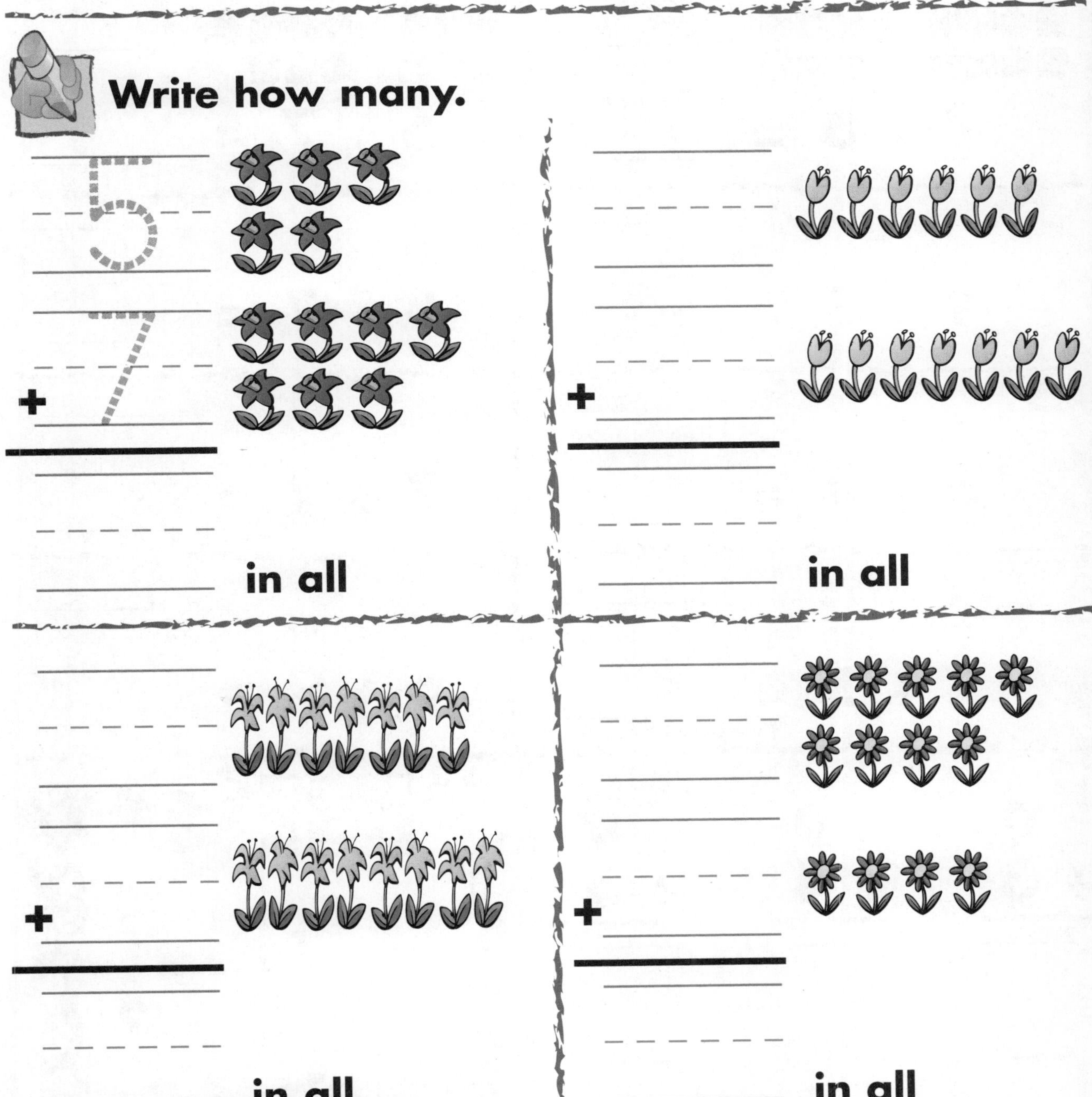

in all

in all

in all

in all

ADDITION

Cars and Blocks

8 + 7 = 15

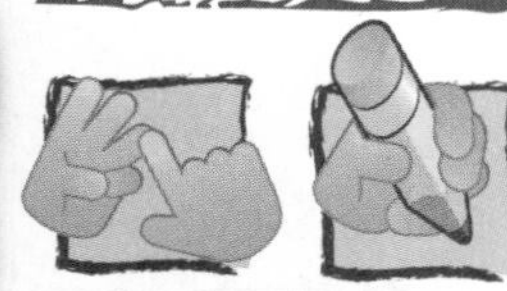

Add. Write each sum.

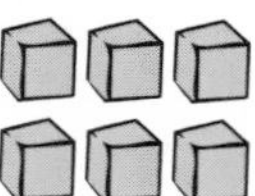

8 + 6 = 14

6 + 7 = ____

9 + 5 = ____

8 + 7 = ____

6 + 8 = ____

7 + 4 = ____

7 + 7 = ____

6 + 9 = ____

$$\begin{array}{r} 9 \\ +\ 3 \\ \hline \end{array} \qquad \begin{array}{r} 9 \\ +\ 4 \\ \hline \end{array} \qquad \begin{array}{r} 9 \\ +\ 5 \\ \hline \end{array}$$

Lots of Socks

Add.
Write each sum.

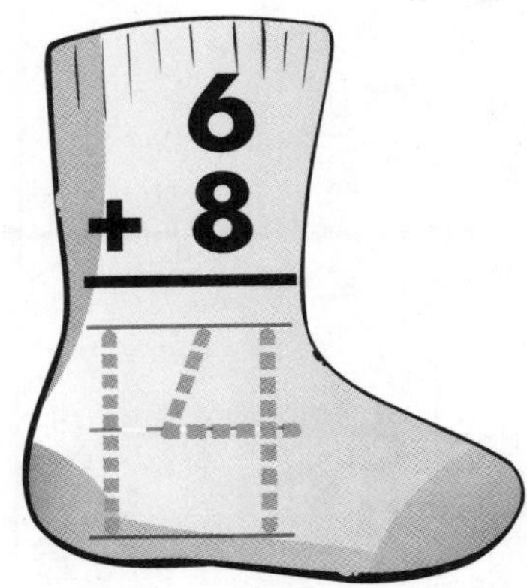

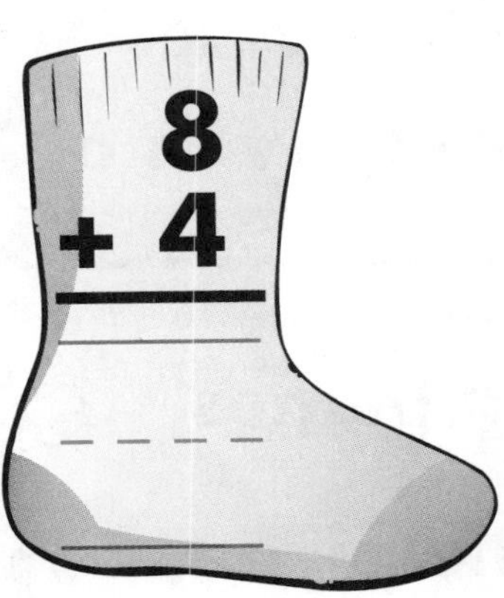

ADDITION

Flying High

4 kites in the sky
+ 8 more kites fly

12 kites in all

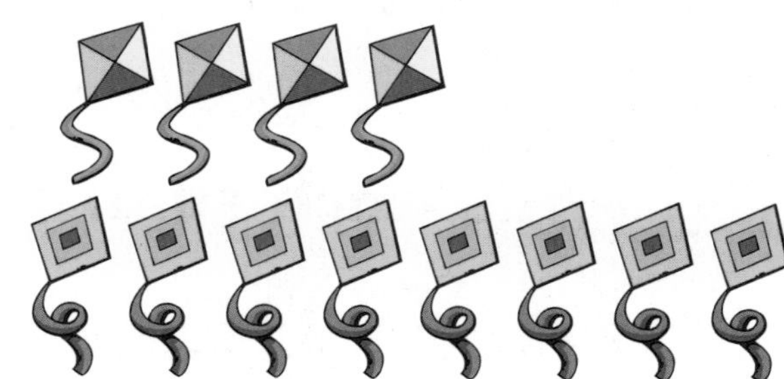

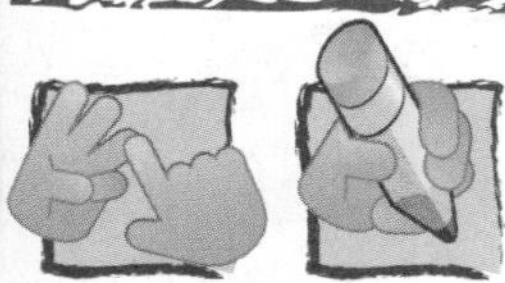

Add. Write each sum.

7 balloons

8 more balloons

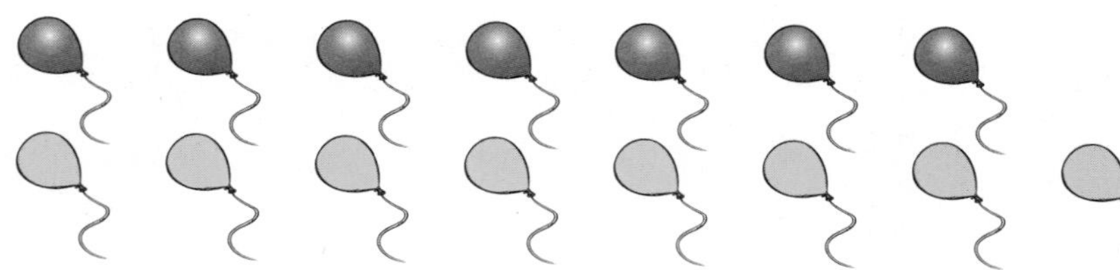

How many in all? ____ balloons

5 big planes

8 little planes

How many in all? ____ planes

9 flags

6 more flags

How many in all? ____ flags

Sum Money

$$\begin{array}{r} 7¢ \\ +\ 8¢ \\ \hline 15¢ \end{array}$$

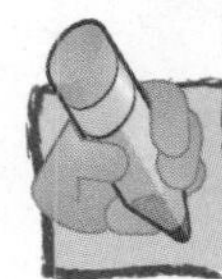

Write how much money.

9 ¢
+ 4 ¢
13 ¢

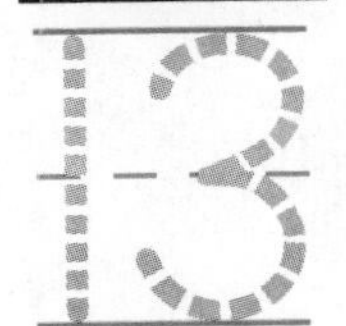

8 ¢
+ 5 ¢
____ ¢

6 ¢
+ 8 ¢
____ ¢

7 ¢
+ 7 ¢
____ ¢

Circle each bag with 15¢.

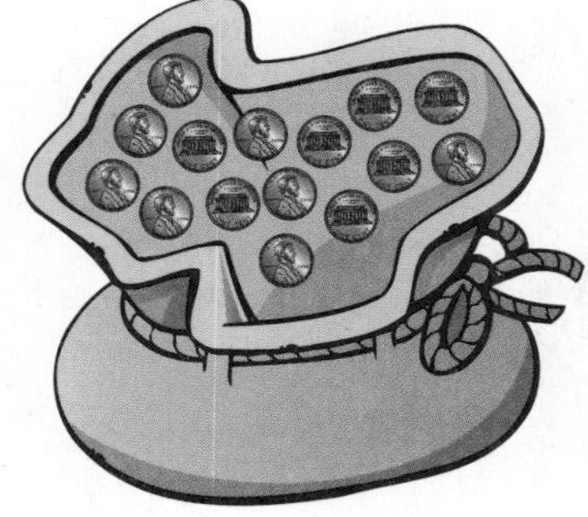

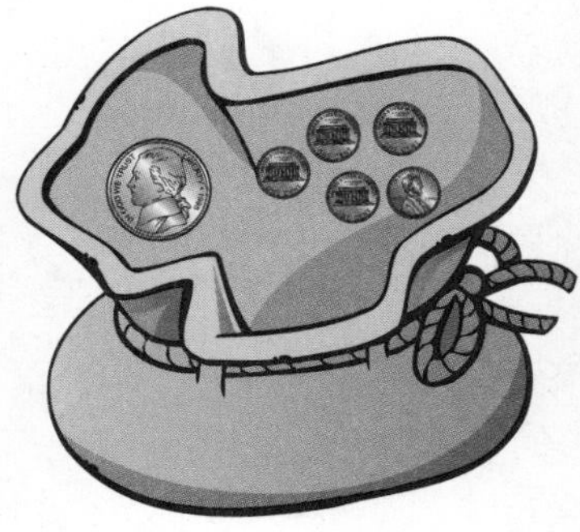

ADDITION

Play Ball!

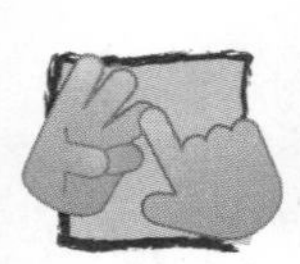
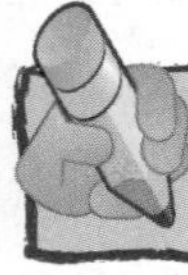

Add. Write each sum.

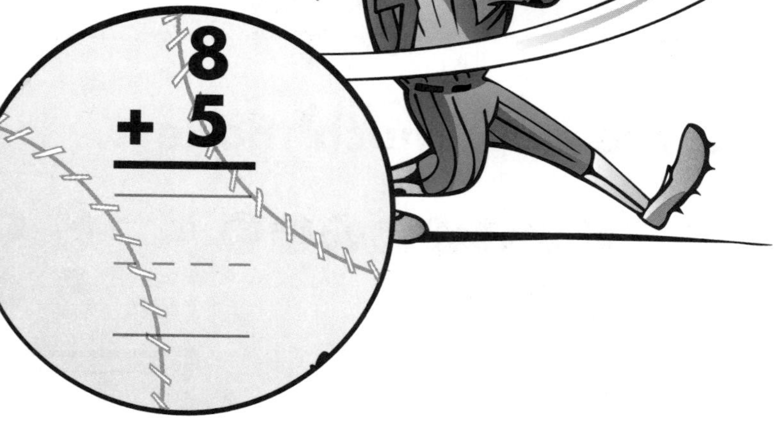

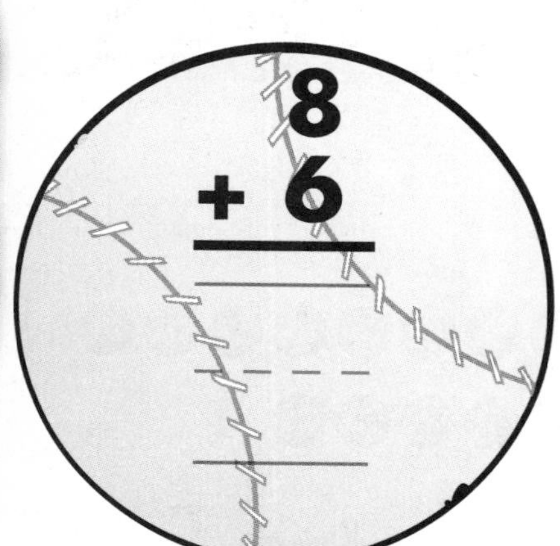

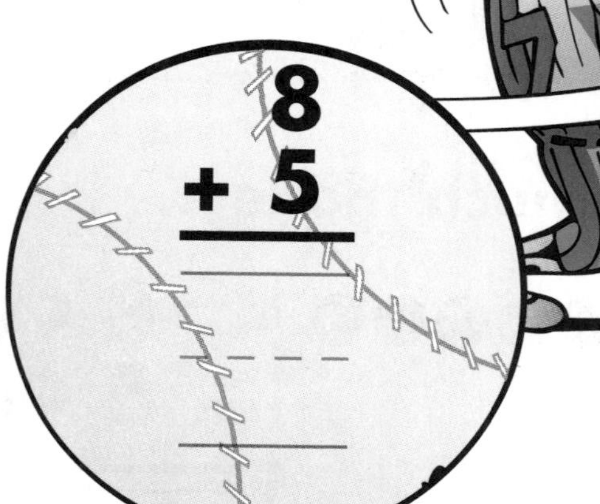

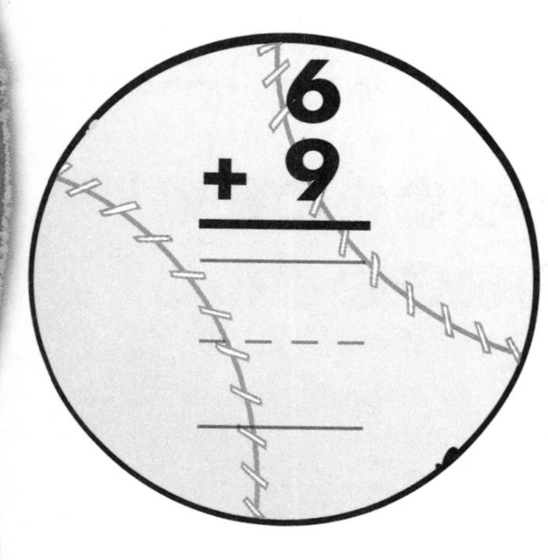

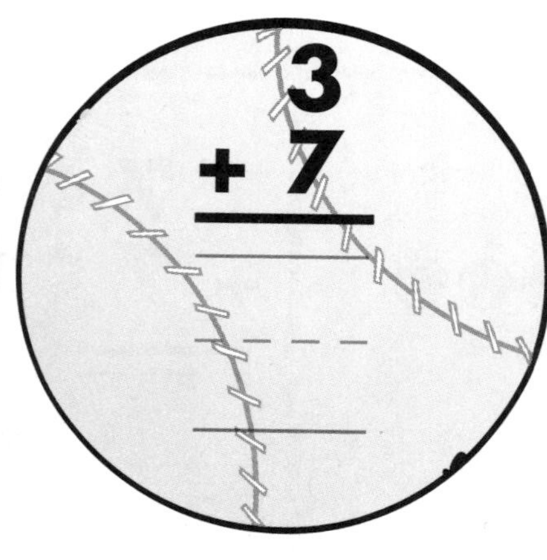

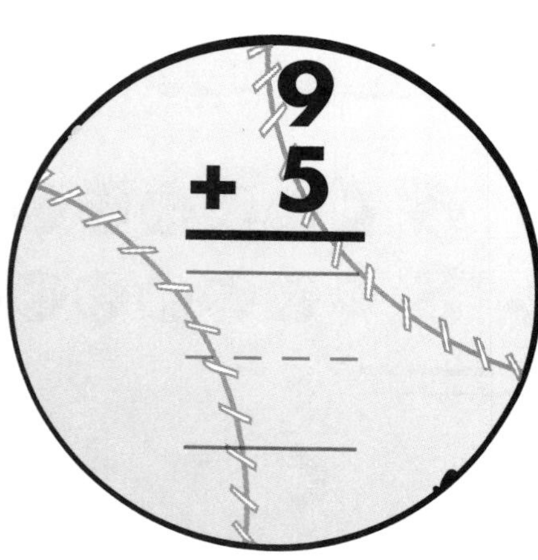

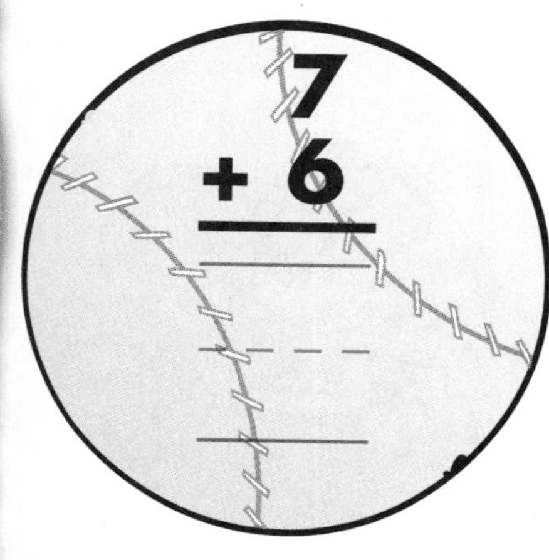

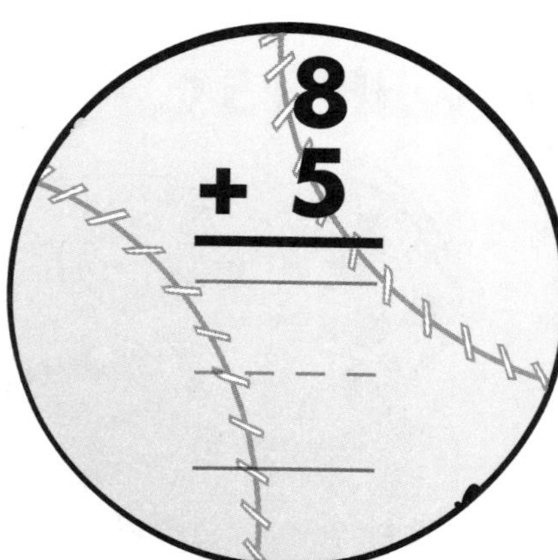

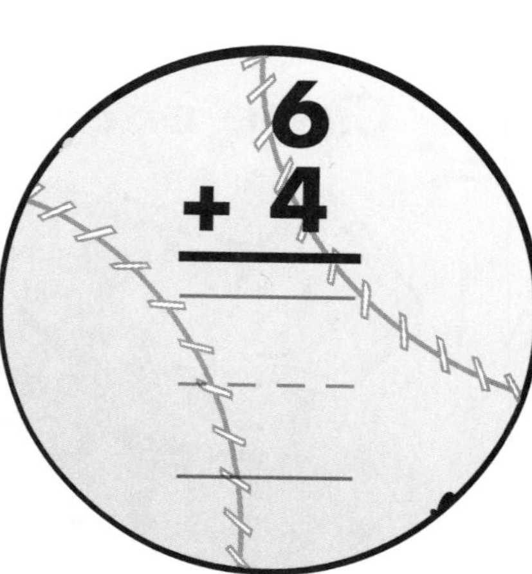

Review

Add. Write each sum.

$$\begin{array}{r} 5 \\ +\,6 \\ \hline \end{array} \quad \begin{array}{r} 3 \\ +\,9 \\ \hline \end{array} \quad \begin{array}{r} 6 \\ +\,7 \\ \hline \end{array} \quad \begin{array}{r} 9 \\ +\,4 \\ \hline \end{array}$$

$$\begin{array}{r} 8 \\ +\,6 \\ \hline \end{array} \quad \begin{array}{r} 2 \\ +\,9 \\ \hline \end{array} \quad \begin{array}{r} 3 \\ +\,10 \\ \hline \end{array} \quad \begin{array}{r} 8 \\ +\,3 \\ \hline \end{array} \quad \begin{array}{r} 7 \\ +\,4 \\ \hline \end{array}$$

$$\begin{array}{r} 9 \\ +\,5 \\ \hline \end{array} \quad \begin{array}{r} 7 \\ +\,7 \\ \hline \end{array} \quad \begin{array}{r} 4 \\ +\,4 \\ \hline \end{array} \quad \begin{array}{r} 9 \\ +\,6 \\ \hline \end{array} \quad \begin{array}{r} 7 \\ +\,3 \\ \hline \end{array}$$

$$\begin{array}{r} 4 \\ +\,8 \\ \hline \end{array} \quad \begin{array}{r} 6 \\ +\,2 \\ \hline \end{array} \quad \begin{array}{r} 6 \\ +\,6 \\ \hline \end{array} \quad \begin{array}{r} 8 \\ +\,5 \\ \hline \end{array} \quad \begin{array}{r} 7 \\ +\,8 \\ \hline \end{array}$$

On the Go

Subtract. Write each answer.

How many are left?

6 – 2 = 4

How many are left?

9 – 3 = ____

How many are left?

10 – 8 = ____

Circle the correct answer.

What has no hands but can wave all day?

Animal Action

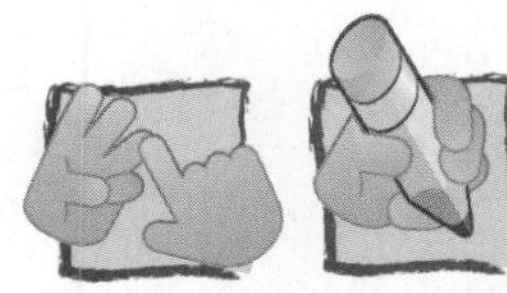

Subtract. Write each answer.

How many are left?

7 – 5 =

How many are left?

9 – 4 = ____

How many are left?

10 – 3 = ____

How many are left?

8 – 8 = ____

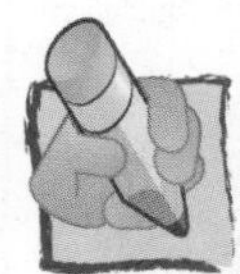

Write the missing numbers.

10, 9, 8, ____, 6, 5, ____, 3, 2, 1

More Animals

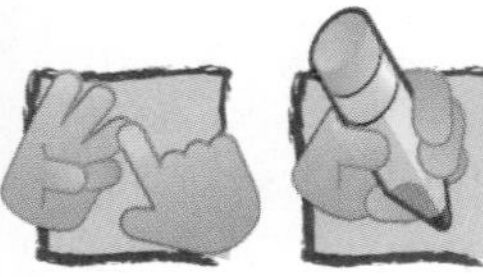
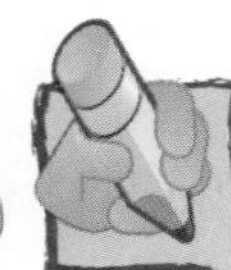

X out. Subtract. Write each answer.

How many are left?

$$\begin{array}{r} 9 \\ -\ 6 \\ \hline 3 \end{array}$$

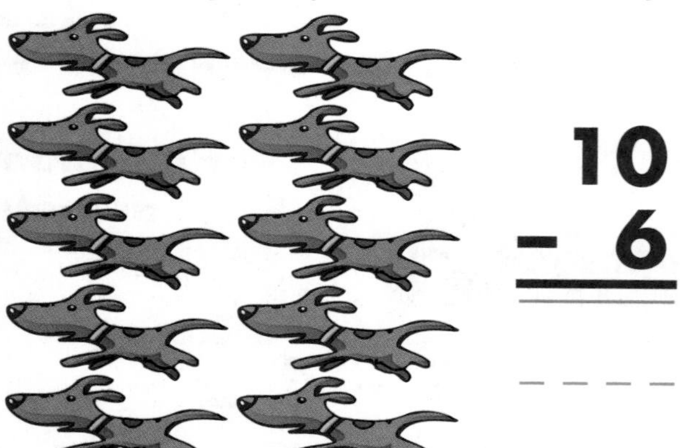

$$\begin{array}{r} 10 \\ -\ 6 \\ \hline \end{array}$$

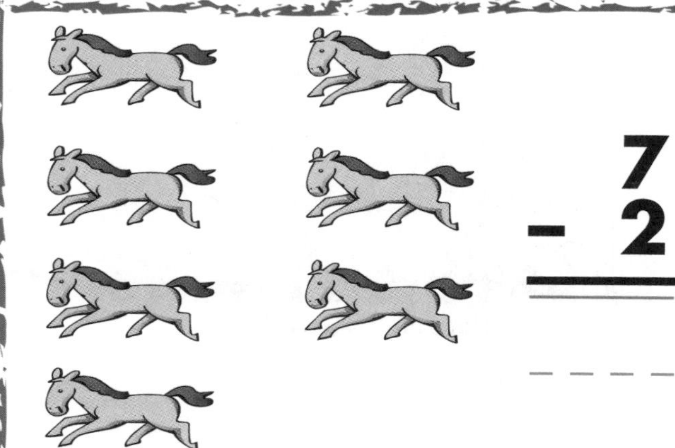

$$\begin{array}{r} 7 \\ -\ 2 \\ \hline \end{array}$$

$$\begin{array}{r} 8 \\ -\ 5 \\ \hline \end{array}$$

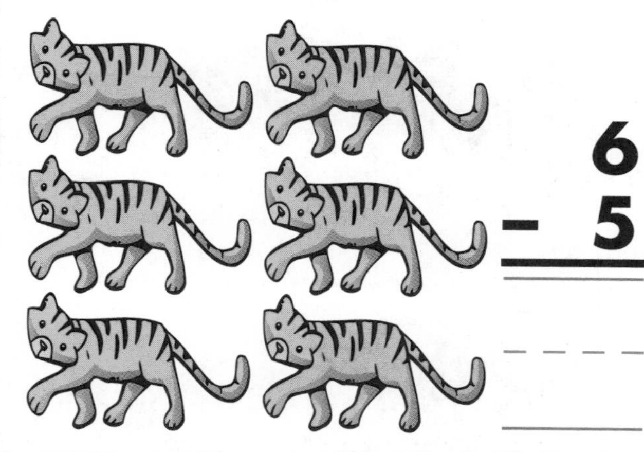

$$\begin{array}{r} 6 \\ -\ 5 \\ \hline \end{array}$$

Circle the correct answer.

Which animal is easy to spot?

Party Time

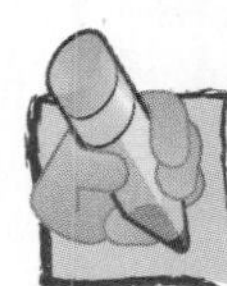

Write how many are left.

How many are left?

14 – 8 = 6

13 – 6 = ____

12 – 7 = ____

9 – 0 = ____

11 – 5 = ____

Don't Bug Me!

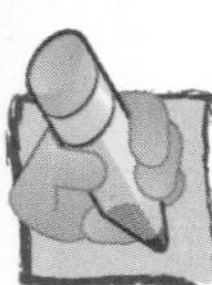

Write how many are left.

14 – 5 = 9

13 – 9 = ____

11 – 3 = ____

12 – 5 = ____

Circle the correct answer.

What has 6 wheels and flies?

Nutty Cross Out

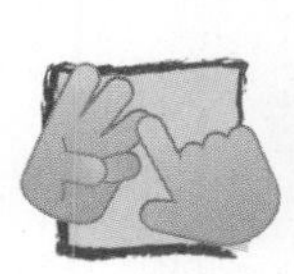  **Subtract. Write how many are left.**

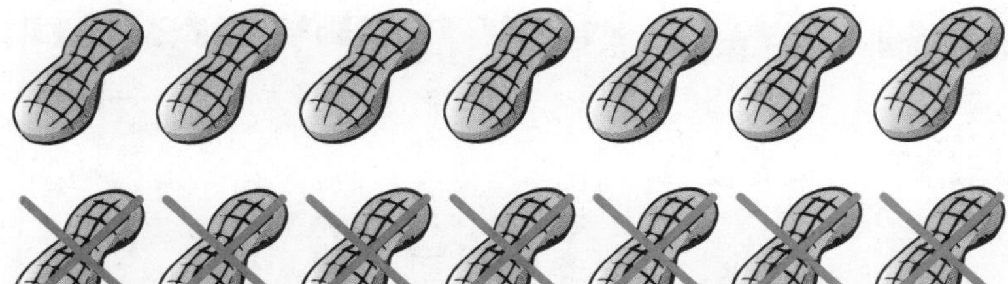

14 − 7 = 7

11 − 2 = ____

13 − 8 = ____

12 − 9 = ____

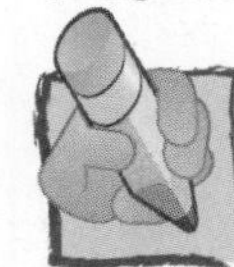 **Write the answer.**

A  **got 10**  **s. The**  **ate 7**  **s.**

How many  **s are left?** ____

SUBTRACTION

Home Sweet Home

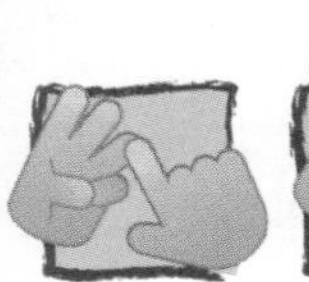

X out. Subtract. Write how many are left.

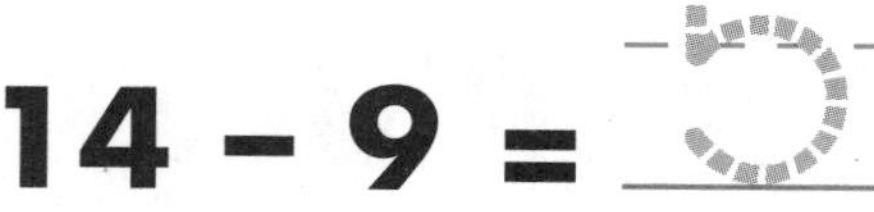

14 – 9 = 5

10 – 7 = ____

12 – 6 = ____

13 – 5 = ____

Circle the correct answer.

What animal never leaves home?

Down We Go

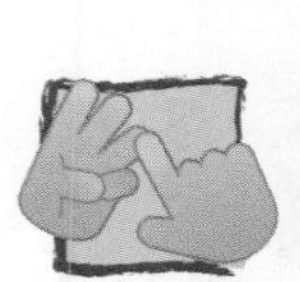 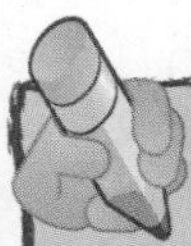

Subtract. Write how many are left.

How many are left?

$$\begin{array}{r} 11 \\ -\ 5 \\ \hline 6 \end{array}$$

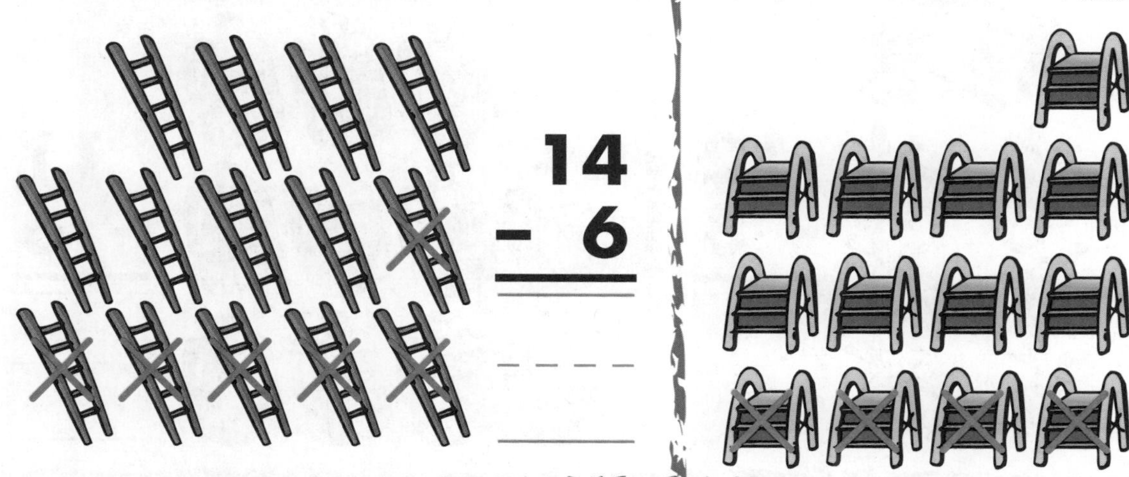

$$\begin{array}{r} 14 \\ -\ 6 \\ \hline \end{array}$$

$$\begin{array}{r} 13 \\ -\ 4 \\ \hline \end{array}$$

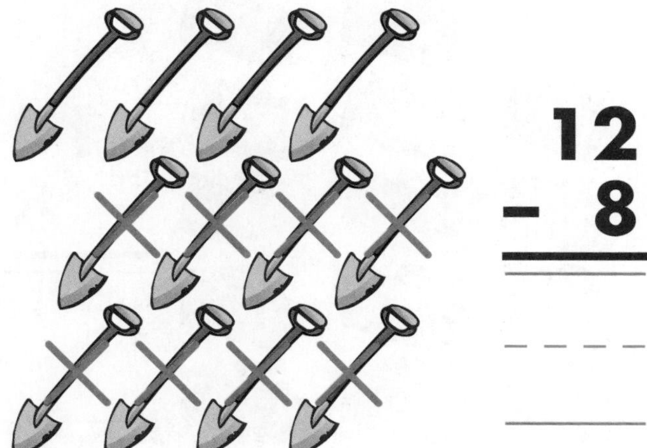

$$\begin{array}{r} 12 \\ -\ 8 \\ \hline \end{array}$$

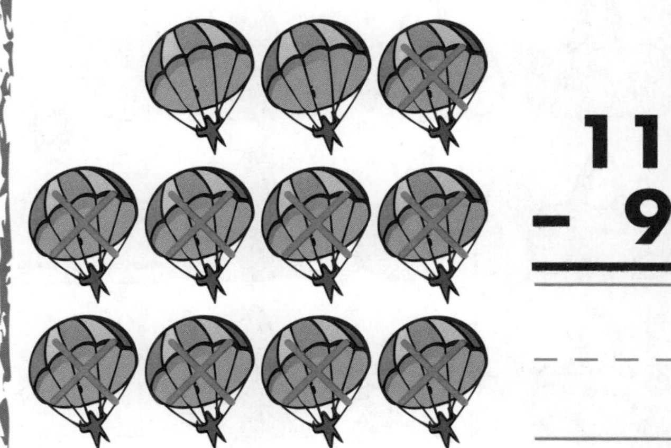

$$\begin{array}{r} 11 \\ -\ 9 \\ \hline \end{array}$$

Write the missing numbers.

14, 12, ____, 8, ____, 4, 2

SUBTRACTION

SUBTRACTION

Have a Nice Trip

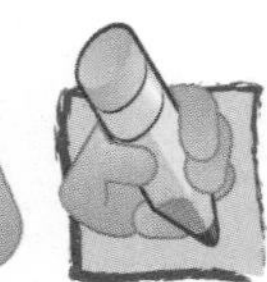

X out. Subtract. Write how many are left.

$$\begin{array}{r} 13 \\ -\ 7 \\ \hline 6 \end{array}$$

How many are left?

$$\begin{array}{r} 12 \\ -\ 3 \\ \hline \end{array}$$

$$\begin{array}{r} 11 \\ -\ 6 \\ \hline \end{array}$$

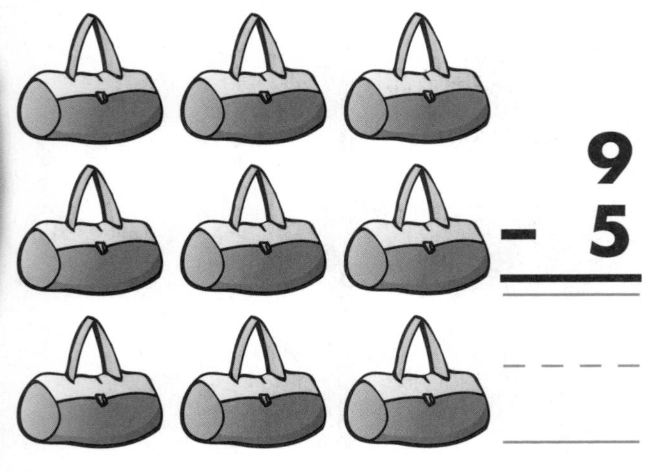

$$\begin{array}{r} 9 \\ -\ 5 \\ \hline \end{array}$$

$$\begin{array}{r} 14 \\ -\ 8 \\ \hline \end{array}$$

Circle the correct answer.

What can travel all over but never leaves the corner?

On the Lines

Subtract.
Write each answer.

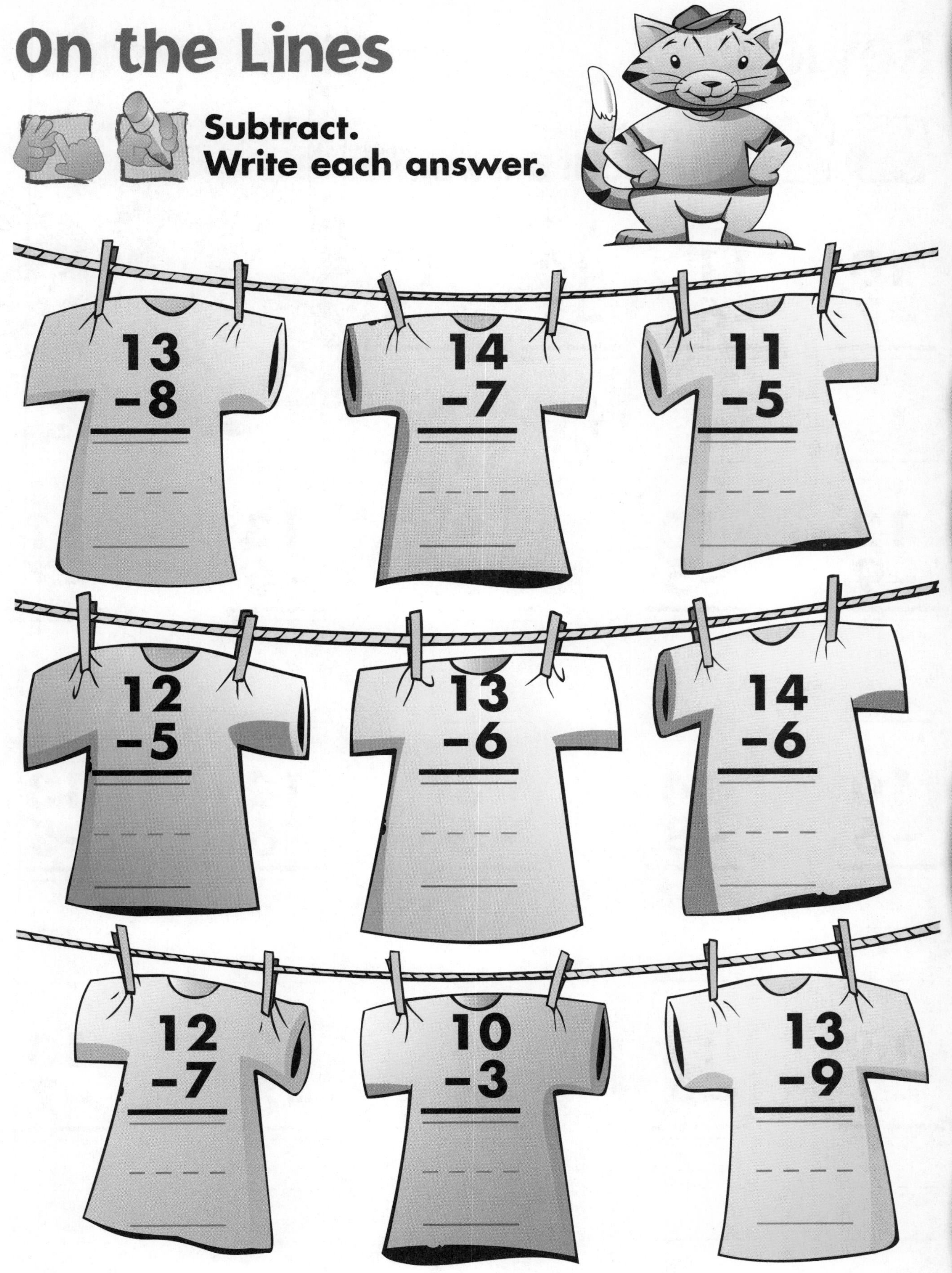

Review

Subract.
Write each answer.

10 − 7	11 − 6	14 − 5	13 − 3	
12 − 9	10 − 5	9 − 7	13 − 6	11 − 7
10 − 6	14 − 8	8 − 6	12 − 6	13 − 5
11 − 2	12 − 4	14 − 6	12 − 8	13 − 7

When the farmer got to the apples his wife cried, "Why, this morning I could not spare one apple for our neighbor. Now I have a whole sack! How wonderful!"

So the two rich men had to pay $100 to the farmer for the sack of rotten apples.

And that, of course, was the very best trade of all!

What Can You Get for a Horse?

A farmer and his wife lived on a little farm with their horse.

One day the farmer said, "Let's sell the horse for something better."

"Fine with me," the wife said.

The farmer took the horse to the fair. On the way he met a man with a cow.

"Would you like to trade?" asked the man.

"Well," said the farmer, "my horse is worth more money. But a cow is better. It will give us milk."

And so they traded.

$18 - $12 = $6 lost

The men laughed. "We'll bet $100 to your sack of apples that your wife will be angry."

So off they went, and the farmer told the story all over again. His wife clapped at every trade!

Soon the farmer met two rich men. He told them about his trades.

"Why, you fool!" said the men. "Your wife will be very angry."

"I don't think so," said the farmer.

Next the farmer met a man with a sheep.

"Would you like to trade?" asked the man.

"Well," said the farmer, "My cow is worth more money. But a sheep is better. It will give us wool to keep us warm."

So they traded.

$12 - $9 = $3 lost

Then a woman with a goose came along.

"Would you like to trade?" asked the woman.

"Well," said the farmer, "My sheep is worth more money. But a goose is better. It will give us beautiful feathers."

And so they traded.

$9 - $7 = $2 lost

Next the farmer met a man with a sack of rotten apples.

"Would you like to trade?" asked the man.

"Well," said the farmer, "My goose is worth more money. But my wife would like those better. Last year we had only one rotten apple on our tree."

And so they traded.

$7 - $2 = $5 lost

Month 6 Checklist

Hands-on activities to help your child in school!

ADDITION WITH SUMS THROUGH 18

Adding with Sums to 18: pages 163-174, 177-178
Applying Addition Concepts: pages 171-178

In this month, your child will continue to learn addition facts—including sums through 18.

- ❑ Complete the worksheets.
- ❑ With your child, count out up to 18 small items and separate them into two groups. Write a number sentence with the total number of items as the sum and the number of items in each group as the addends. After doing this activity a few times, your child can repeat it independently. Challenge him or her to find and record all the combinations for any given sum.
- ❑ Have your child write a story about an addition fact and then tell the story to other family members. For example, "What happened when the 3 bears were joined by 11 cousins? There were 14 bears, and there was no room for Goldilocks!"
- ❑ To reinforce the "make a ten" strategy for finding sums, cut an egg carton so that it has 10 sections. Using an addition sentence such as 8 + 9, have your child place 8 objects in the egg carton, then add 2 more to make 10. With 7 left over, your child proves that 8 + 9 = 10 + 7, or 17. Repeat for several other facts.
- ❑ Have your child roll three dice and name the numbers. Then, challenge him or her to find the sum of the numbers using objects, counting on, or other addition strategies.
- ❑ With your child, draw or paint a picture that illustrates a hard-to-learn fact.

SUBTRACTION FROM NUMBERS THROUGH 18

Subtracting with Differences to 18: pages 182-188, 191-192
Applying Subtraction Concepts: pages 179-181, 189-191

In this month, your child will explore the concepts of subtraction more closely, examining subtraction as it is used to take away, compare, or find how many more are needed. He or she will also get ample practice in subtracting from numbers through 18.

- ❑ Complete the worksheets.
- ❑ Play "How Many More?" Create groups of 13 pennies and 8 pennies. Have your child compare to find which group has more pennies, then subtract to find how many more. Repeat the activity using penny groups of different amounts, such as 12 pennies and 7 pennies, to reinforce the concept of using subtraction to compare.
- ❑ Play "Under the Cup." Show your child a collection of up to 14 small items. Hide some of the items under the cup and challenge your child to tell how many are hidden by counting those that remain. Reverse roles and play again. Repeat as time and interest permit.
- ❑ Have your child make up a funny story, a poem, a jingle, or a song to reinforce facts. Then encourage him or her to repeat the story, poem, jingle, or song to other family members to gain confidence and additional practice.

Kitten Mischief

9 + 9 = 18 in all

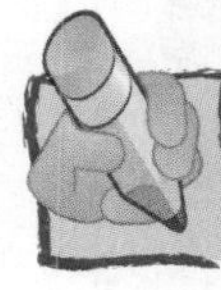

Write how many.

8 + 9 = ____ in all

____ + ____ = ____ in all

____ + ____ = ____ in all

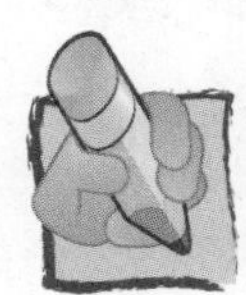

Write the answer.
If 1 cat has 9 lives, how many lives do 2 cats have?

____

ADDITION

Marching Band

$$\begin{array}{r} 9 \\ +\ 8 \\ \hline 17 \end{array}$$

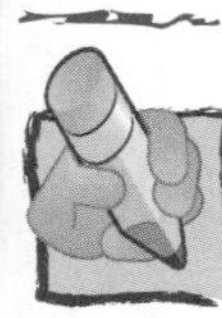

Write how many in all.

$$\begin{array}{r} 8 \\ +\ 7 \\ \hline 15 \end{array}$$

15 in all

$$\begin{array}{r} 8 \\ +\ 9 \\ \hline \end{array}$$

_____ in all

$$\begin{array}{r} 9 \\ +\ 7 \\ \hline \end{array}$$

_____ in all

$$\begin{array}{r} 6 \\ +\ 9 \\ \hline \end{array}$$

_____ in all

$$\begin{array}{r} 6 \\ +\ 7 \\ \hline \end{array}$$

_____ in all

$$\begin{array}{r} 7 \\ +\ 7 \\ \hline \end{array}$$

_____ in all

On the Green

9 + 9 = 18

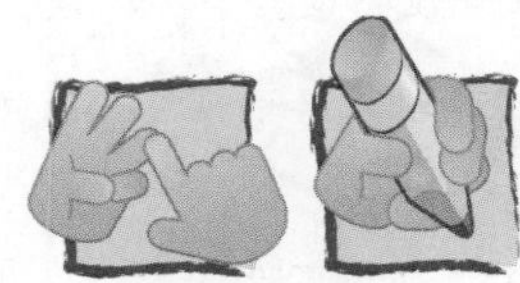

Add. Write each sum.

9 + 8 = 17

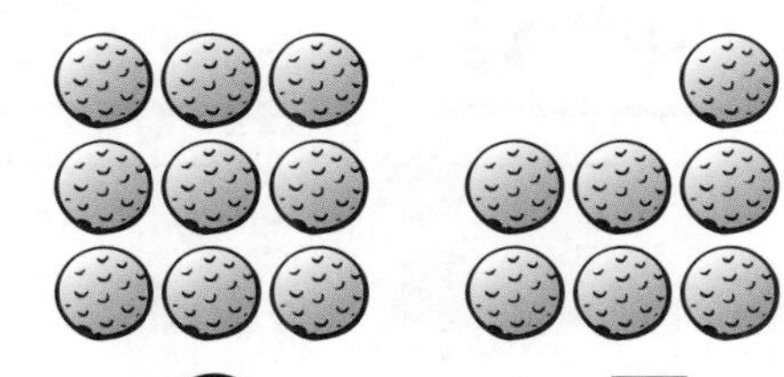

9 + 7 = ____

8+9= ____ 7+9= ____ 9+6= ____

8+8= ____ 7+3= ____ 0+7= ____

2+6= ____ 8+0= ____ 6+3= ____

In the Alley

$$\begin{array}{r} 10 \\ +\ 8 \\ \hline 18 \end{array}$$

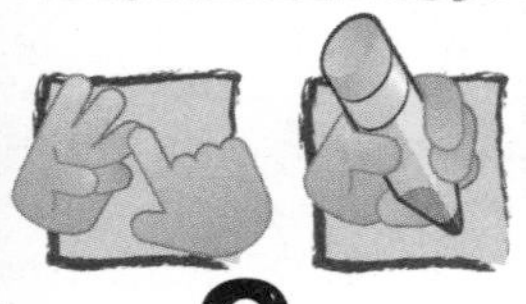

Add. Write each sum.

$$\begin{array}{r} 9 \\ +\ 8 \\ \hline 17 \end{array} \qquad \begin{array}{r} 10 \\ +\ 0 \\ \hline \end{array} \qquad \begin{array}{r} 9 \\ +\ 9 \\ \hline \end{array} \qquad \begin{array}{r} 6 \\ +\ 8 \\ \hline \end{array}$$

$$\begin{array}{r} 6 \\ +\ 9 \\ \hline \end{array} \qquad \begin{array}{r} 7 \\ +\ 6 \\ \hline \end{array} \qquad \begin{array}{r} 9 \\ +\ 5 \\ \hline \end{array} \qquad \begin{array}{r} 8 \\ +\ 8 \\ \hline \end{array}$$

$$\begin{array}{r} 10 \\ +\ 5 \\ \hline \end{array} \qquad \begin{array}{r} 10 \\ +\ 6 \\ \hline \end{array} \qquad \begin{array}{r} 10 \\ +\ 7 \\ \hline \end{array} \qquad \begin{array}{r} 10 \\ +\ \square\ ? \\ \hline \square\ ? \end{array}$$

What's Missing?

7 + 4 = 11

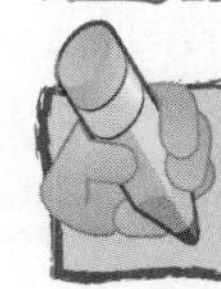

Write the missing number.

6 + ___ 14	___ + 9 12	8 + ___ 13	___ + 9 17
___ + 8 16	___ + 7 7	9 + ___ 18	10 + ___ 13
3 + ___ 11	___ + 7 15	5 + ___ 15	

Falling Leaves

Add. Color the leaves according to the code.

15 =

17 =

16 =

18 =

8 + 8 | **10 + 8** | **7 + 8**

9 + 8 | **8 + 9** | **9 + 9**

10 + 8 | **9 + 7** | **8 + 8**

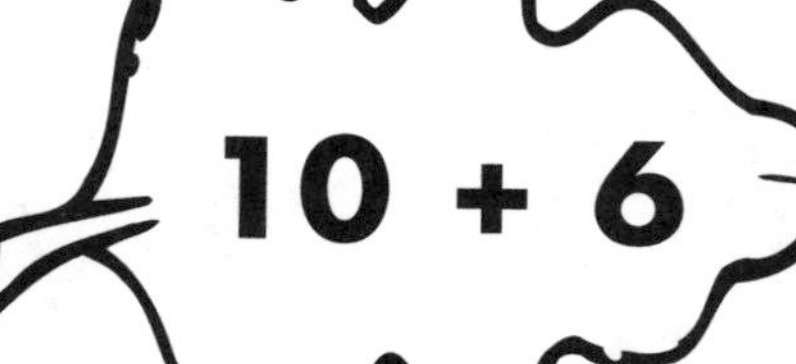

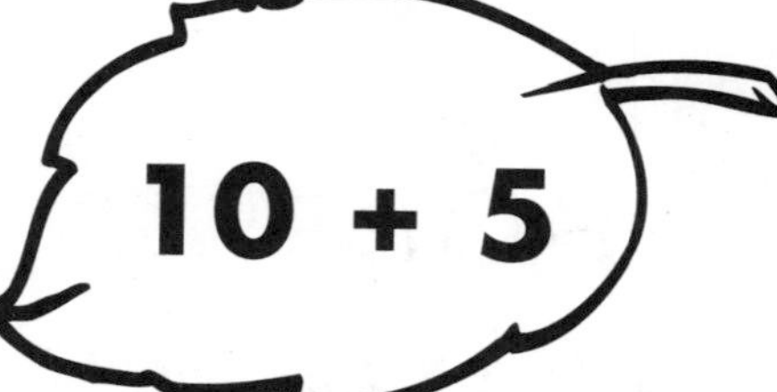

On Target

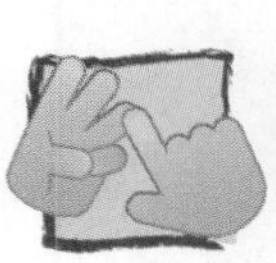

Add and write the answers to complete the wheels.

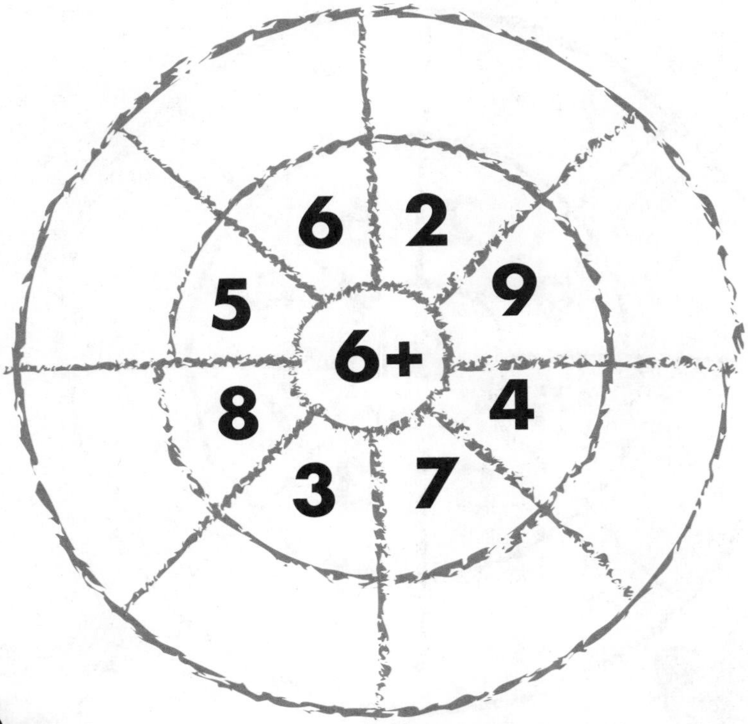

6+

6 2 9 4 7 3 8 5

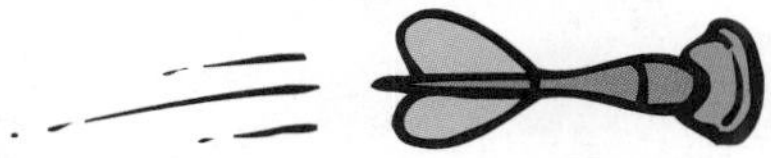

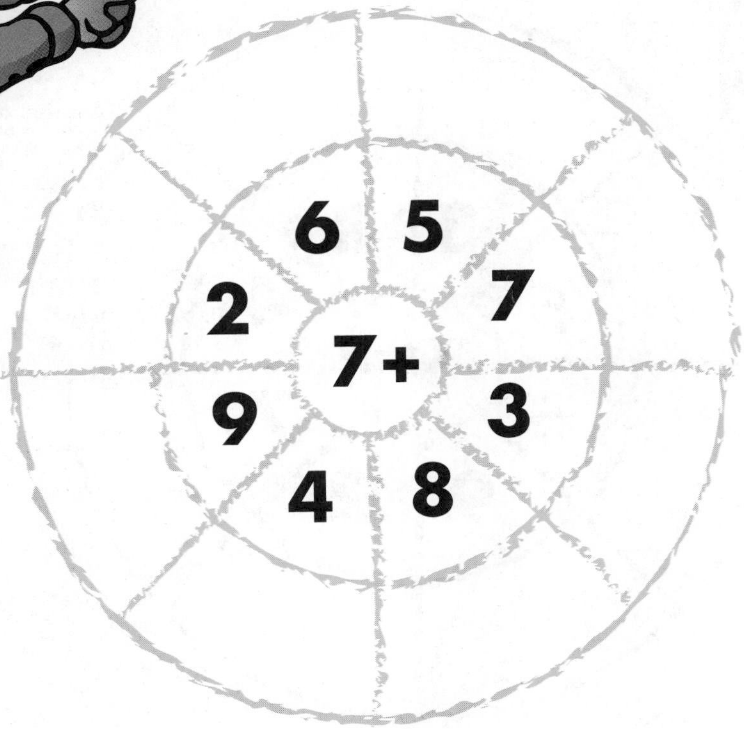

7+

6 5 7 3 8 4 9 2

ADDITION

More Target Practice

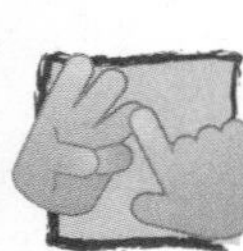

Add and write the answers to complete the wheels.

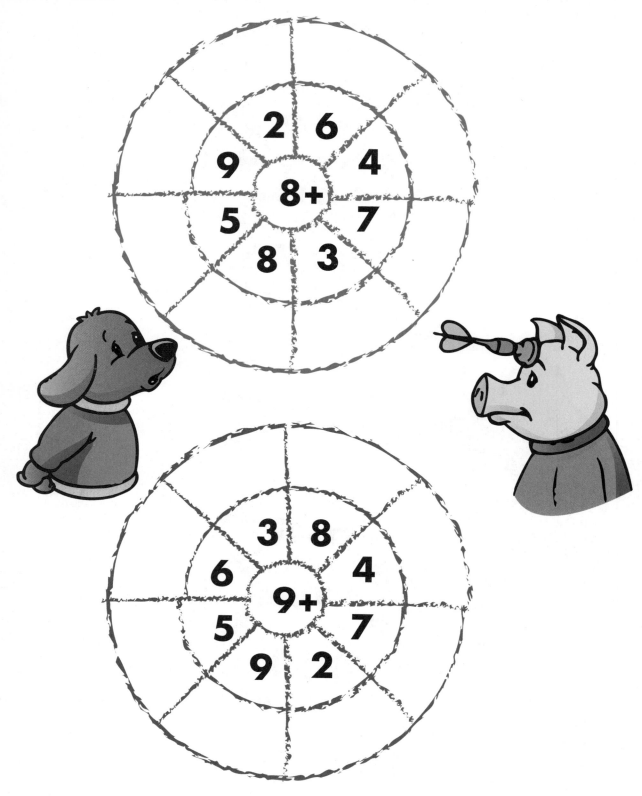

8+

2 6
9 4
5 7
8 3

9+

3 8
6 4
5 7
9 2

At last the stranger said, "The soup is done!"

And everyone in the town, including the clever stranger, enjoyed the stone soup.

Long ago, in a far away land, the people of a small town were very poor.

One day a stranger came to town and asked for food. The people said they had nothing to give him.

But the stranger was very smart.

He asked, "Do you have a big black pot?"

The people said, "Oh, yes."

He asked, "Do you have cold, fresh water?"

And the people said, "Oh, yes."

Just then a hunter came back from his hunt with 8 rabbits. They were added to the soup, too.

The stranger stirred the pot for a very long time.

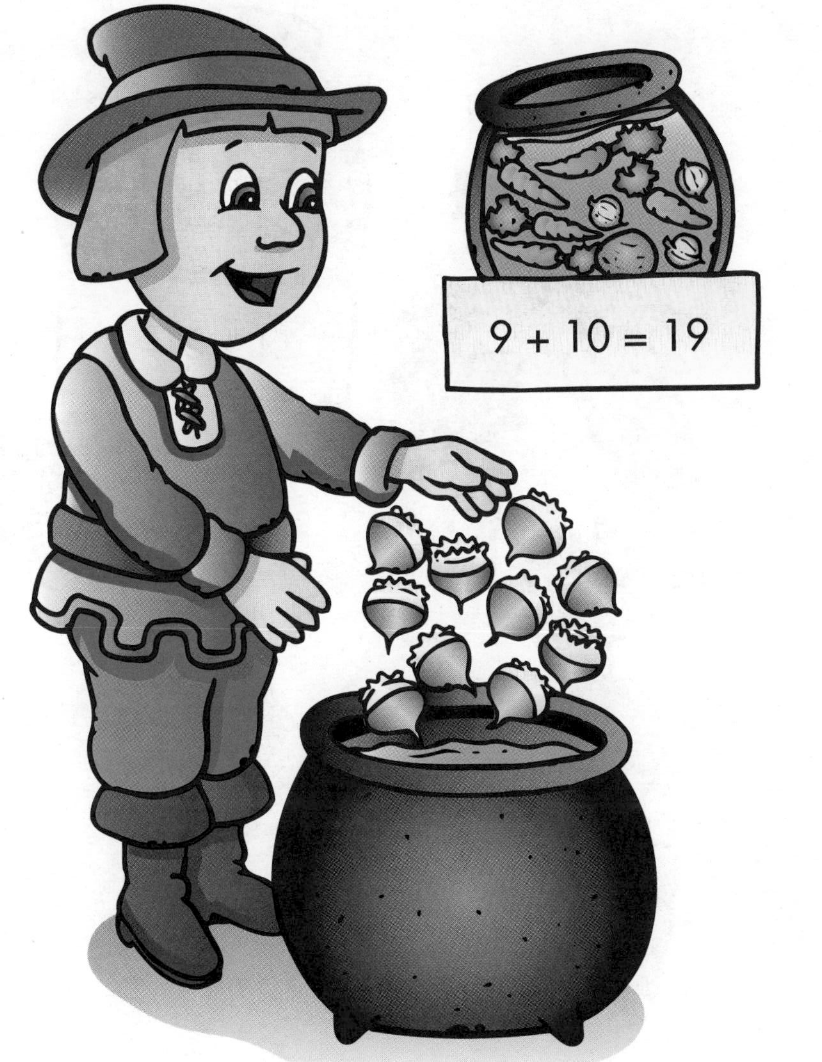

"A turnip or two would really be nice," said the stranger.

"Oh, yes," said the people. And they went and got 10 tiny turnips.

The stranger said, "Then fill the pot with water, for I have a soup stone."

"A soup stone? What is that?" asked the people.

"Why, a soup stone makes soup," the stranger said.

So he put 1 stone in the pot of water.

Then the stranger said, "Do you have an onion or two?"

"Oh, yes," the people said. And they put in 3 large onions.

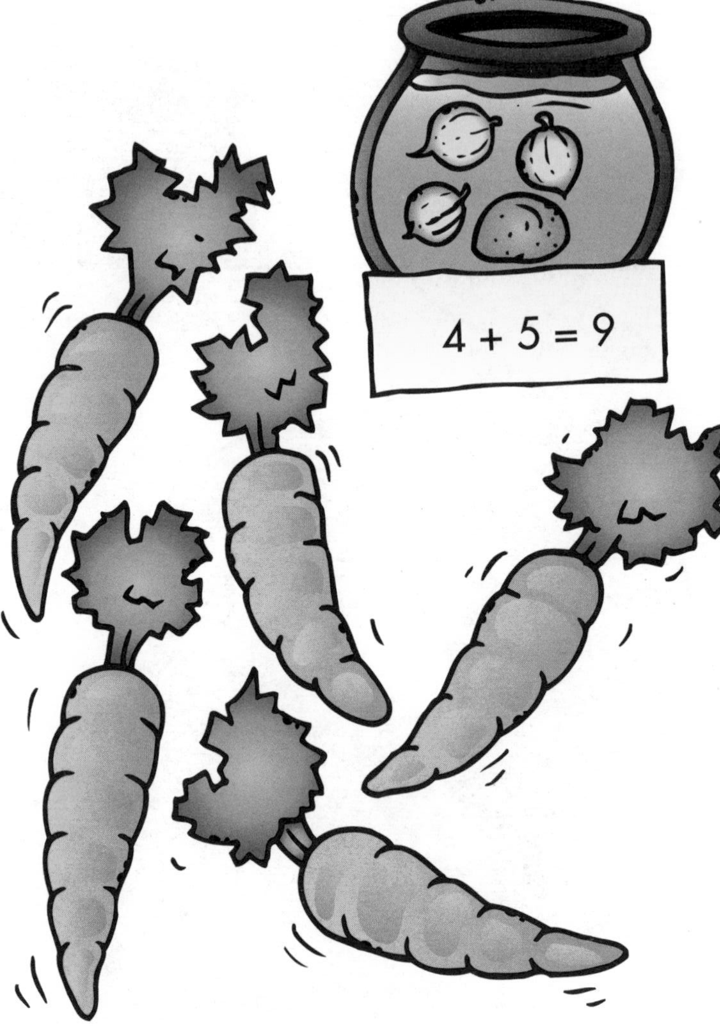

"Maybe you have a carrot?" the stranger asked.

"Oh, yes," the people said. And they found 5 fat carrots.

Addition Stories

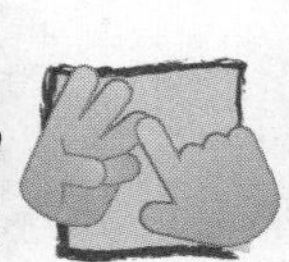

Read each story. Add.
Write each sum.

Kim has 5  **s.**

She got 6 more  **s.**

How many  **s does she have now?**

$$\begin{array}{r} 5 \\ +\ 6 \\ \hline \end{array}$$

Rick found 8  **s.**

Pam found 7  **s.**

How many shells did they find in all?

$$\begin{array}{r} 8 \\ +\ 7 \\ \hline \end{array}$$

Matt has 6  **s.**

Rob has 9  **s.**

How many cars do they have in all?

$$\begin{array}{r} 6 \\ +\ 9 \\ \hline \end{array}$$

Pat has 7  **s.**

Her mother gave her 4 more.

How many  **s does she have now?**

$$\begin{array}{r} 7 \\ +\ 4 \\ \hline \end{array}$$

Add Them All

3	4
2	5
+ 4	+ 7
9	16

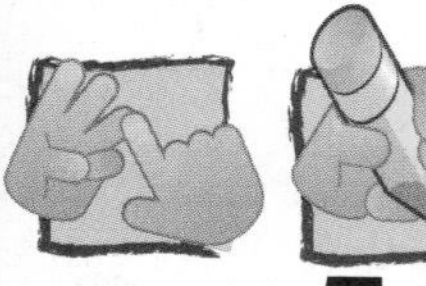

Add. Write each sum.

5	4	3	3	3
3	1	4	2	4
+ 6	+ 9	+ 8	+ 7	+ 5
14				

4	3	2	6	5
4	6	5	6	2
+ 9	+ 7	+ 3	+ 6	+ 6

Review

Help Spot run home. Add. Write each sum.

START

$$\begin{array}{r} 7 \\ +\ 9 \\ \hline \end{array}$$

$$\begin{array}{r} 7 \\ +\ 8 \\ \hline \end{array}$$

$$\begin{array}{r} 6 \\ +\ 8 \\ \hline \end{array}$$

$$\begin{array}{r} 4 \\ +\ 9 \\ \hline \end{array}$$

$$\begin{array}{r} 9 \\ +\ 5 \\ \hline \end{array}$$

$$\begin{array}{r} 6 \\ +\ 5 \\ \hline \end{array}$$

$$\begin{array}{r} 7 \\ +\ 7 \\ \hline \end{array}$$

ADDITION

Practice Test

I can add across.

4 + 3 = 7
- ❍ 6
- ● 7
- ❍ 8

Add. Write each sum and fill in the circle next to the correct answer.

A. 3 + 4 = ____
- ❍ 5
- ❍ 6
- ❍ 7

B. 5 + 6 = ____
- ❍ 11
- ❍ 12
- ❍ 13

C. 0 + 6 = ____
- ❍ 0
- ❍ 6
- ❍ 1

D. 7 + 4 = ____
- ❍ 10
- ❍ 11
- ❍ 12

E. 2 + 9 = ____
- ❍ 9
- ❍ 10
- ❍ 11

F. 4 + 9 = ____
- ❍ 12
- ❍ 13
- ❍ 14

G. 8 + 6 = ____
- ❍ 12
- ❍ 13
- ❍ 14

H. 9 + 9 = ____
- ❍ 17
- ❍ 18
- ❍ 19

Teddy Bear Take Away

Subtract means take away.

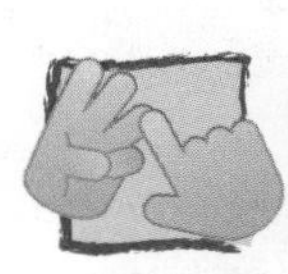 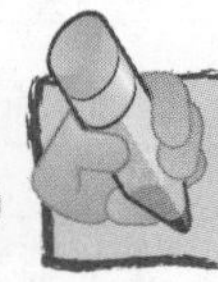 **Subtract. Write how many are left.**

$$\begin{array}{r} 11 \\ -2 \\ \hline 9 \end{array}$$

$$\begin{array}{r} 13 \\ -5 \\ \hline \end{array}$$

$$\begin{array}{r} 15 \\ -8 \\ \hline \end{array}$$

 **Circle the correct answer.**

Take away 2 [honey jar] s.
Then take away 2 more.
How many are left by the door?

1 **2**

SUBTRACTION

More Doors

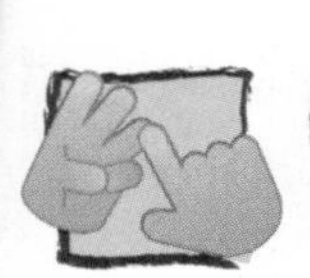

Subtract to compare two sets. What is the difference between the two sets? Write the difference.

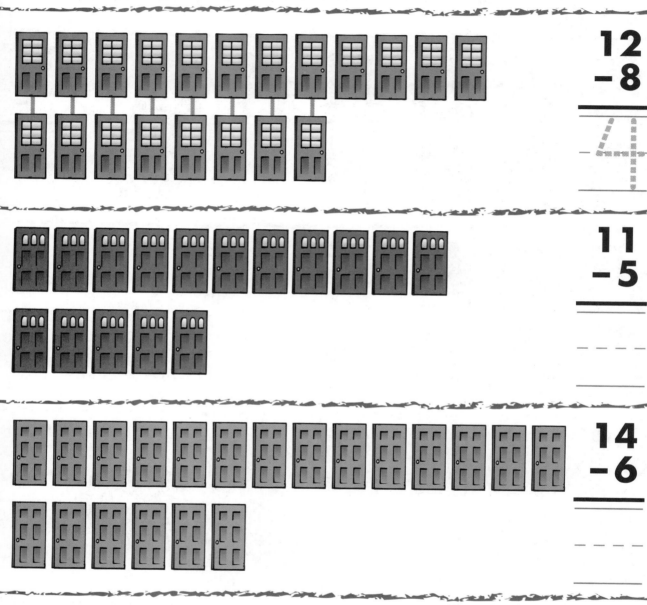

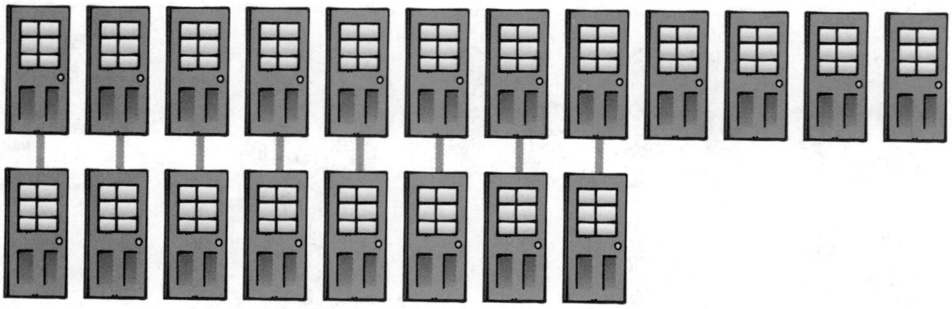

$$\begin{array}{r} 12 \\ -8 \\ \hline 4 \end{array}$$

$$\begin{array}{r} 11 \\ -5 \\ \hline \end{array}$$

$$\begin{array}{r} 14 \\ -6 \\ \hline \end{array}$$

$$\begin{array}{r} 13 \\ -7 \\ \hline \end{array}$$

I Need Some More

Subtract. Write how many more are needed.

$$\begin{array}{r} 9 \\ -5 \\ \hline 4 \end{array}$$

$$\begin{array}{r} 10 \\ -7 \\ \hline \end{array}$$

$$\begin{array}{r} 10 \\ -5 \\ \hline \end{array}$$

Circle the correct answer in the box.

 **has 8 s.**

He wants 10 s.

How many more  **s does he need?**

2	3

SUBTRACTION

Rolling Along

Write how many are left.

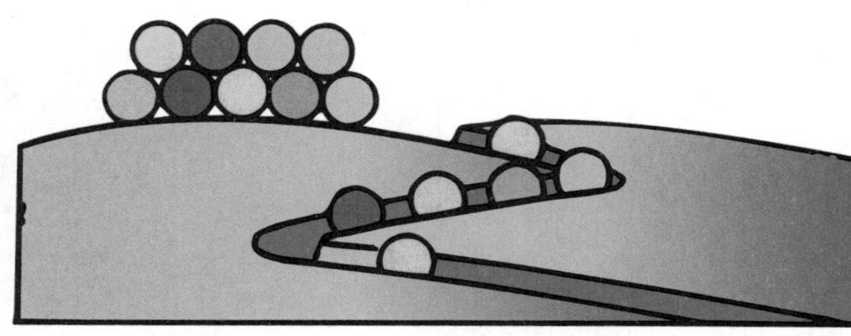

15 − 6 = 9

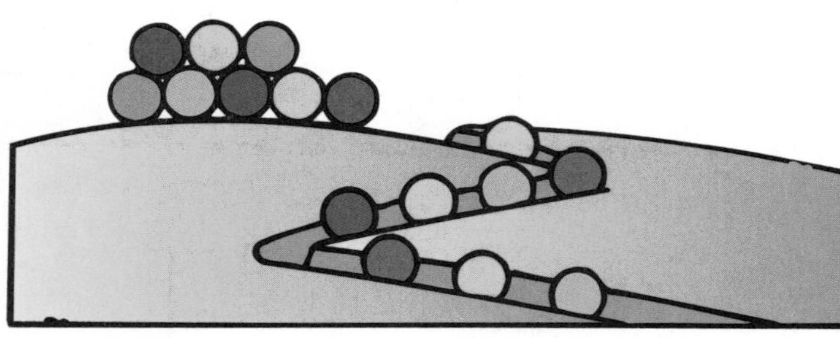

16 − 8 = ____

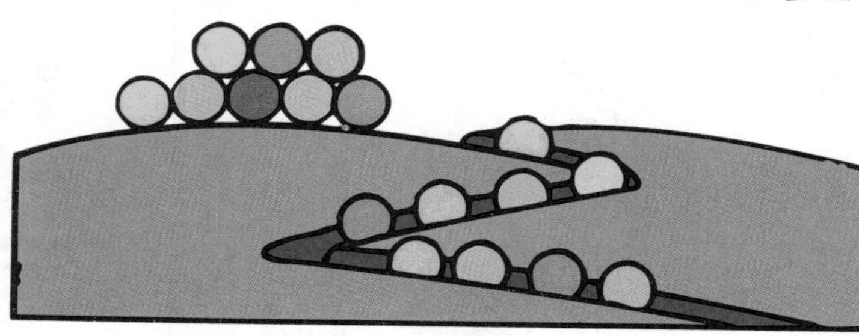

17 − 9 = ____

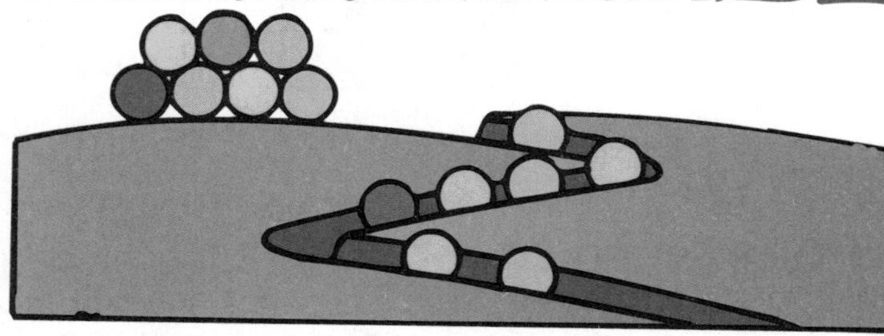

14 − 7 = ____

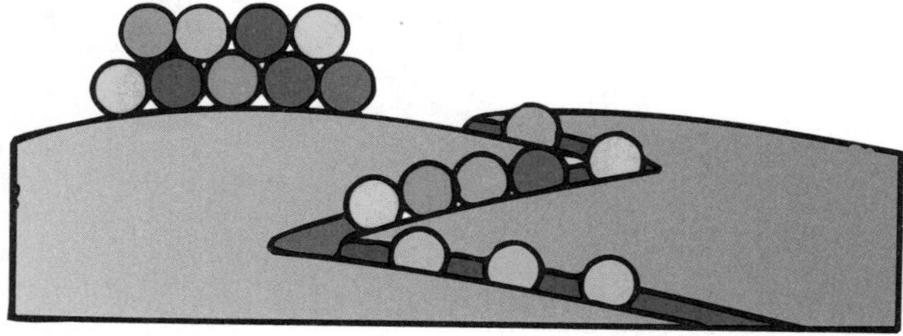

18 − 9 = ____

Fishy Facts

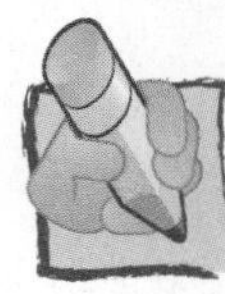

Write how many are left.

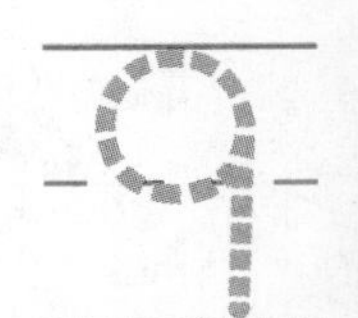

How many are left? 18 − 9 =

17 − 8 =

16 − 9 =

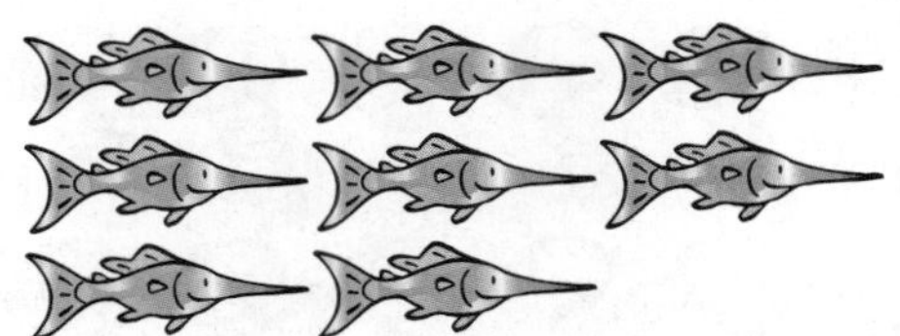

15 − 8 =

16 − 7 =

SUBTRACTION

Nuts and Bolts

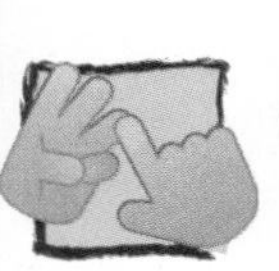

Subtract. Write how many are left.

How many are left? 15 – 8 = 7

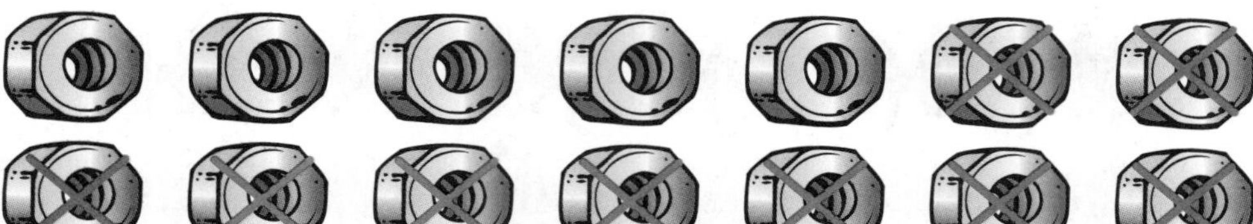

14 – 9 = ____

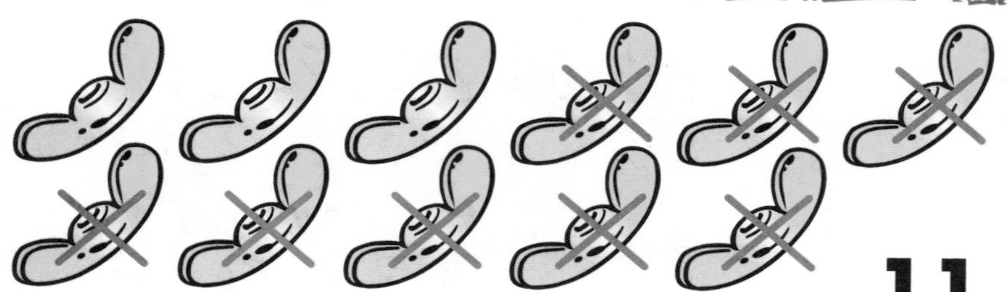

11 – 8 = ____

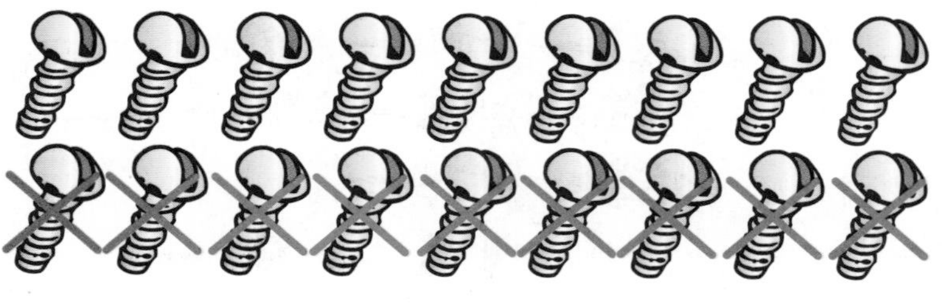

18 – 9 = ____

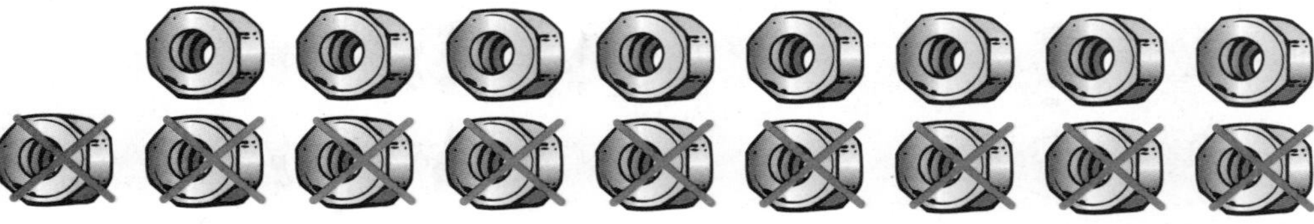

17 – 9 = ____

Too Many Tools

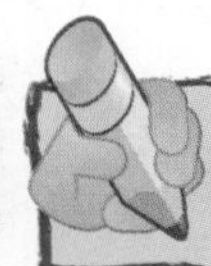

X out. Subtract. Write how many are left.

$$\begin{array}{r} 15 \\ -7 \\ \hline 8 \end{array}$$

How many are left?

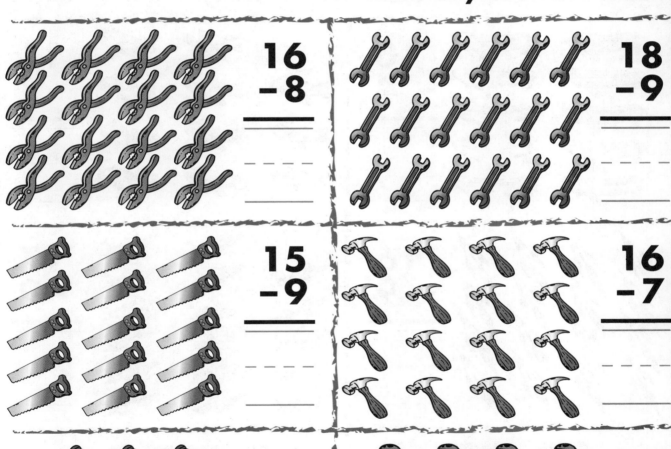

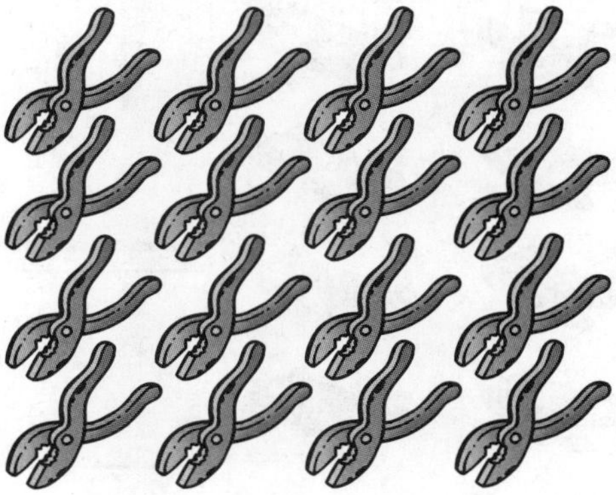

$$\begin{array}{r} 16 \\ -8 \\ \hline \end{array}$$

$$\begin{array}{r} 18 \\ -9 \\ \hline \end{array}$$

$$\begin{array}{r} 15 \\ -9 \\ \hline \end{array}$$

$$\begin{array}{r} 16 \\ -7 \\ \hline \end{array}$$

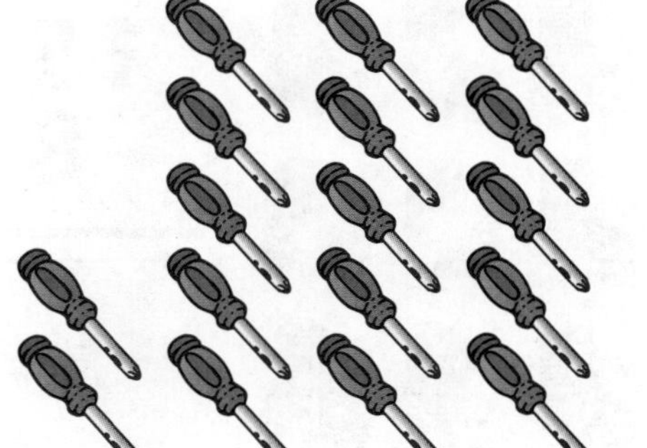

$$\begin{array}{r} 17 \\ -8 \\ \hline \end{array}$$

$$\begin{array}{r} 12 \\ -7 \\ \hline \end{array}$$

Subtracting numbers 0-9 from numbers through 18 in vertical form

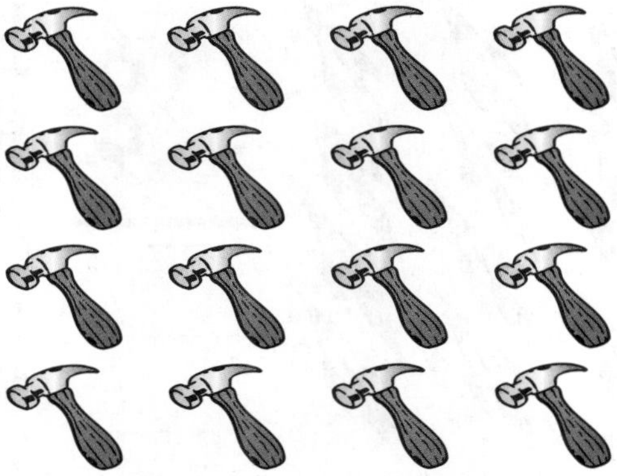

SUBTRACTION

Zoom Along

X out. Subtract.
Write how many are left.

$$\begin{array}{r} 12 \\ -4 \\ \hline \end{array}$$

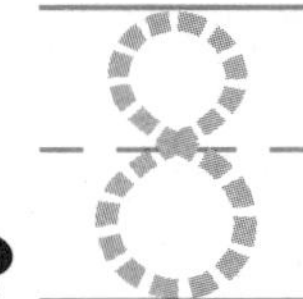

How many are left?

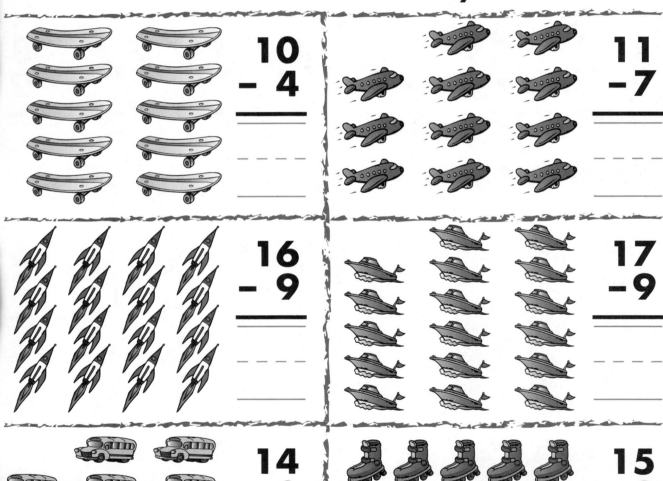

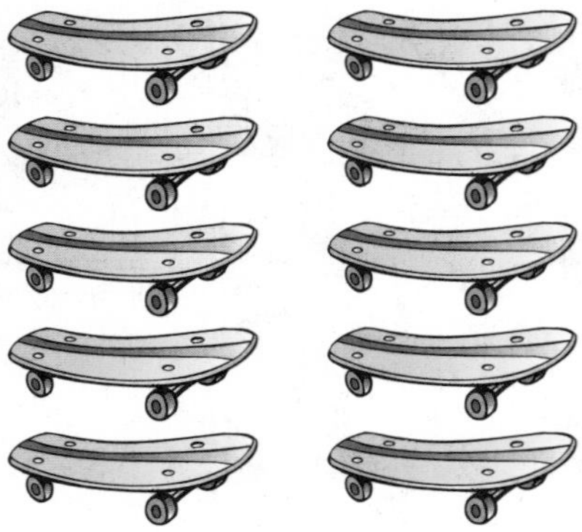

$$\begin{array}{r} 10 \\ -\ 4 \\ \hline \end{array}$$

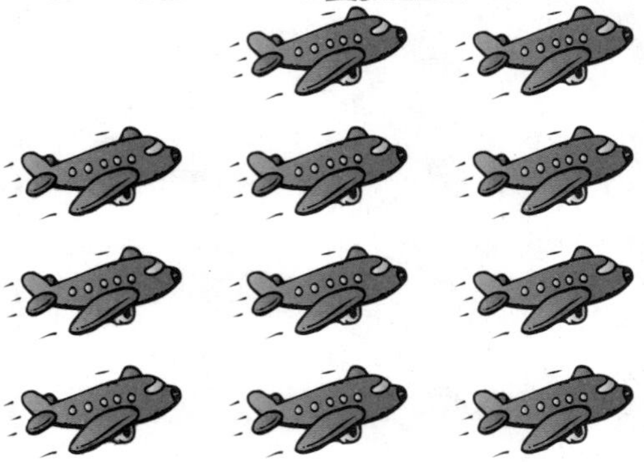

$$\begin{array}{r} 11 \\ -7 \\ \hline \end{array}$$

$$\begin{array}{r} 16 \\ -\ 9 \\ \hline \end{array}$$

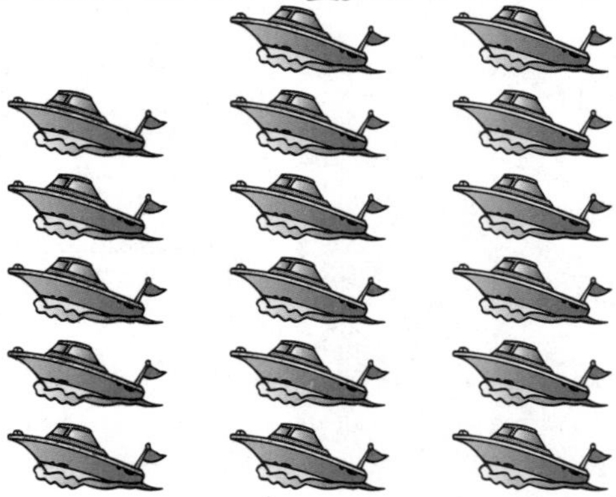

$$\begin{array}{r} 17 \\ -9 \\ \hline \end{array}$$

$$\begin{array}{r} 14 \\ -\ 8 \\ \hline \end{array}$$

$$\begin{array}{r} 15 \\ -8 \\ \hline \end{array}$$

Subtracting numbers 0-9 from numbers through 18 in vertical form

Yummy Cookies

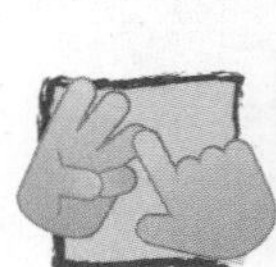

Subtract. Write each answer.

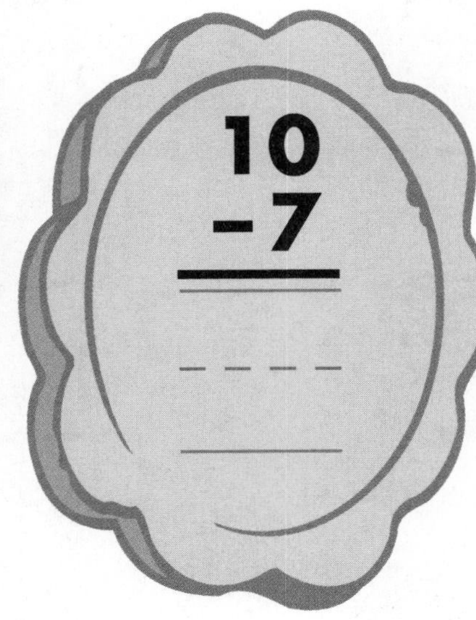

SUBTRACTION

It's a Match!

Draw lines between the equations with the same answer.

15 – 8	16 – 8
12 – 6	14 – 9
10 – 5	14 – 7
17 – 9	13 – 9
11 – 7	13 – 7

What's Missing?

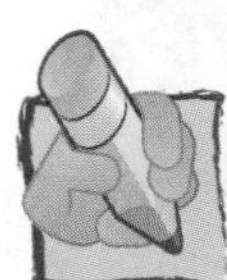

Write the missing number in each equation.

$14 - \_\_ = 6$

$12 - \_\_ = 9$

$\_\_ - 5 = 7$

$10 - \_\_ = 7$

$\_\_ - 8 = 8$

$18 - \_\_ = 9$

$13 - \_\_ = 6$

$\_\_ - 4 = 8$

$17 - \_\_ = 8$

$\_\_ - 7 = 4$

$14 - \_\_ = 9$

$9 - \_\_ = 5$

$\_\_ - 6 = 3$

$10 - \_\_ = 8$

SUBTRACTION

Subtraction Stories

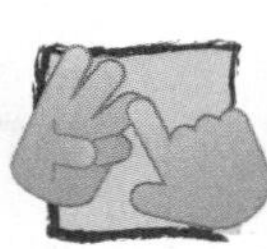

Read the story. Subtract. Write the answers.

I had 11  **s.**

5  **s popped.**

How many  **s are left?**

$$\begin{array}{r} 11 \\ -5 \\ \hline \end{array}$$

I saw 13  **s.**

4  **s swam away.**

How many  **s are left?**

$$\begin{array}{r} 13 \\ -4 \\ \hline \end{array}$$

I have 9  **s.**

I need 16  **s.**

How many more  **s do I need?**

$$\begin{array}{r} 16 \\ -9 \\ \hline \end{array}$$

I had 16  **s.**

I gave away 8  **s.**

How many  **s do I have left?**

$$\begin{array}{r} 16 \\ -8 \\ \hline \end{array}$$

Review

 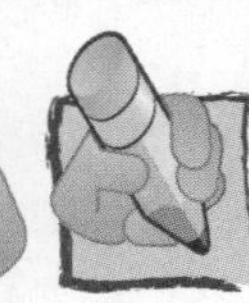

Subtract. Write each answer.

10 −7	12 −6	18 −9	16 −7	12 −8
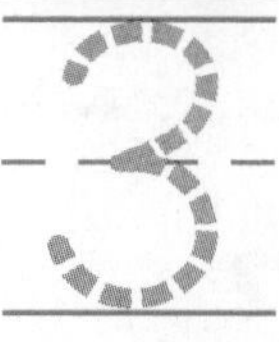				
15 −7	13 −9	17 −8	11 −8	14 −6
13 −5	11 −6	15 −8	16 −9	
13 −7	15 −9	17 −9	16 −8	12 −7

Practice Test

I know my subtraction facts.

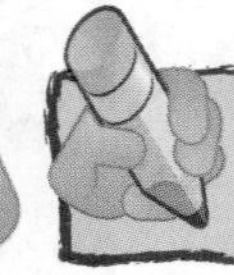

Subtract. Write each answer and fill in the circle next to each answer.

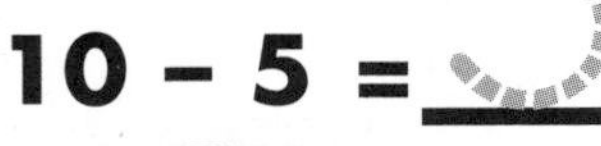

10 – 5 = 5 ○ 6 ● 5 ○ 4

A. 18 – 9 = ____ ○ 9 ○ 8 ○ 7

B. 13 – 7 = ____ ○ 8 ○ 7 ○ 6

C. 15 – 8 = ____ ○ 8 ○ 7 ○ 6

D. 12 – 9 = ____ ○ 5 ○ 3 ○ 1

E. 9 – 9 = ____ ○ 2 ○ 1 ○ 0

F. 14 – 6 = ____ ○ 9 ○ 8 ○ 7

G. 11 – 7 = ____ ○ 4 ○ 3 ○ 2

H. 16 – 8 = ____ ○ 9 ○ 8 ○ 7

Month 7 Checklist

Hands-on activities to help your child in school!

TIME AND MONEY

Telling Time: pages 195-213

In this month, your child will learn about the parts of a clock face. He or she will also practice telling and showing time to the hour and half hour, matching digital and analog clock times, and completing time word problems. Use the following activities to support this practice:

- ❑ Complete the worksheets.
- ❑ Help your child find and count all the clocks in the house. Be sure not to overlook clocks on ovens, VCRs, microwaves, radios, etc. To practice telling time, on the hour or half hour, call attention to each clock and ask, "What time is it?" If you are looking at an analog clock, ask your child to describe the position of the hour (short) hand and the minute (long) hand.
- ❑ Write the numbers 1-12 around a paper plate to look like a clock face. Using cardboard or heavy paper, cut out a long and short arrow to represent the hands. Use a paper fastener to attach the hands to the center of the paper plate. Then name times to the hour and half hour and ask your child to position the hands on the clock to show each time.
- ❑ Over the course of a week, help your child record his or her bedtime or wake-up time to the nearest hour or half hour. Compare the times at the end of the week.

TIME AND MONEY

Recognizing and Using Money: pages 214-224

Two coins are introduced this month: pennies and nickels. The following activities provide ways to practice recognizing and counting pennies and nickels and completing word problems with money:

- ❑ Complete the worksheets.
- ❑ Provide a collection of real pennies and nickels and have your child sort them by type. Ask your child questions to encourage discussion about the coins. For example: *How are the coins alike?* (They are round; They have pictures and numbers on them.) *How are the coins different?* (They are different colors and sizes; The pictures on them are different). *Can you point to a coin that is worth 1 cent?* (penny) *Can you point to a coin that is worth 5 cents?* (nickel)
- ❑ On index cards or slips of paper write amounts from 1¢ to 25¢. Put the cards in a stack face down on a table and provide a collection of pennies and nickels nearby. Have your child turn over a card, read the amount, and count out coins to show that amount. If the amount is over 5¢, you might challenge your child to show it more than one way. For example, 12¢ can be shown as 12 pennies, 1 nickel and 7 pennies, or 2 nickels and 2 pennies.
- ❑ Make several arrangements of pennies and nickels to show different amounts. Write the corresponding amounts on index cards or paper slips. Ask your child to place the cards next to the appropriate groups of coins to match the amounts.
- ❑ Provide two different arrangements of pennies and nickels. Ask your child to count the coins in each group and tell you the amount. Then ask your child to compare the two amounts. *Which is worth more? Which is worth less?*

It's Time

The numbers show the time.
The short hand shows the hour.
The long hand shows the minutes.
The time is 4 o'clock.

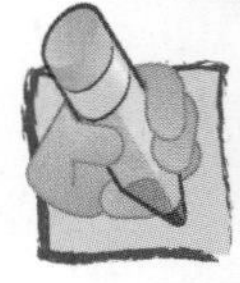

Write the clock numbers.

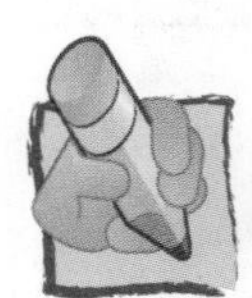

Write the numbers.

The hour hand is on _____.

The minute hand is on _____.

It is _____ o'clock.

T I M E

What Time Is It?

The **minute hand** is on 12.
The **hour hand** is on 3.
It is 3 o'clock.

Color the hour hand red.
Circle the correct time.

5 o'clock

7 o'clock

12 o'clock

1 o'clock

10 o'clock

8 o'clock

11 o'clock

9 o'clock

6 o'clock

7 o'clock

3 o'clock

2 o'clock

Time Match-Up

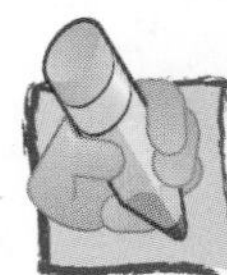

Draw a line from each clock to the matching time.

1 o'clock

6 o'clock

8 o'clock

2 o'clock

9 o'clock

4 o'clock

TIME

Watch the Time!

Write the time.

3 o'clock  ___ o'clock  ___ o'clock

___ o'clock  ___ o'clock  ___ o'clock

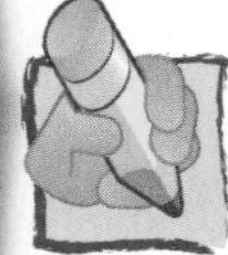

Unscramble the letters to answer the riddle.

What time is it when an elephant steps on your watch?

____ __ ___ _ ___ ______

i T m e o t t g e a w e n a c w h t !

Answer: Time to get a new watch!

Digital Time

A digital clock tells time with just numbers. It tells the hour and the minutes.

Write the time on the digital clocks.

2:00

__:00

__:00

__:00

__:00

__:00

Party Time

Draw the hour hand on each clock to show the time.

7:00

2:00

5:00

11:00

8:00

1:00

4:00

9:00

10:00

Showing time to the hour on an analog clock

Daily Doings

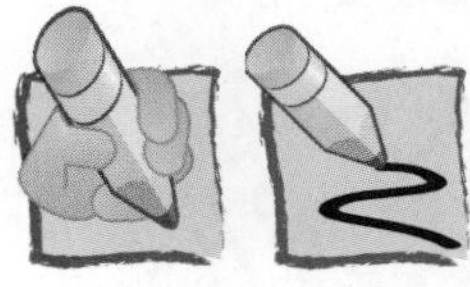

Look at the pictures. Write the hour you do each activity. Draw hands to show the time.

___ :00

___ :00

___ :00

___ :00

___ :00

___ :00

Now and Later

Now it is 2 o'clock.

One hour later it will be 3 o'clock.

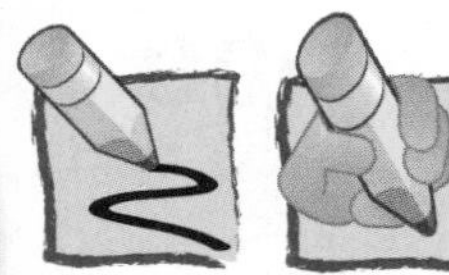

Draw clock hands to show the time one hour later. Write the time.

NOW **LATER**

4 o'clock **___ o'clock**

7 o'clock **___ o'clock**

10 o'clock **___ o'clock**

So Many Clocks

4 o'clock

4:00

Draw lines to match the clocks that show the same time.

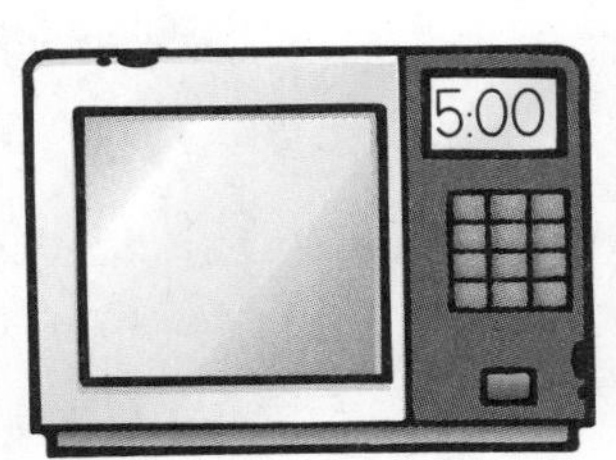

TIME

Clock Maze

Follow the path that shows times in order. Draw a line from the bus to the school.

START

4:00

1:00

11:00

10:00

6:00

12:00

STOP

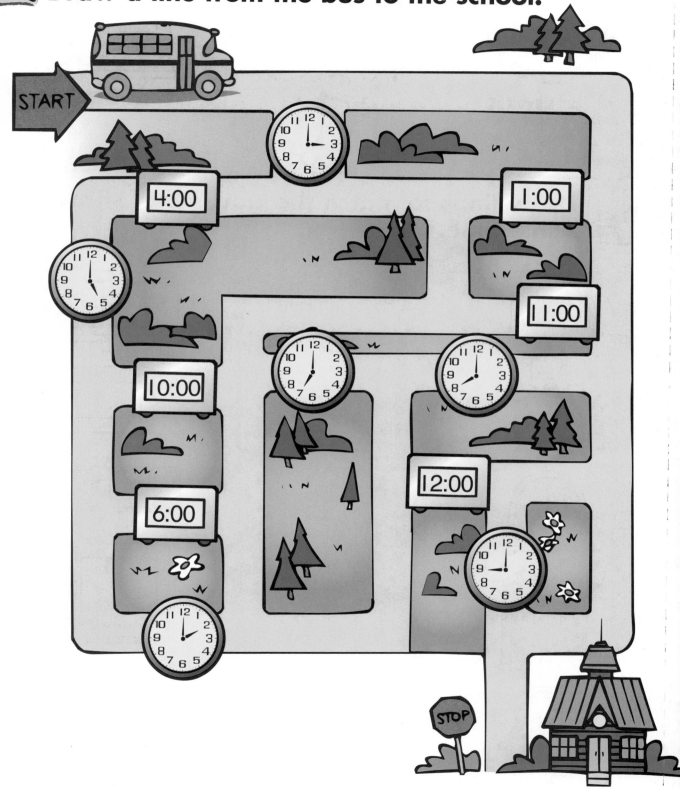

Completing a maze to show time in order

Summer Time Fun

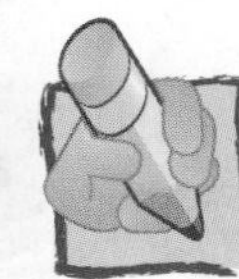

Read each problem.
Write the answer.

Eric left home at 11 o'clock.
It took 1 hour to get to the beach.
What time did Eric get to the beach?

____

Kate goes to camp at 8 o'clock.
Pat goes to camp at 9 o'clock.
Who goes to camp first?

____

Samir got to the park at 3 o'clock.
He went home at 5 o'clock.
How long was Samir at the park?

____

The soccer game starts at 6 o'clock.
It ends one hour later.
What time does the soccer game end?

____

Meg left home at 9 o'clock.
It took her 2 hours to get to Aunt Lin's.
What time did Meg get to Aunt Lin's?

____

Ben went to the pool at 2:00.
He stayed for 3 hours.
What time did Ben go home?

____

Solving word problems that involve time

Time to the Half Hour

Minute hand on the 6.
Hour hand between 8 and 9.
8:30

8:30 or eight thirty

Circle the correct time.

9:30
8:30

1:30
11:30

8:30
7:30

5:30
6:30

three thirty
two thirty

nine thirty
eight thirty

Fishing for Time

Draw a line from each clock to the fish with the matching time. Color the fish to match.

6 o'clock

7:30

12:30

Time to Clown Around

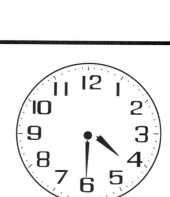

Write the time.

Snack Time

The minute hand is on the 6.
The hour hand is between 3 and 4.
The time is 3:30.

Draw the hour hand to show the time.

8:30  **5:30**  **10:30**

12:00  **4:30**  **11:30**

Clock Shop

Draw hour and minute hands to show the time.

11:30

1:00

3:30

9:00

10:30

12:00

5:00

2:30

4:00

Showing time to the hour and half hour

Clock Match

Draw lines to match the clocks with the same time.

Telling time to the hour and half hour; matching clock faces with digital clocks

Racing Time

Write the time.

7:00

Reading and writing time to the hour and half hour

Review

Circle the time.

ten thirty	4 o'clock	6:00
eleven thirty	2 o'clock	12:00

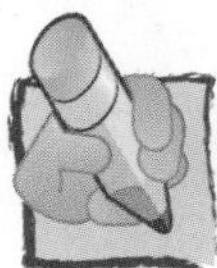

Write the time.

______ ______ ______

Draw hands to show the time.

3:00 **seven thirty** **11:30**

MONEY

Penny Pockets

This is a penny.
A penny has two sides.

heads **tails**

1 penny = 1 cent
1¢

2 pennies = 2 cents
2¢

Color each penny. Circle the pocket that has more pennies.

Penny Paths

= 4¢

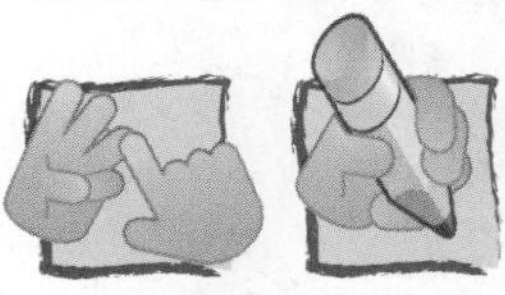

Count the pennies. Write how many cents.

3 ¢

____ ¢

____ ¢

____ ¢

Penny Jars

Draw lines to match each set of pennies with the correct amounts.

Be a Detective

This is a nickel.
A nickel has two sides.

heads **tails**

1 nickel = 5 cents
5¢

Circle each nickel.
Draw a line under each penny.

Identifying nickels; distinguishing between pennies and nickels

How Much Money?

Start with the nickel.
Then count on.
5¢ 6¢ 7¢ 8¢ 9¢

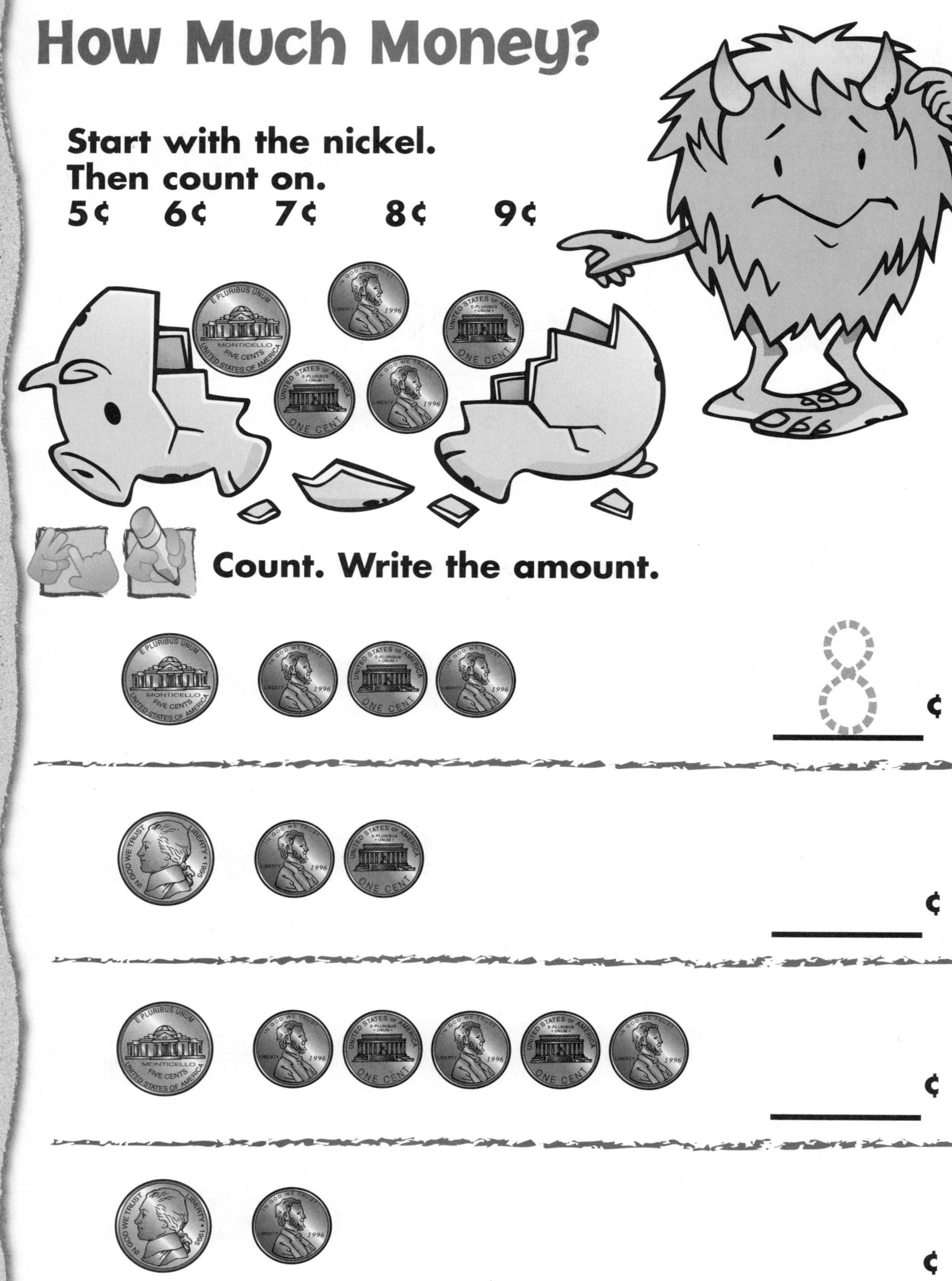

Count. Write the amount.

8 ¢

___ ¢

___ ¢

___ ¢

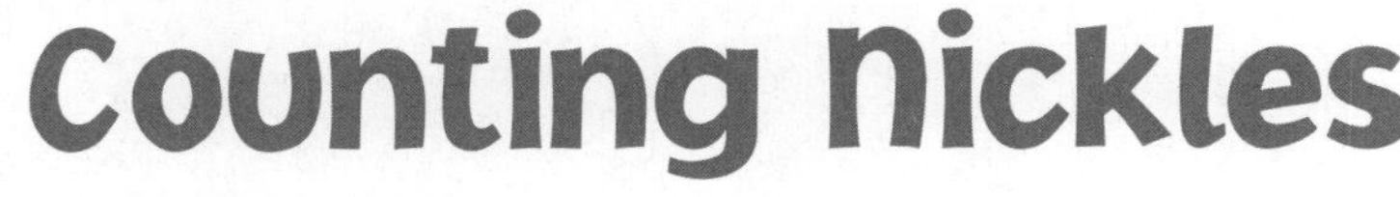

Counting Nickles

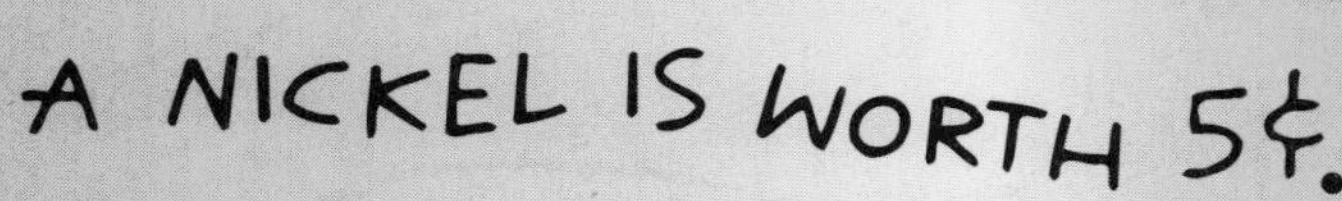

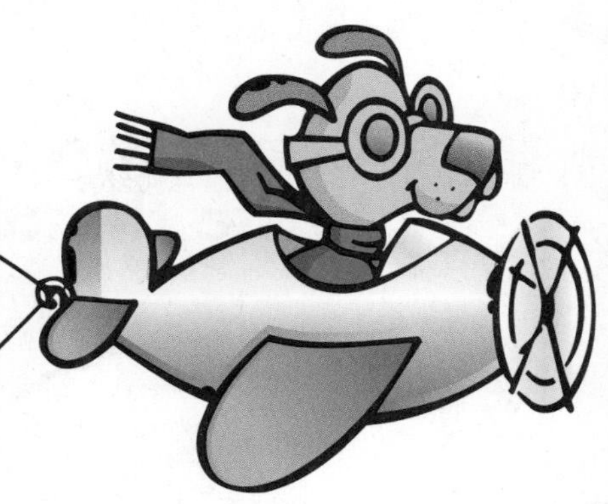

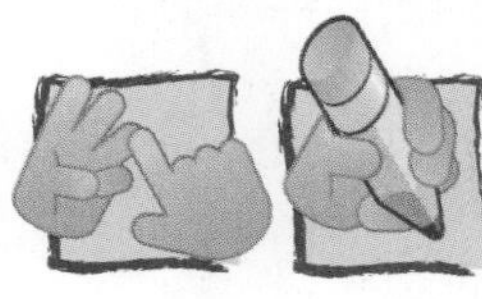

Count by 5's. Write the amount.

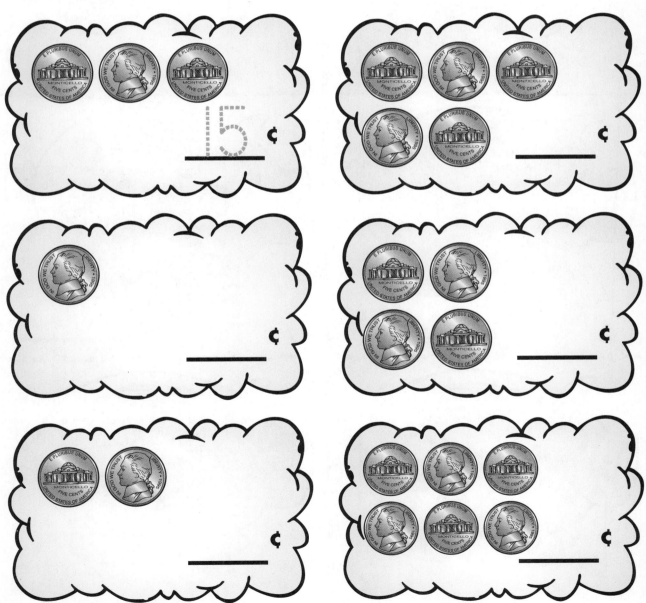

15 ¢

____ ¢

____ ¢

____ ¢

____ ¢

____ ¢

Coin Count

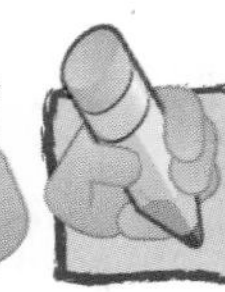

Count the money in each bank.
Write the amount.

_____ ¢

_____ ¢

_____ ¢

_____ ¢

_____ ¢

_____ ¢

Let's Go Shopping

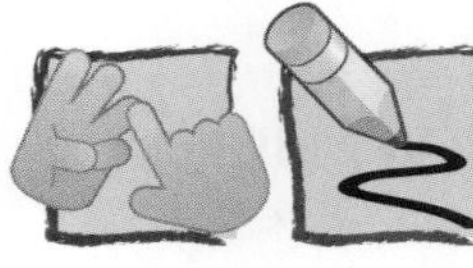

Count the money in each purse.
Draw a line to the item you can buy.

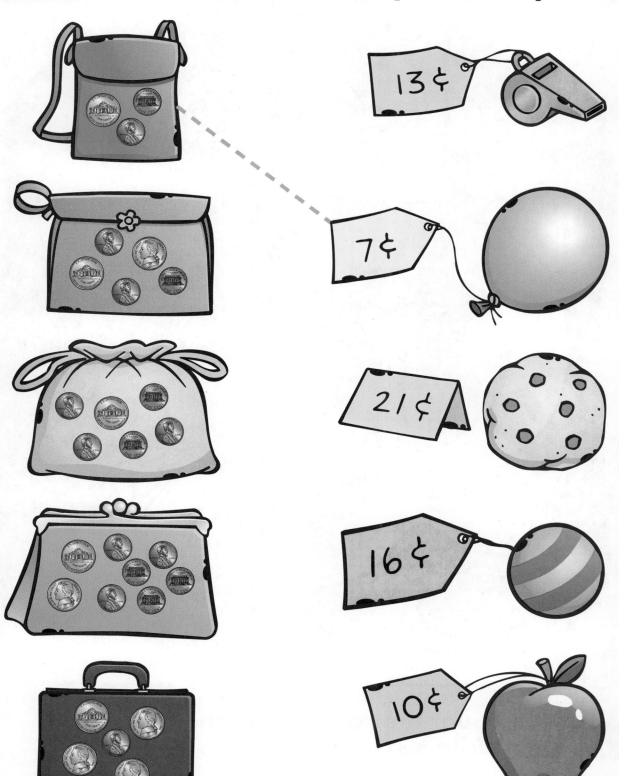

13¢

7¢

21¢

16¢

10¢

Coin Maze

Draw a line to make a path to the doghouse.

START

STOP

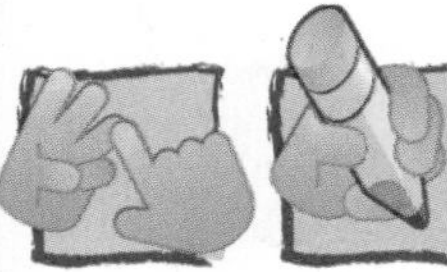

Count the coins along the path. Write the amount.

_____ ¢

Counting nickels and pennies

How Much Money?

Read the problem. Draw a picture to help you solve it. Write the answer.

Rosa has 2 pennies in one hand.

She has 3 pennies in the other hand.

How much money does she have in all?

_______ ¢

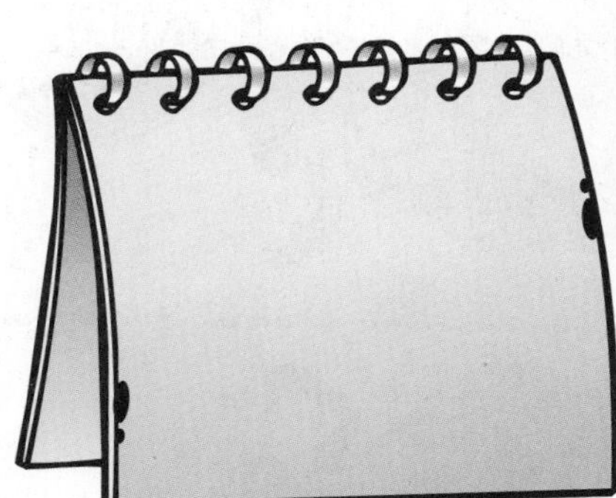

Howard has one nickel.

He saves two nickels.

How much money does he have in all?

_______ ¢

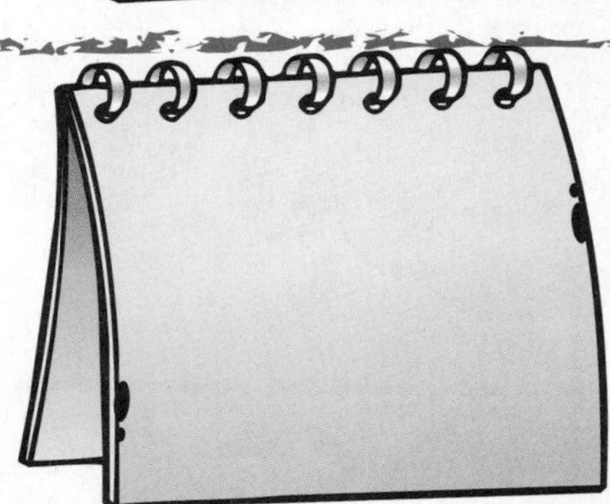

Todd had 1 nickel.

He found 2 pennies.

How much money does Todd have now?

_______ ¢

Jill has 3 nickels.

Paul has 5 pennies.

Who has more money?

_______ ¢

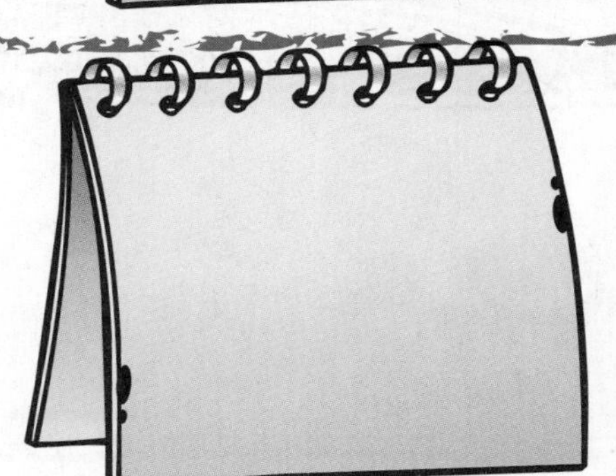

Review

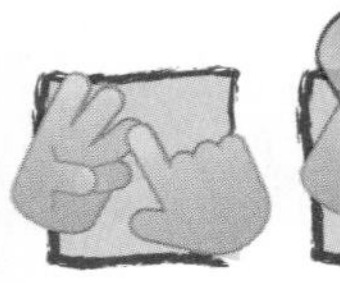
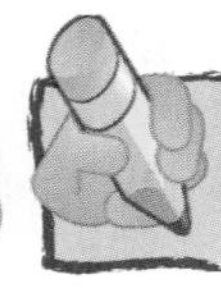

Count the coins. Write each amount.

_______ ¢

_______ ¢

_______ ¢

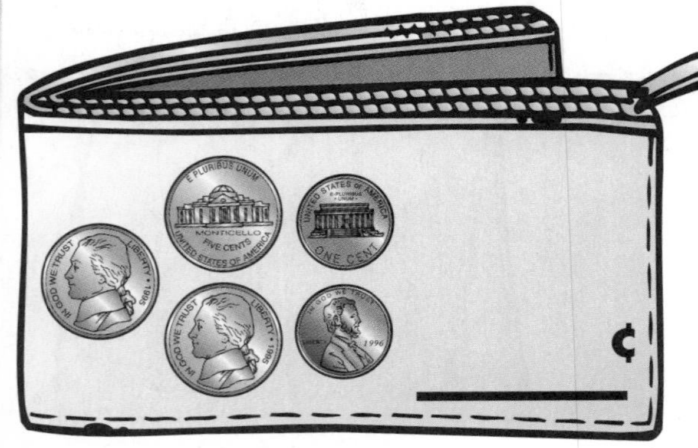

_______ ¢

_______ ¢

Month 8 Checklist

Hands-on activities to help your child in school!

TIME AND MONEY

Money Recognition and Usage: pages 227-242

In this month, your child will practice counting pennies, nickels, dimes, and quarters; adding with money; and solving money word problems.

- ❑ Complete the worksheets.
- ❑ Display a collection of real coins (pennies, nickels, dimes, and quarters) and have your child sort them by type. Ask questions to encourage discussion. For example: *How are the coins alike?* (They are round; They have pictures and numbers on them.) *How are the coins different?* (They are different colors and sizes; The pictures on them are different.) *Can you point to a coin that is worth 10 cents?* (dime) *Can you find a coin that is worth 25 cents?* (quarter)
- ❑ Display a collection of real coins that totals up to 99¢. Have your child place the coins in a line in order from greatest to least value. Then have your child "count" the coins to find the total amount. Repeat using different coin combinations.
- ❑ Set up a "store" by arranging several items on a table. On index cards or slips of paper, write a price ranging from 10¢ to 99¢ for each item. Then invite your child to "go shopping" with a collection of coins you've provided. When an item is chosen, ask "Which coins do you need to buy it?" Challenge your child to find more than one combination of coins for each price. For example, an item that costs 30¢ can be "bought" with 3 dimes or 1 quarter and 1 nickel or 2 dimes and 2 nickels, and so on.
- ❑ Make several arrangements of quarters, dimes, nickels, and pennies to show different amounts. Write the corresponding amounts on index cards or paper slips. Ask your child to place the cards next to the appropriate groups of coins to match the amounts.
- ❑ Provide two different arrangements of coins. Ask your child to count the coins in each group and tell you the amount. Then ask your child to compare the two amounts. *Which is worth more? Which is worth less?*
- ❑ Place different combinations of pennies, nickels, dimes, and quarters in three clear plastic zipper bags. Challenge your child to guess which bag he or she thinks is worth the most. Then have your child count the money in each bag and arrange the bags in order from least value to greatest value.
- ❑ Play an "exchange" game with your child. Give your child a collection of pennies, nickels, and dimes. Then display a coin, such as a quarter, and ask your child to exchange some of his or her coins for the quarter. Challenge your child to exchange the quarter for different combinations of coins.

TIME AND MONEY

Telling and Showing Time: pages 243-252
Reading a Calendar: pages 253-255

In this month, your child will also learn to tell time to the quarter hour and in 5-minute intervals. He or she will also practice reading a calendar and identify the months of the year.

❑ Complete the worksheets.

❑ If you and your child made a paper plate clock in Month 7, use it now to show time in 5-minute intervals. Say a time, such as 10:25, and ask your child to move the hands on the clock to show that time. Repeat with other times such as 1:15, 9:30, 12:55, and so on.

❑ Ask your child to name a favorite TV show and tell what time it starts and ends. Then ask, "How many minutes or hours long is the show?"

❑ Make up story problems for your child to solve. For example: We started to eat lunch at 12:00. We were done 30 minutes later. At what time were we done eating lunch?

❑ On index cards or slips of paper, write times in 15-minute intervals. Make 3 cards for each time: for example, draw a clock face to show 8:30 on one card, write *8:30* on another card, and write *30 minutes after 8 o'clock* on another card. Make cards for at least three different times. Then shuffle the cards and arrange them face down in a grid to play a game. You and your child take turns turning over two cards. If the cards match, you keep them. If they don't match, you put them back face down. Play until you've made all the pairs possible.

❑ Display a calendar and help your child note holidays, birthdays, and other special dates on the calendar. Then have him or her point to a date on the calendar and tell you the month, the day of the week, and the date.

❑ Write the names of the months on index cards. Mix the cards and ask your child to arrange them to show the order of the months. Also try this activity with weekday names.

Lemonade for Sale

This is a dime.
A dime has two sides.

1 dime = 10 cents
10¢

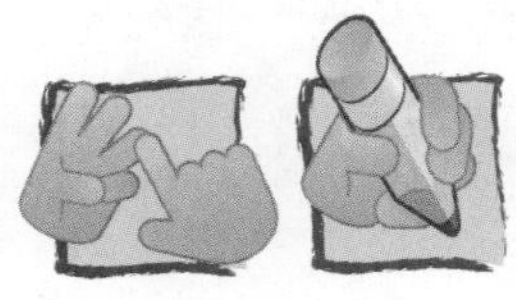

Count the money. Write the amount.

10 ¢

____ ¢

____ ¢

____ ¢

MONEY

Counting Dimes

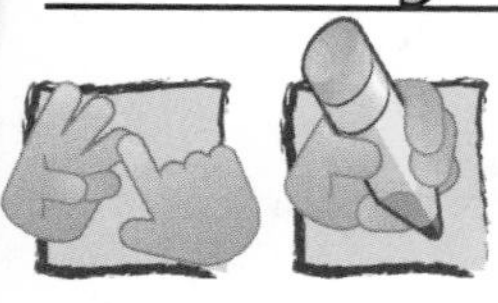

Count by tens. Write the amount.

40 ¢

______ ¢

______ ¢

______ ¢

______ ¢

______ ¢

Treasure Chests

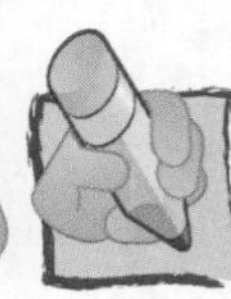

Count the money in each treasure chest. Write the amount.

22 ¢

____ ¢

____ ¢

____ ¢

____ ¢

____ ¢

Circle the treasure chest with the most money.

Counting dimes and pennies

MONEY

Adding Money

 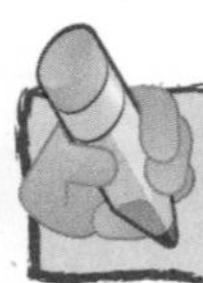

**Count dimes and pennies.
Add to find the total.**

_____ ¢ + _____  =  ¢

_____ ¢ + _____  = _____ ¢

_____ ¢ + _____  = _____ ¢

_____ ¢ + _____ ¢ = _____ ¢

_____ ¢ + _____ ¢ = _____ ¢

Drawing Coins

Draw dimes and pennies to show the amount.

10¢ 1¢ 1¢ 1¢

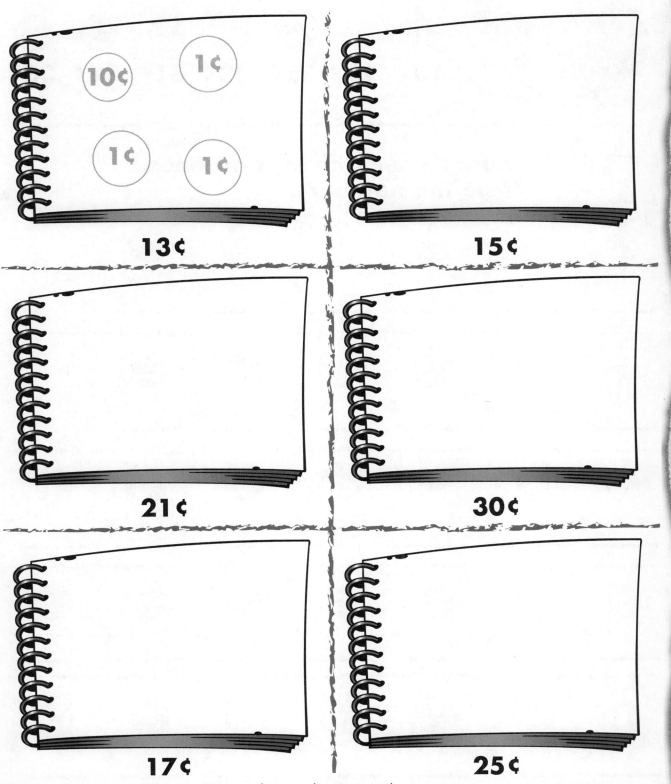

13¢

15¢

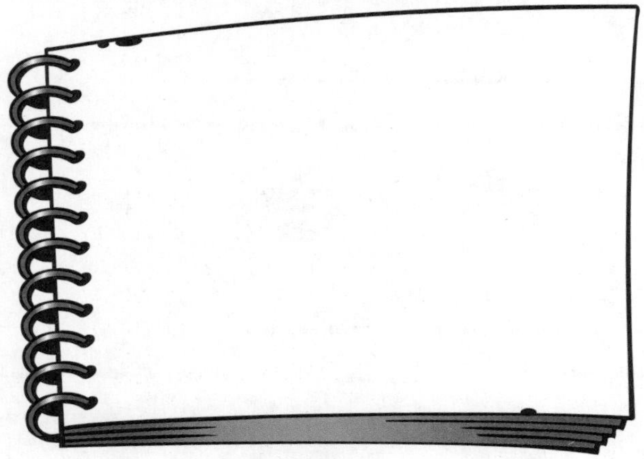

21¢

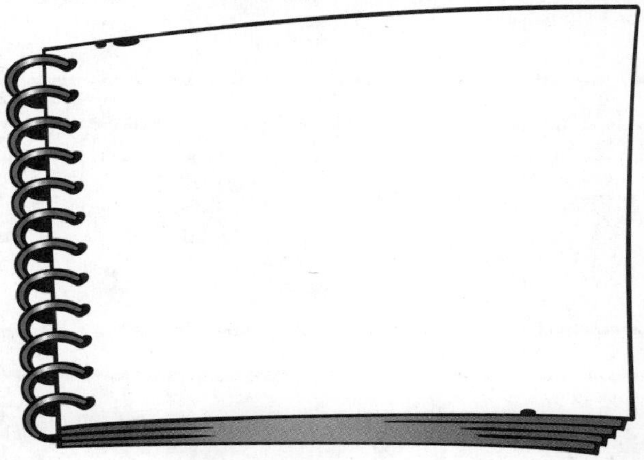

30¢

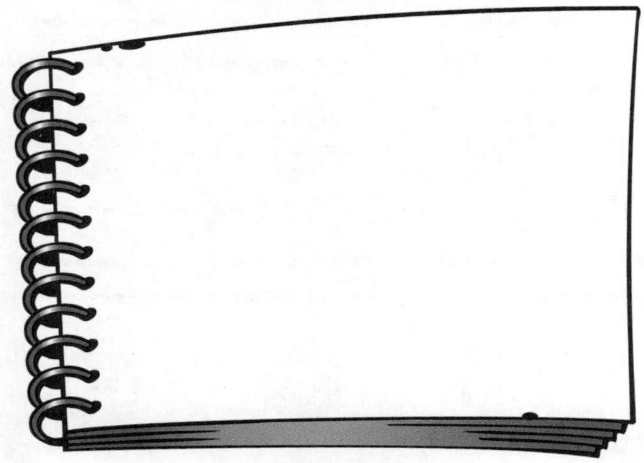

17¢

25¢

Counting Coins

Start counting by tens. Then count on by fives and ones.

10¢ 20¢ 25¢ 30¢ 31¢ 32¢ 33¢

 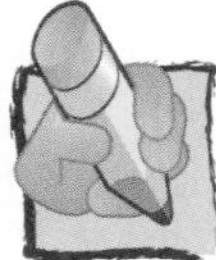

Count by tens, fives, and ones. Write the numbers.

10 ¢ 20 ¢ 30 ¢ 35 ¢ 40 ¢ 41 ¢

___¢ ___¢ ___¢ ___¢ ___¢ ___¢

___¢ ___¢ ___¢ ___¢ ___¢ ___¢ ___¢

___¢ ___¢ ___¢ ___¢ ___¢ ___¢ ___¢

___¢ ___¢ ___¢ ___¢ ___¢ ___¢ ___¢

How Much Money?

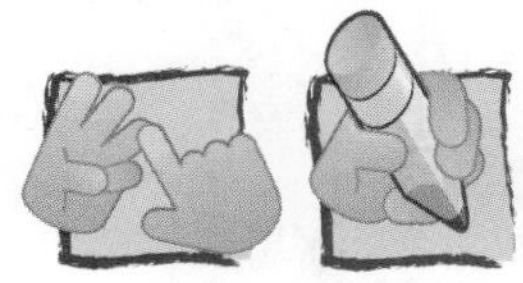

Count the money. Write the amount.

MONEY

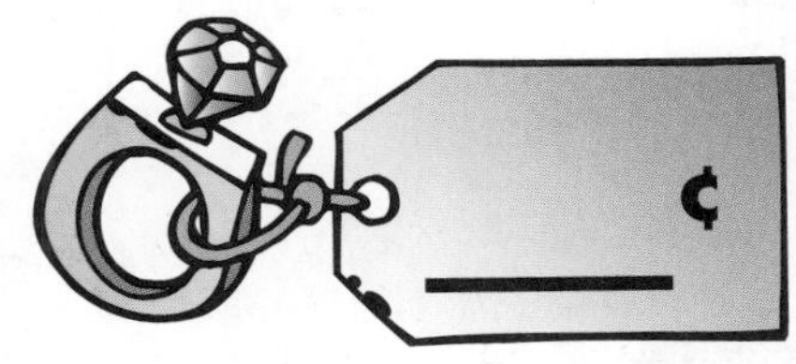

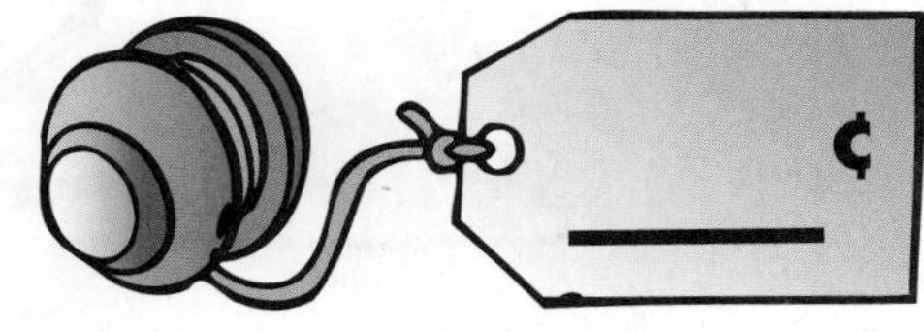

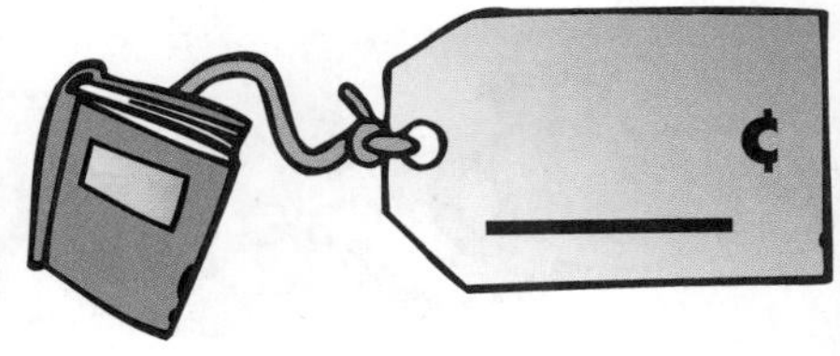

Go Shopping!

Draw lines between the matching amounts.

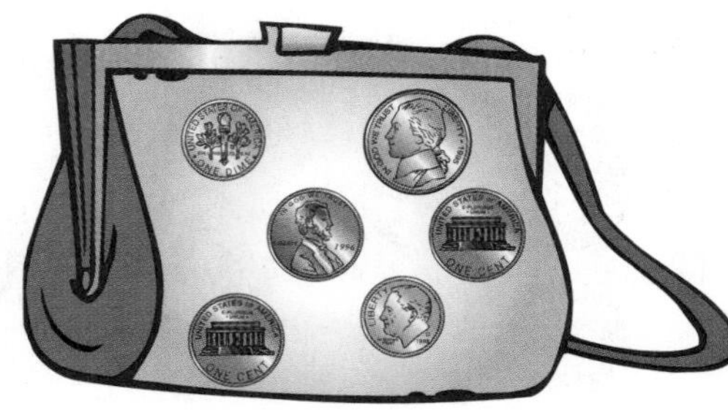

Coin Riddles

Read the riddles. Circle the answers.

Josh has 24¢ in his pocket. He has 6 coins. Which coins does Josh have?

Kim has 30¢ in her pocket. She has 3 coins. Which coins does Kim have?

Matt has 16¢ in his pocket. He has 4 coins. Which coins does Matt have?

Jake has more than 3 nickels, but fewer than 2 dimes.

How much money does Jake have?

18¢ 25¢ 30¢

Lara has fewer than 4 nickels, but more than 8 pennies.

How much money does Lara have?

5¢ 15¢ 20¢

Treasure Hunt

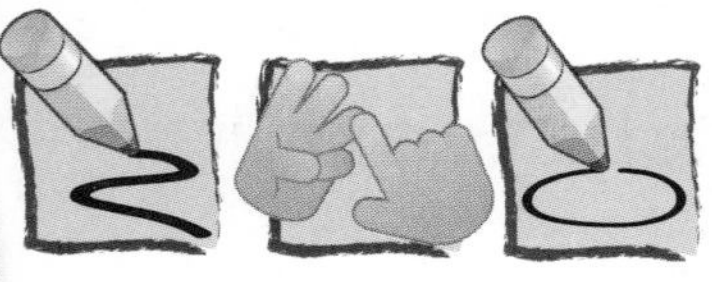

Draw lines to show 3 paths to the treasure. Count the money on each path. Circle the boat on the path with the most money.

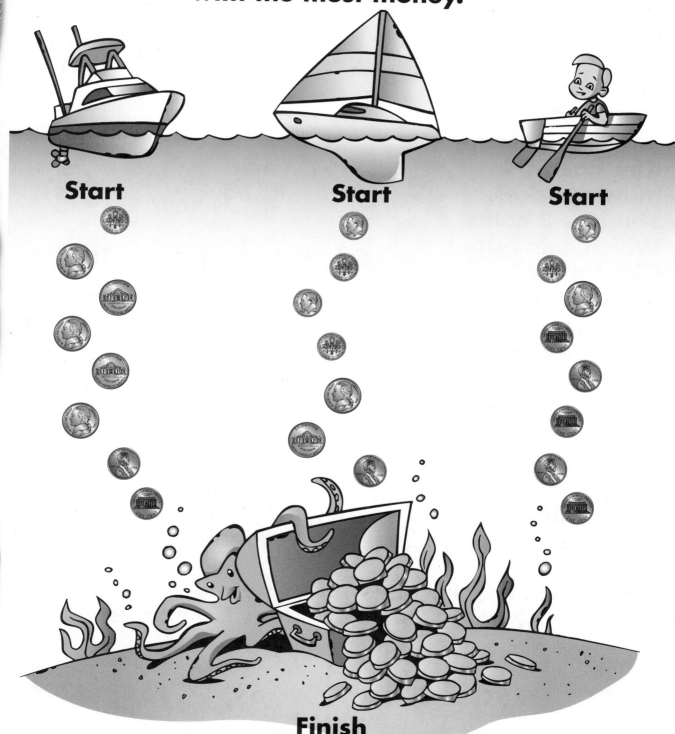

Start **Start** **Start**

Finish

Quarters Anyone?

This is a quarter.
A quarter has two sides.

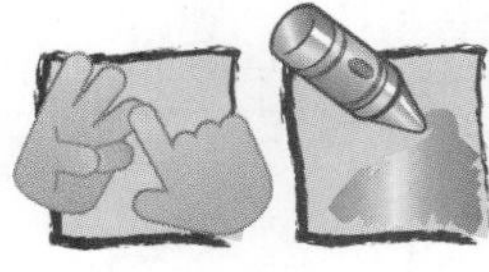

Count the money in each purse. Color the purse if the amount equals a quarter.

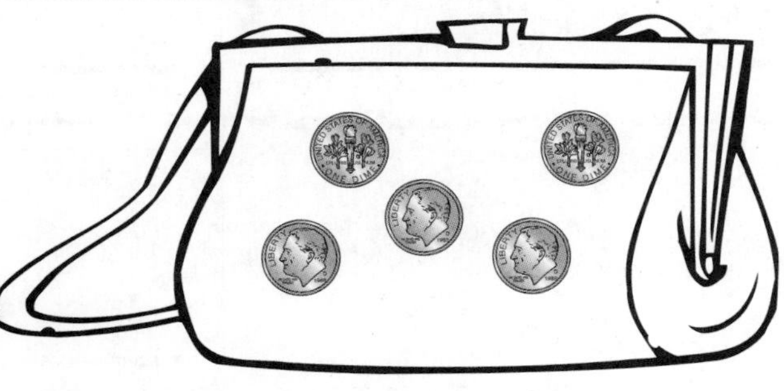

Coin Collections

Start with the coin that is worth the most. Then count on by tens, fives, and ones.

25¢ 35¢ 40¢ 45¢ 46¢ 47¢ ____

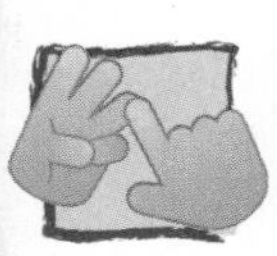 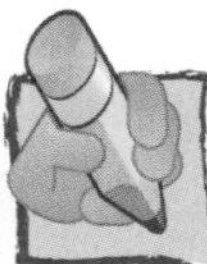

Count the coins.
Write the amount in the box.

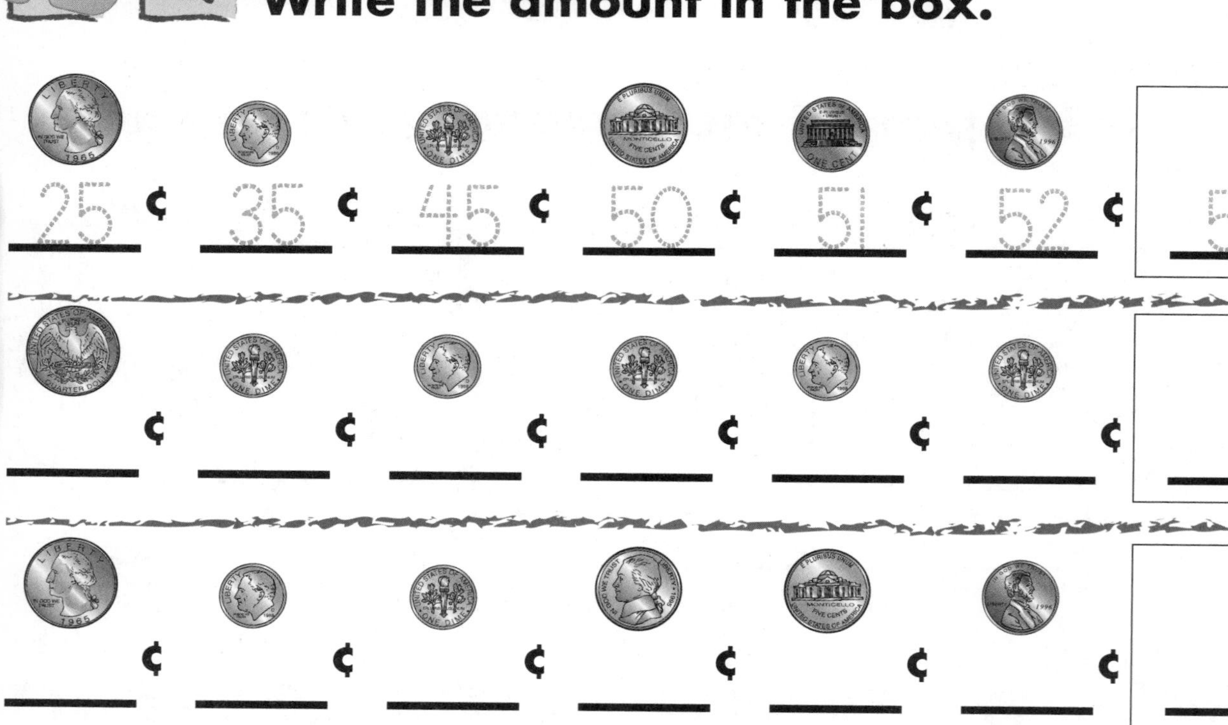

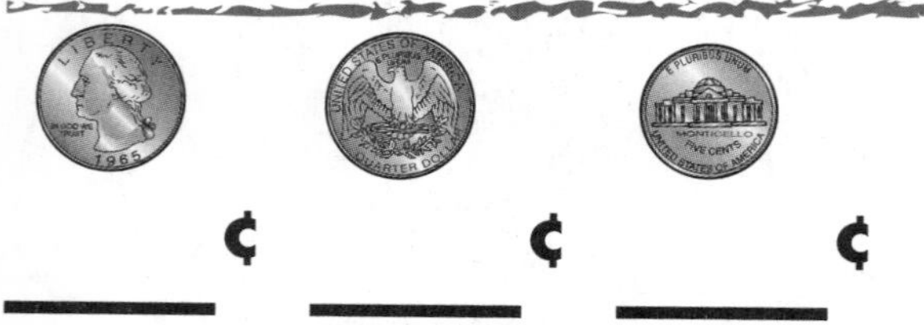

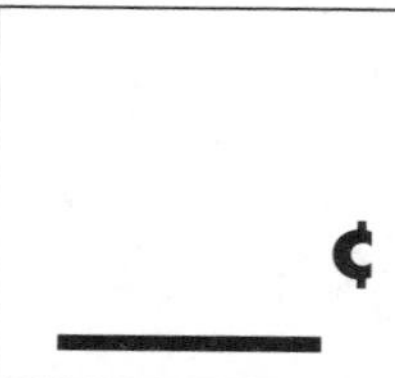

Count and Color

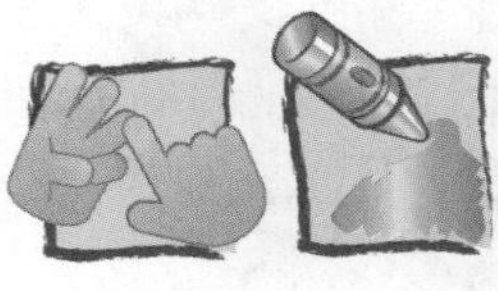

**Count the money in each jar.
Color the jar to match the amounts in the code.**

25¢ = **40¢ =** **55¢ =**

Monster Match

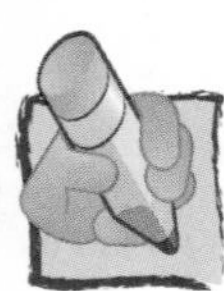

Draw lines to match the coins with the amounts on the tags.

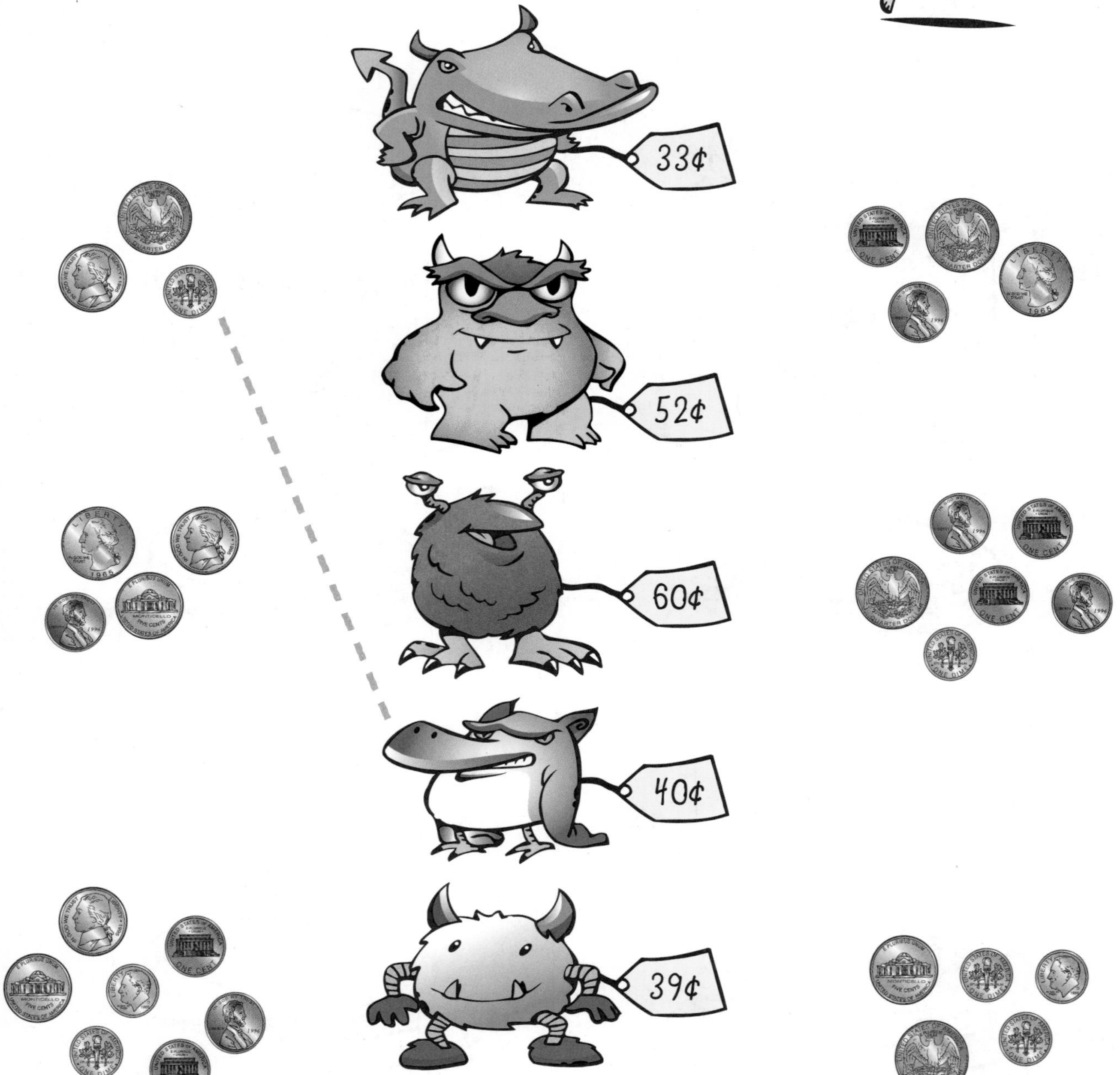

33¢

52¢

60¢

40¢

39¢

36¢

Snack Bar

I can use 1 quarter and 1 dime.
35¢

Read the price of each item. Draw the coins you need to buy it. Write the number of coins.

45¢

25¢ 10¢ 10¢

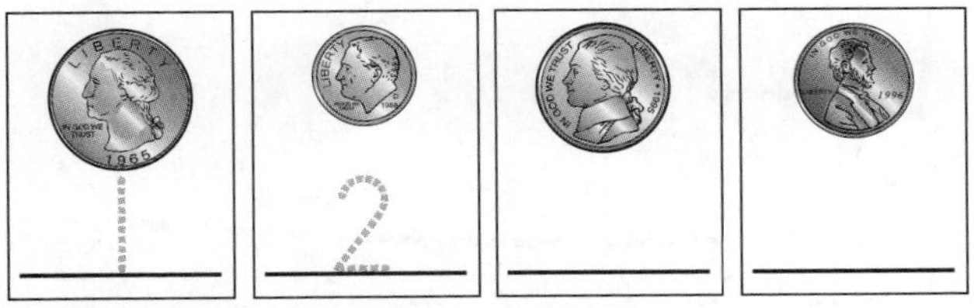

1 2

64¢

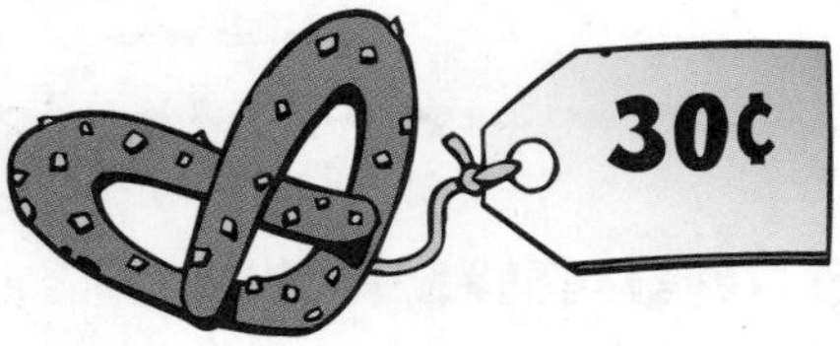

30¢

42¢

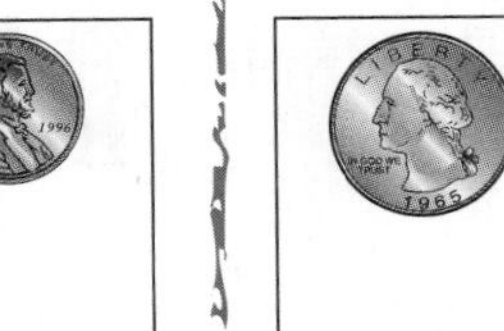   

Solving problems using money

Review

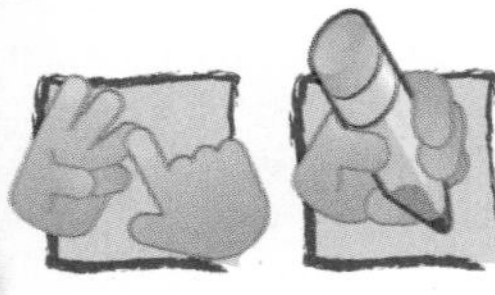

Count the money. Write the amount.

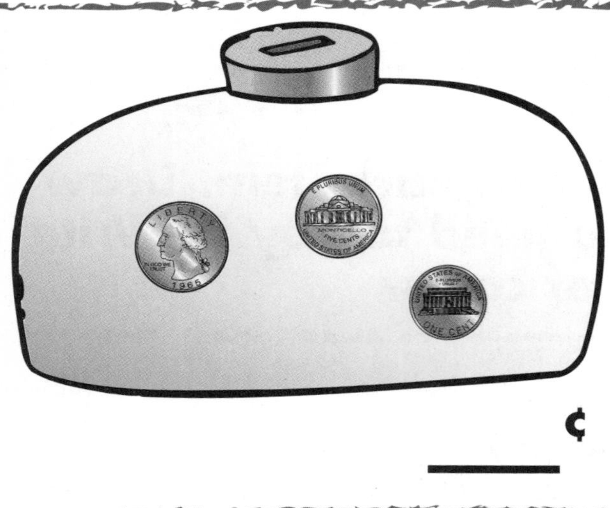

_____ ¢

_____ ¢

_____ ¢

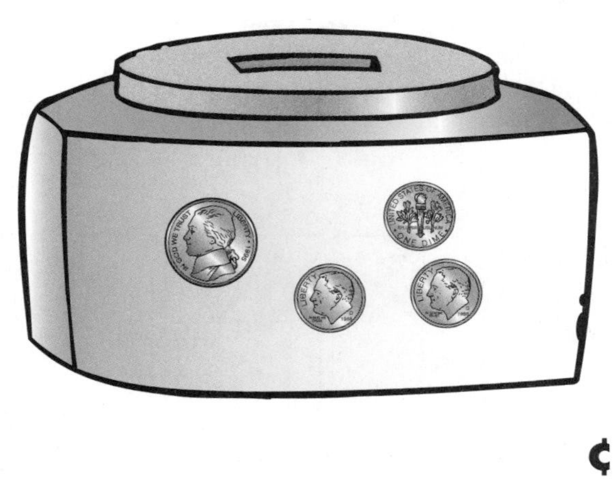

_____ ¢

Read the problem. Circle the answer.

Bob has 1 dime, 2 nickels, and 5 pennies. Is that equal to 1 quarter?

yes **no**

Kara has 1 quarter and 2 dimes. Lynn has 4 dimes, 2 nickels, and 6 pennies. Who has more money?

Kara **Lynn**

Race Around the Clock

It is 15 minutes after 7 o'clock.
It is 7:15.

There are 60 minutes in 1 hour.
Count by 5's to find the minutes after the hour.

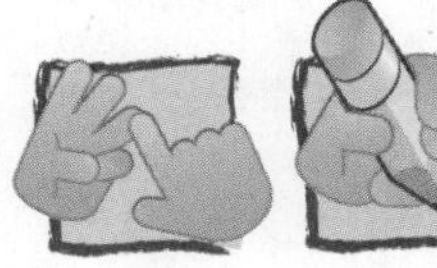

Count by 5's. Write the numbers around the clock.

You Can Say That Again!
It is 15 minutes after 4 o'clock.
It is 4:15.
Count by 5's to find the time. Write the time two ways.
15 minutes after 8 o'clock
8 : 15
_____ minutes after _____ o'clock
_____ : _____
_____ minutes after _____ o'clock
_____ : _____
_____ minutes after _____ o'clock
_____ : _____

What Time Is It?

The hour hand is between 5 and 6
The minute hand is on 3.
The clock shows 5:15.

Trace the minute hand with red.
Circle the correct time.

8:30

9:15

12:00

1:15

11:30

11:45

8:30

6:15

5:30

7:30

8:45

9:30

T I M E

Riddle Time

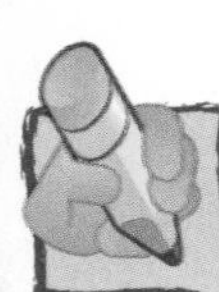

Write the time.

___ : ___ ___ : ___

___ : ___ ___ : ___

___ : ___ ___ : ___

Unscramble the letters to answer the riddle.

What did one clock say to the other clock?

___ ___ ___ ___ ___ ___ ___ ___ ___ ___ ?

t G o a t e m n i u

Answer: Got a minute?

On Time

It is 4:20.

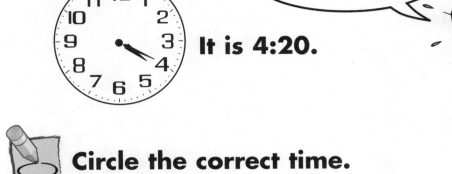

Circle the correct time.

1:10

1:15

3:15

3:40

9:35

9:20

2:45

2:05

7:35

7:20

1:10

10:55

6:50

6:15

8:30

8:25

Cat Clocks

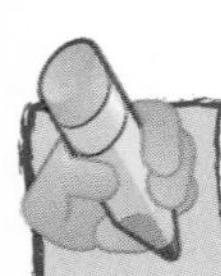

Write the time.

____:____ ____:____ ____:____

____:____ ____:____ ____:____

____:____ ____:____ ____:____

Telling time in 5-minute intervals

Time for Robots

Draw hands on the clocks to show the time.

7:30

2:10

10:25

12:05

6:45

3:40

5:15

1:55

9:20

Time to Play Ball!

Draw lines to match the clocks with the same time.

Both clocks show 9:20.

In a While, Crocodile

Now it is 4:00.

30 minutes later it will be 4:30.

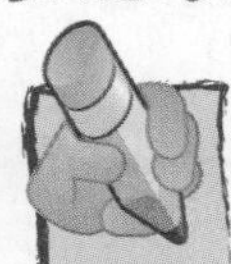

Draw the clock hands to show the time 30 minutes later. Write the time.

Now | **30 minutes later**

5:30

___ : ___

8:00

1:15

2:45

At the Museum

Draw hands on the clocks to help you solve the problem. Write the answer on the line.

Kristen woke up at 9:00. She left for the museum 30 minutes later. What time did Kristen leave for the museum?

____ : ____

Brad got to the museum at 10:20. Pat got to the museum 25 minutes later. What time did Pat get to the museum?

____ : ____

Lindsay got to the museum at 1:00. She went home 3 hours later. What time did Lindsay go home?

____ : ____

The dinosaur show starts at 2:15. It lasts 30 minutes. What time does the dinosaur show end?

____ : ____

Calendar Time

Circle the name of the month.

Color the first day of the month blue.
Color the last day of the month red.

Draw a ▲ on every Wednesday.

JULY
Sunday
Monday
Tuesday
Wednesday
Thursday
Friday
Saturday
1 2 3 4 5
6 7 8 9 10 11 12
13 14 15 16 17 18 19
20 21 22 23 24 25 26
27 28 29 30 31

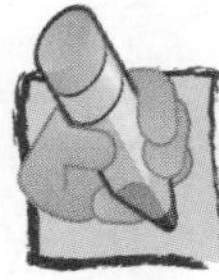

Write the answers.

What is the first day of the week? ____________

How many days are in one week? ____________

How many Mondays are in this month? ______

What day of the week is July 10? ____________

Which Month?

January February March April May June July August September October November December

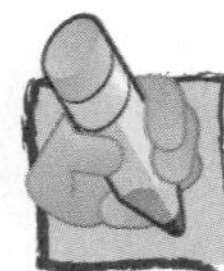

Read the clue. Write the name of the month.

1. First month of the year ___January___
2. Last month of the year ______
3. Month after June ______
4. Month before September ______
5. Month between May and July ______
6. Second month of the year ______
7. Tenth month of the year ______
8. Third month of the year ______
9. Month between March and May ______
10. Fifth month of the year ______
11. Month before October ______
12. Month before December ______

Identifying the names and order of the months of the year

Review

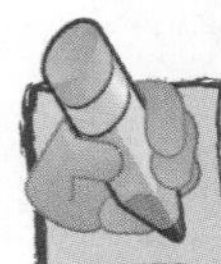

Write the time.

___:___ ___:___ ___:___

Draw hands on each clock to show the time.

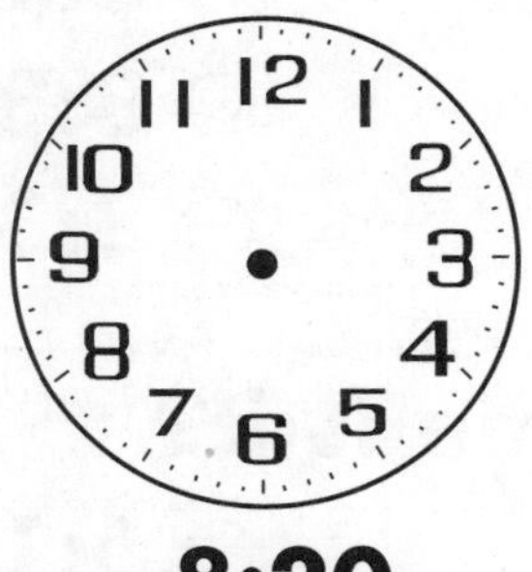

8:20

5:45

12:35

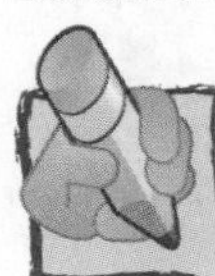

Write the answers.

NOVEMBER

Sunday	Monday	Tuesday	Wednesday	Thursday	Friday	Saturday
				1	2	3
4	5	6	7	8	9	10
11	12	13	14	15	16	17
18	19	20	21	22	23	24
25	26	27	28	29	30	

Which day of the week is the first day of this month? ____________

How many Tuesdays are in this month? ____________

What month will come after this month? ____________

Practice Test

How much money?

- ❍ 2¢
- ❍ 10¢
- ● 20¢

Fill in the circle next to the correct answer.

1. How much money?

- ❍ 5¢
- ❍ 23¢
- ❍ 32¢

2. How much money?

- ❍ 10¢
- ❍ 11¢
- ❍ 21¢

3. How much money?

- ❍ 60¢
- ❍ 50¢
- ❍ 40¢

4. How much money?

- ❍ 29¢
- ❍ 9¢
- ❍ 14¢

5. What time is it?

- ❍ 8:15
- ❍ 8:30
- ❍ 3:30

6. What time is it?

- ❍ 6:15
- ❍ 6:30
- ❍ 6:45

7. What time is it?

- ❍ 2:00
- ❍ 2:20
- ❍ 4:10

8. What time is it?

- ❍ 8:45
- ❍ 8:55
- ❍ 9:00

Month 9 Checklist

Hands-on activities to help your child in school!

NUMBERS

Sequencing Numbers to 100 and Number Patterns: pages 259-260, 267-269, 270, 272

Comparing and Ordering Numbers to 100: pages 261-267, 271

The worksheets in this section will help your child build skills in counting, sequencing, ordering, and comparing numbers, including identifying the number that is greater or less than another number and ordering a group of three or more numbers.

❑ Complete the worksheets.

❑ Take a walk along a residential street. Ask your child to read the house numbers. Call attention to the use of odd and even numbers, and look for patterns together.

❑ Write a secret number between 1 and 100. Have your child guess the number, and respond by saying, "This number is greater than ___" or "This number is less than ___." Continue until your child guesses the number. Reverse roles and play again.

❑ Say a number, and ask your child to supply three numbers that are greater and three numbers that are less than that number. Then, reverse roles and repeat the activity.

❑ Place a collection of up to 100 beans in a jar. Discuss how to make a good estimate. Then, ask your child to guess the number of beans. Spill them out and count together. Repeat the activity, using a different number of beans. Note how your child's estimation and number sense skills improve with each trial!

NUMBERS continued

Place Value—Tens and Ones: pages 274-281
Place Value—Hundreds, Tens, and Ones: pages 282-287

Now that your child can read and write numbers through 100, he or she is ready to learn how to construct them using tens and ones. These worksheets focus on the concepts of 2-digit numbers consisting of groups of tens and ones, and 3-digit numbers consisting of groups of hundreds, tens, and ones.

- ❑ Complete the worksheets.
- ❑ Relate the idea of 2-digit place value to dimes and pennies. Write a number, such as 38, and challenge your child to show the number using dimes and pennies.
- ❑ Have your child make a web for any 3-digit number. For the number 234, for example, your child would write the number in a center circle. In four spokes coming out of the circle, he or she would write (a) 200 + 30 + 4, (b) two hundred thirty-four, (c) 2 hundreds, 3 tens, 4 ones, and (d) a picture showing 2 hundreds, 3 tens, and 4 ones.
- ❑ Have your child choose three numbers, such as 5, 7, and 4. Challenge your child to write as many different 2-digit numbers and 3-digit numbers as possible using each number only once.

Garden Path

Color the boxes from 75 to 100, in order, to make a path from Start to Finish.

Start

75	76	77	80	81	93	94
78	71	78	79	91	80	83
72	89	79	83	93	94	95
82	81	80	88	92	91	96
83	88	79	72	91	98	97
84	76	75	78	90	92	98
85	86	87	88	89	93	99
88	92	94	93	91	87	100

Finish

Roller Coaster

Write the missing numbers.

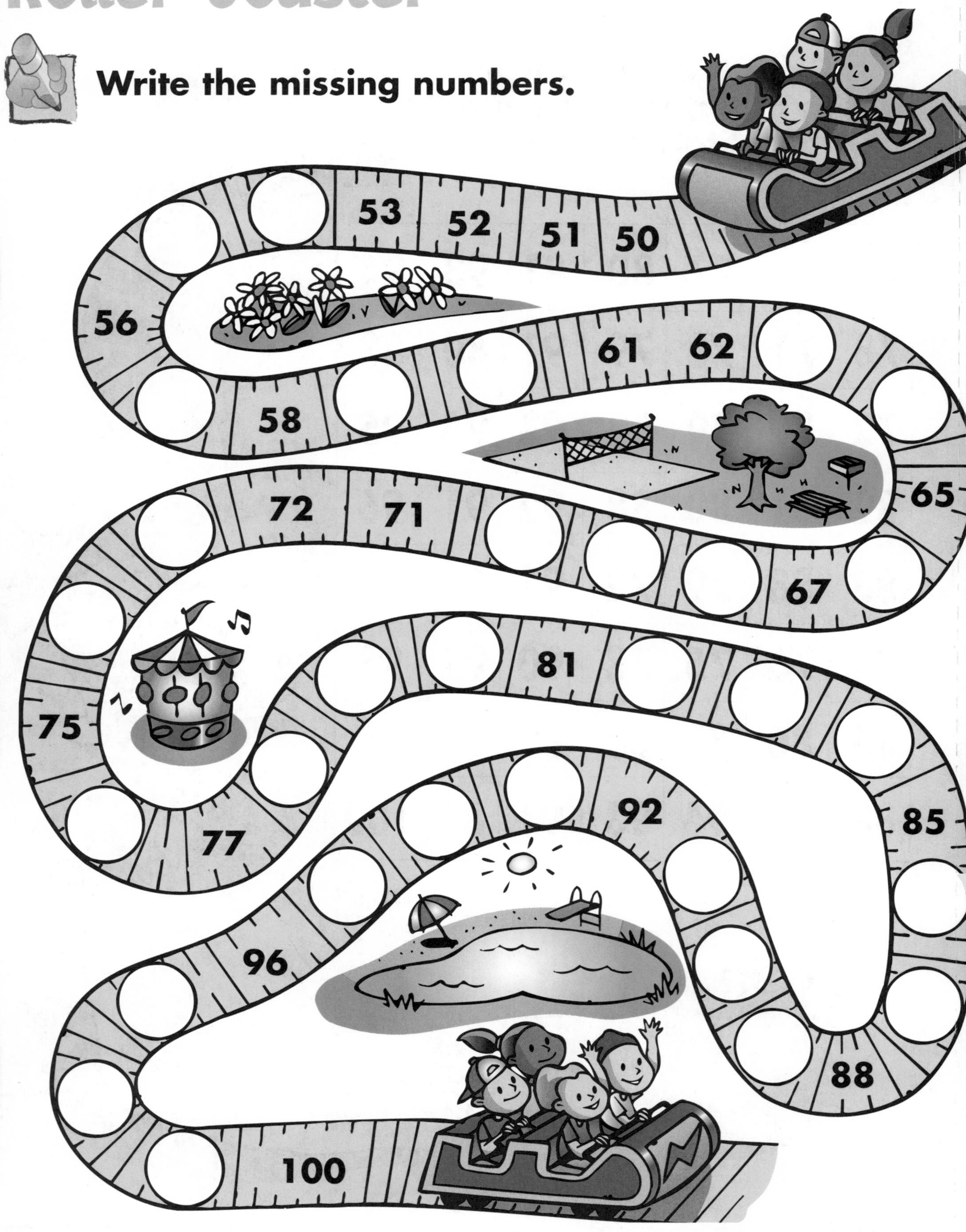

Book Look

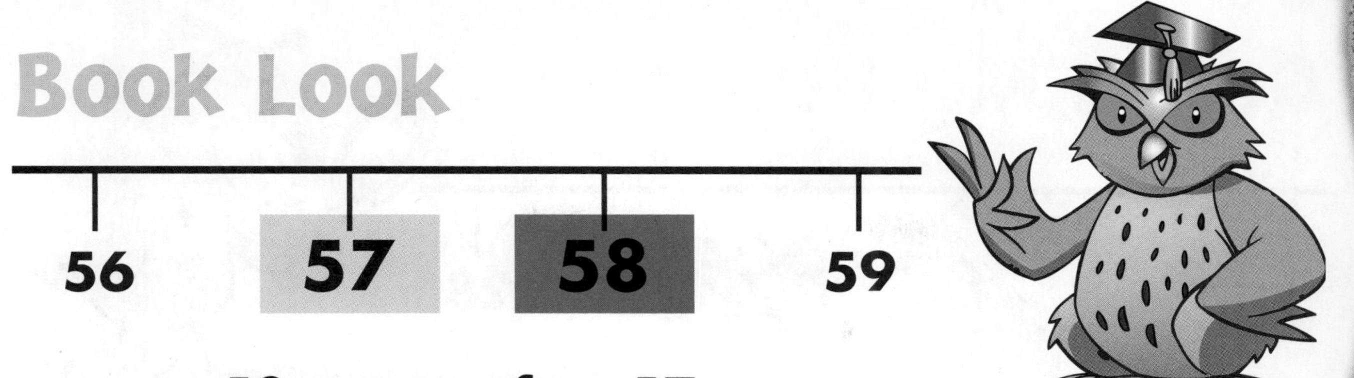

58 comes after 57.

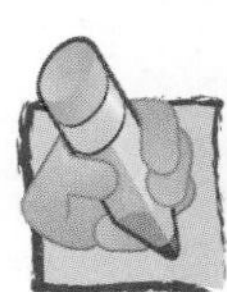

Write the number that comes after.

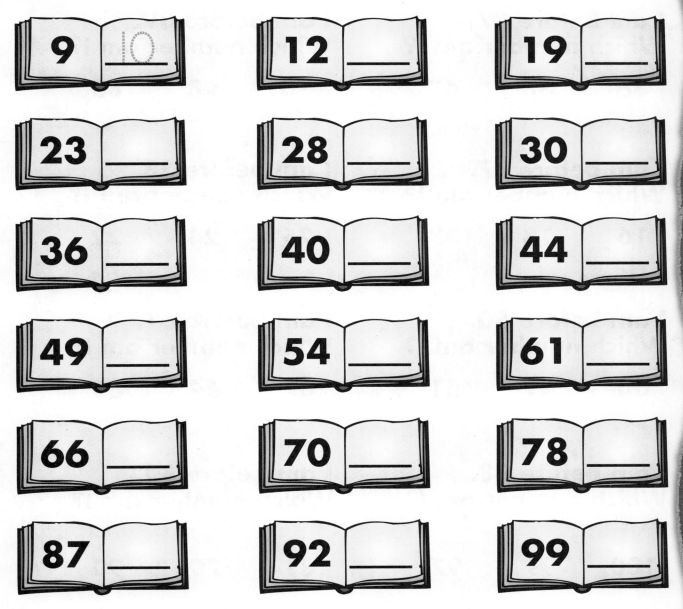

9 10	12 ____	19 ____
23 ____	28 ____	30 ____
36 ____	40 ____	44 ____
49 ____	54 ____	61 ____
66 ____	70 ____	78 ____
87 ____	92 ____	99 ____

Guess My Number

25 | **26** | **27** | 28

26 comes **before** 27.

Circle the number that comes before.

I am before 37.
Which number am I?

36 38 47

I am before 89.
Which number am I?

90 98 88

I am before 17.
Which number am I?

16 18 37

I am before 23.
Which number am I?

25 24 22

I am before 50.
Which number am I?

60 49 51

I am before 61.
Which number am I?

67 64 60

I am before 98.
Which number am I?

100 99 97

I am before 80.
Which number am I?

81 79 90

Bouncing Balls

85 26 60

26 is the smallest number.
85 is the largest number.

Draw a square around the smallest number. Circle the largest number.

9 12 14

15 11 20

19 40 31

50 39 27 42

71 36 17 63

80 37 79 51

76 91 89 40

67 58 49 70

52 84 48 81

50 More or Less

Use the key below to color the boxes.

numbers less than 50

numbers greater than 50

53	75	62	42	61	97	82
78	49	25	38	88	33	73
81	95	55	22	70	27	90
46	10	60	36	77	47	99
12	19	93	43	80	39	98
94	79	83	29	66	61	79

Look at the boxes you colored.

What number do you see? ________________

Some Ducks!

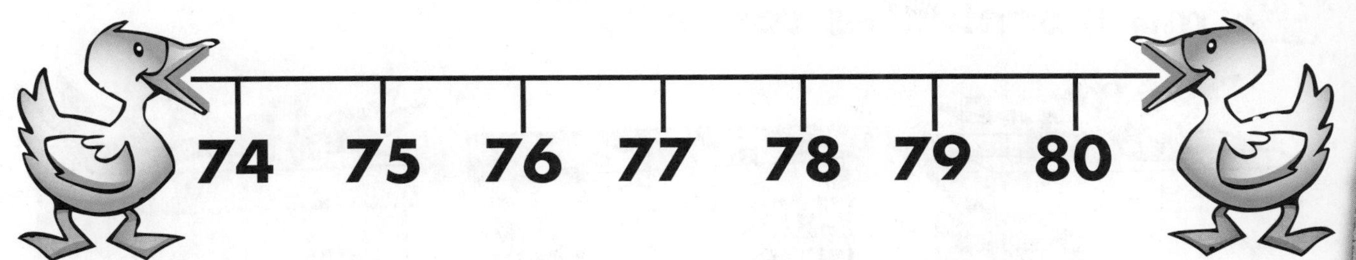

< means "is less than"
76 < 78

> means "is greater than"
77 > 75

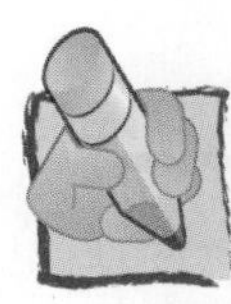

Complete each sentence with < or >. Be sure the duck's mouth is open to the greatest number.

10	9	36	40	18	81
80	68	54	34	16	71
36	39	25	29	50	49
27	72	82	85	71	79
60	59	30	39	48	50
39	31	56	85	19	21

Gift Boxes

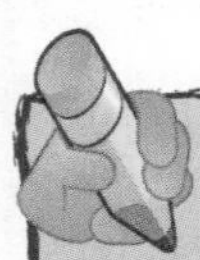

Use each set of numbers to write the math sentences correctly.

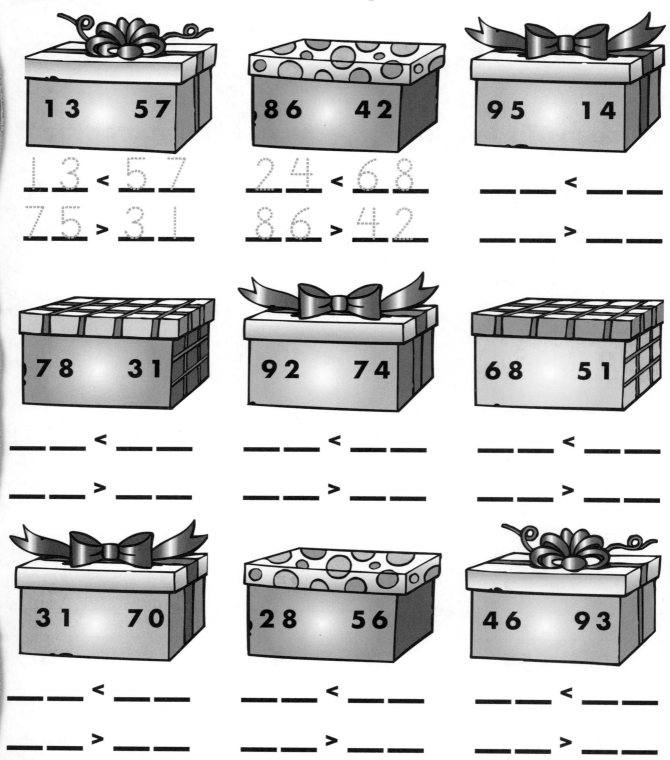

13 57	86 42	95 14
1 3 < 5 7	2 4 < 6 8	___ ___ < ___ ___
7 5 > 3 1	8 6 > 4 2	___ ___ > ___ ___

78 31	92 74	68 51
___ ___ < ___ ___	___ ___ < ___ ___	___ ___ < ___ ___
___ ___ > ___ ___	___ ___ > ___ ___	___ ___ > ___ ___

31 70	28 56	 46 93
___ ___ < ___ ___	___ ___ < ___ ___	___ ___ < ___ ___
___ ___ > ___ ___	___ ___ > ___ ___	___ ___ > ___ ___

Pizza Party

The numbers from least to greatest are 45, 54, 60.

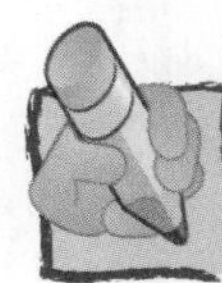

Write each group of numbers from least to greatest.

10 30 20

10 20 30

18 23 14

___ ___ ___

45 48 52

___ ___ ___

34 41 29

___ ___ ___

75 57 68

___ ___ ___

35 27 31

___ ___ ___

67 82 53

___ ___ ___

60 47 59

___ ___ ___

90 68 77

___ ___ ___

Climbing Monkeys

Find the pattern.
Write the missing numbers.

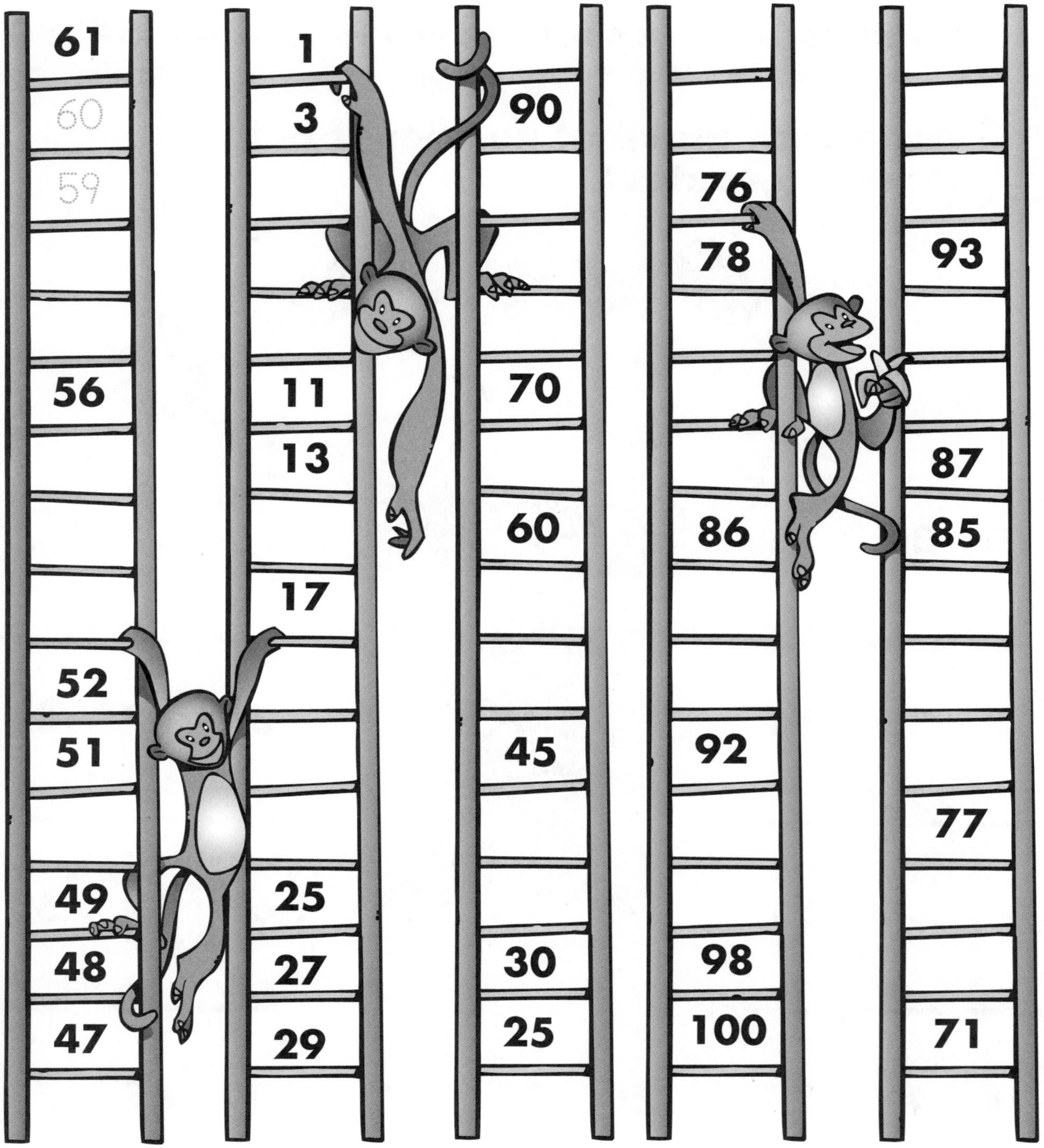

Ladder 1	Ladder 2	Ladder 3	Ladder 4	Ladder 5
61	1			
60	3	90		
59			76	
			78	93
56	11	70		
	13			87
		60	86	85
	17			
52				
51		45	92	
				77
49	25			
48	27	30	98	
47	29	25	100	71

Pattern Puzzles

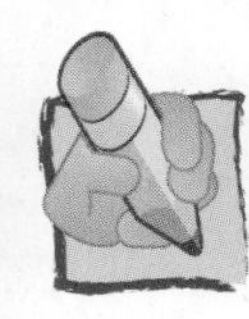

**Find the pattern.
Write the missing numbers.**

43
53
___ 60 61 ___ ___ 64
___ ___
79 ___ ___ ___ 83 ___ 85
91 ___ ___

68 67 66
57
___
___ 36 35 34
___
40 42 ___ 46

Treasure Hunt

Odd numbers end in 1, 3, 5, 7, 9.

Even numbers end in 2, 4, 6, 8, 0.

Color treasures with **odd** numbers purple.

Color treasures with **even** numbers yellow.

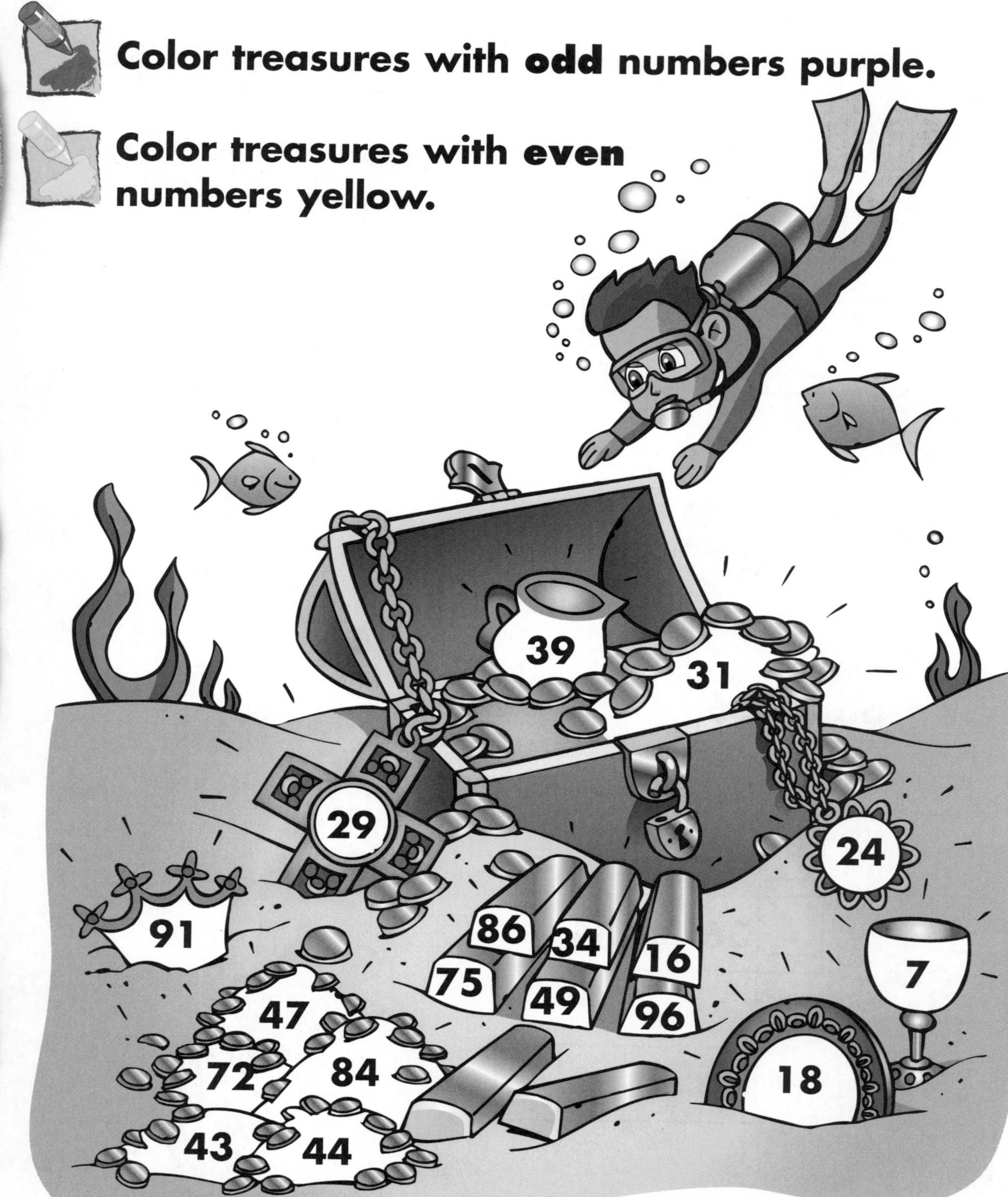

Picking Apples

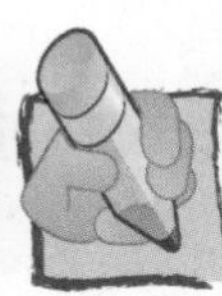

Read the basket labels to find out which apples go in each basket. Write the numbers on the apples.

Wheel Away!

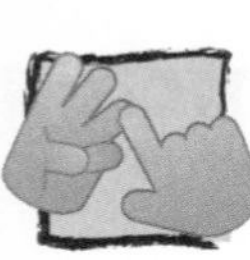

Add the numbers from the inside out. Write the sums.

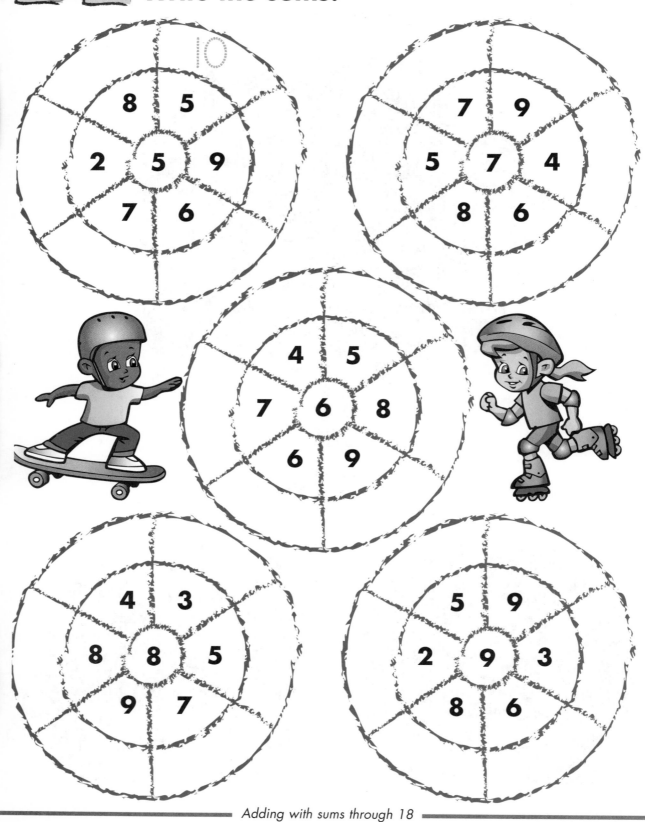

Wheel 1: center 5; inner numbers 8, 5, 9, 6, 7, 2; example answer 10

Wheel 2: center 7; inner numbers 7, 9, 4, 6, 8, 5

Wheel 3: center 6; inner numbers 4, 5, 8, 9, 6, 7

Wheel 4: center 8; inner numbers 4, 3, 5, 7, 9, 8

Wheel 5: center 9; inner numbers 5, 9, 3, 6, 8, 2

Review

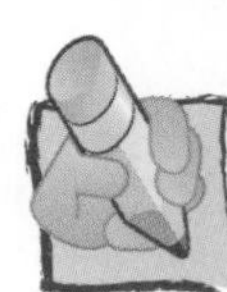

Write the missing numbers.

71	72			75				79	
81			84			87			90
		93			96		98		

Write the missing numbers.

53 ____	87 ____	____ 20	____ 38
75 ____	12 ____	____ 31	____ 49

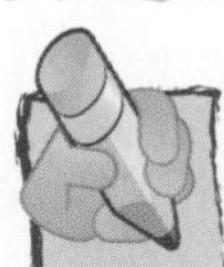

Write two sentences for each number pair. Use < and >.

79 80	65 56	41 38	27 72
________	________	________	________
________	________	________	________

Solve the riddles. Write the numbers.

I am an odd number between 40 and 50. You say my name when you count by 5's. What number am I?

____

I am greater than 89 and less than 93. You say my name when you count by 10's. What number am I?

____

Time for Tens

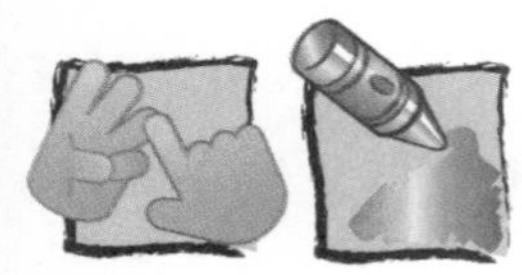

Count by tens. Color the 10 s.

10

20

30

40

50

60

70

80

90

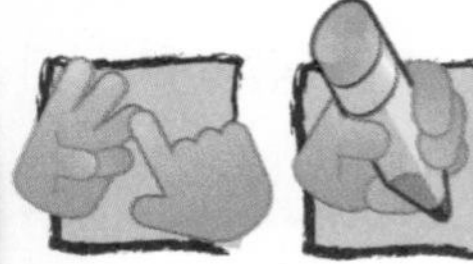

Count by 10's.
Write the missing numbers.

10 **20** ______ **40** ______

60 ______ **80** ______ **100**

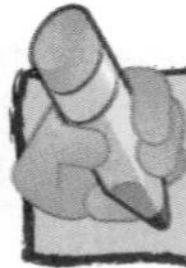

Count back. Write the missing numbers.

100 **90** ______ **70** ______

50 ______ **30** **20** ______

Fish for Tens and Ones

Circle the groups of ten. Write how many tens and ones. Then write the whole number.

2 tens 4 ones = 24

1 tens 7 ones = ____

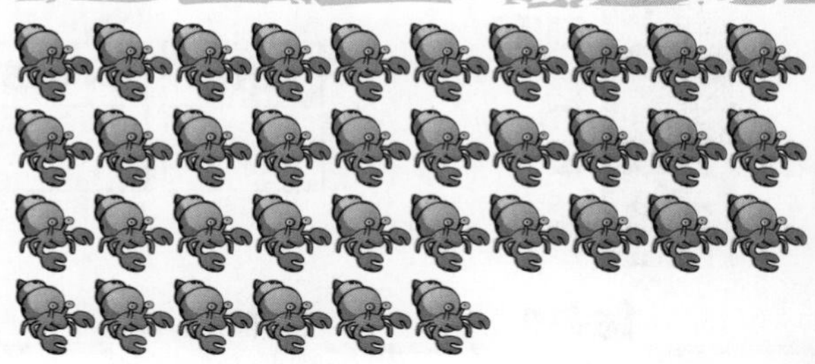

____ tens ____ ones = ____

____ tens ____ ones = ____

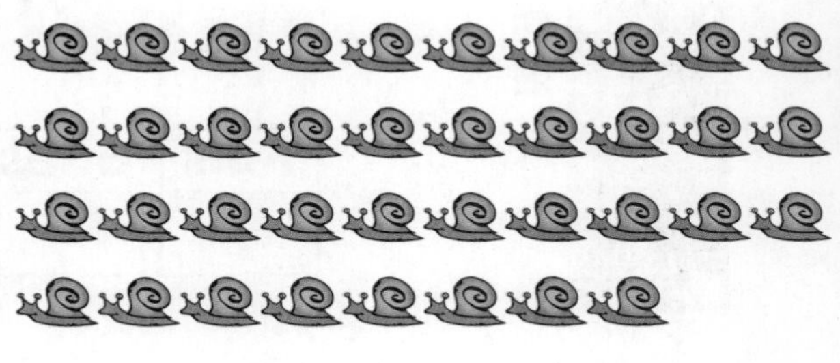

____ tens ____ ones = ____

____ tens ____ ones = ____

____ tens ____ ones = ____

NUMBERS

Block Count

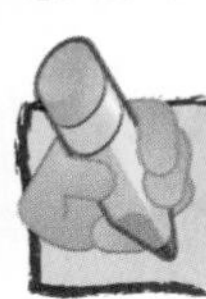

Count tens and ones.
Write how many.
Then write the whole number.

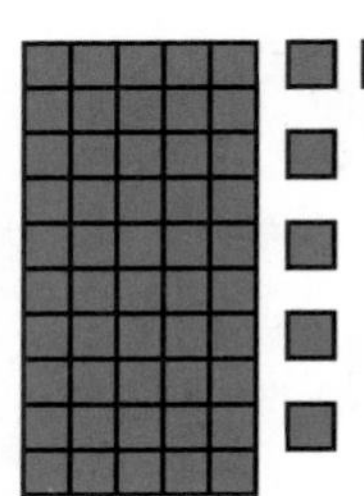

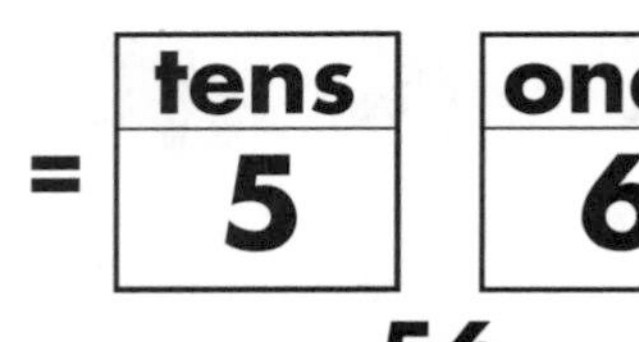

56

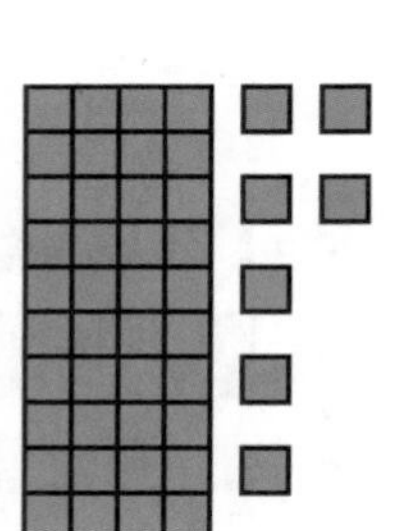

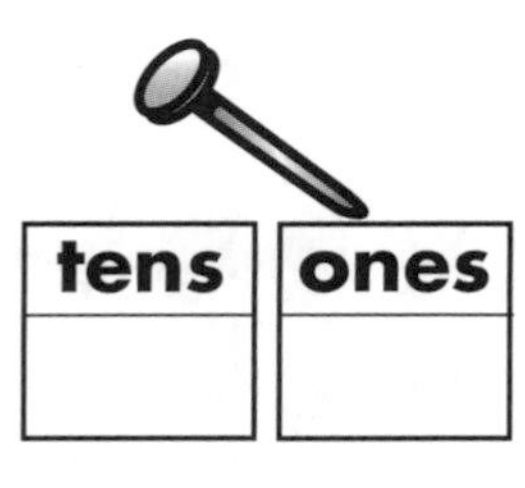

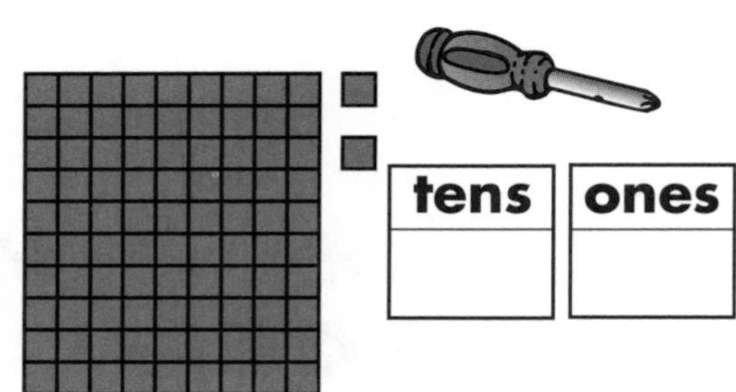

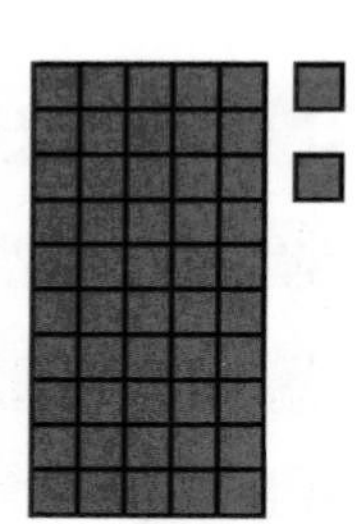

tens	ones

_____ **tens** _____ **ones =** _____

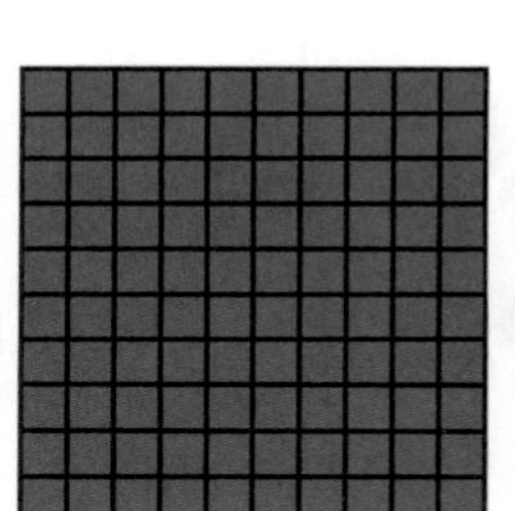

tens	ones

_____ **tens** _____ **ones =** _____

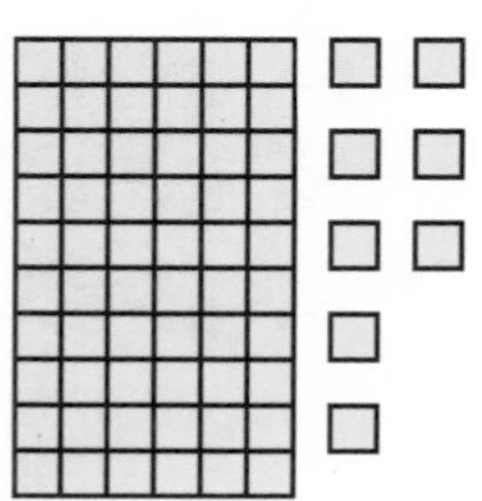

tens	ones

_____ **tens** _____ **ones =** _____

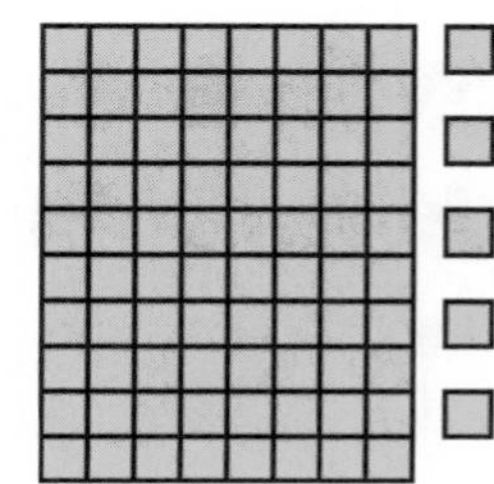

tens	ones

_____ **tens** _____ **ones =** _____

Good and Fruity

Write how many tens and ones. Then write the whole number.

___ ___
tens ones = ________

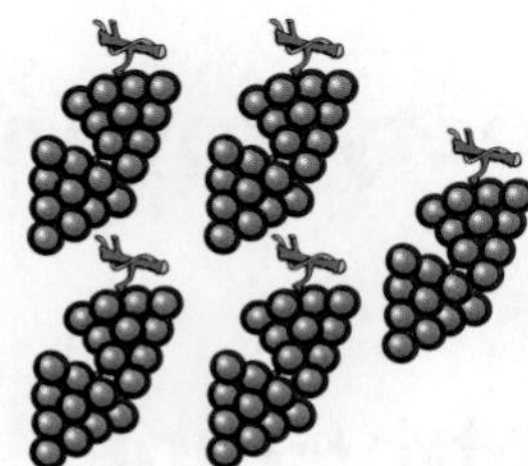 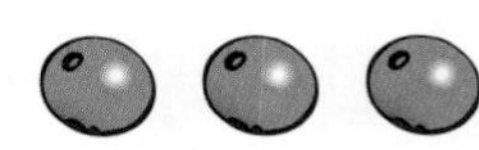

___ ___
tens ones = ________

___ ___
tens ones = ________

Write how many tens and ones.

35 = _____ tens _____ ones | 54 = _____ tens _____ ones

81 = _____ tens _____ ones | 29 = _____ tens _____ ones

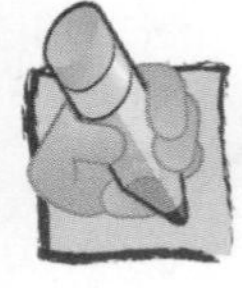

Write the whole number.

4 tens and 3 ones = _____ 1 ten and 6 ones = _____

6 tens and 0 ones = _____ 9 tens and 9 ones = _____

NUMBERS

Match Game

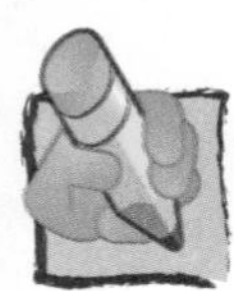

Draw lines to match.

8 tens and 3 ones	97	fifty-eight
5 tens and 8 ones	58	forty-three
3 tens and 1 one	43	ninety-seven
9 tens and 7 ones	26	eighty-nine
8 tens and 9 ones	64	sixty-four
7 tens and 5 ones	83	twenty-six
6 tens and 4 ones	75	thirty-one
2 tens and 6 ones	89	seventeen
1 ten and 7 ones	31	eighty-three
4 tens and 3 ones	17	seventy-five

Dive In!

Solve each addition sentence. Write the number.

30 + 5 = 35 | 80 + 2 = ______ | 70 + 1 = ______

60 + 3 = ______ | 40 + 7 = ______ | 20 + 2 = ______

10 + 9 = ______ | 90 + 1 = ______ | 50 + 6 = ______

30 + 2 = ______ | 80 + 5 = ______ | 60 + 8 = ______

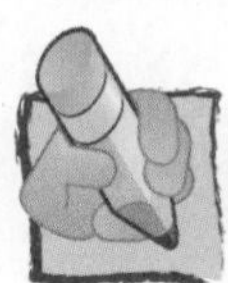

Write an addition sentence.

49 = 40 + 9 | 26 = ____ + ____ | 15 = ____ + ____

53 = ____ + ____ | 45 = ____ + ____ | 62 = ____ + ____

74 = ____ + ____ | 80 = ____ + ____ | 79 = ____ + ____

57 = ____ + ____ | 61 = ____ + ____ | 98 = ____ + ____

Color by Number

Use the key to color.

5 in the ones place 

3 in the ones place 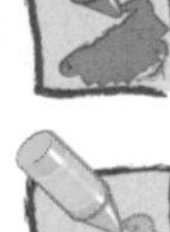

9 in the ones place 

5 in the tens place 

4 in the tens place 

8 in the tens place 

75 50

52 58

40 46

35 25

42 69 19 41

47 29 39 48

80 88

23 13

73 33

15 95

Pop These Number Riddles!

Read the riddles.
Write the number.

I have 4 tens. I have 3 more ones than tens.

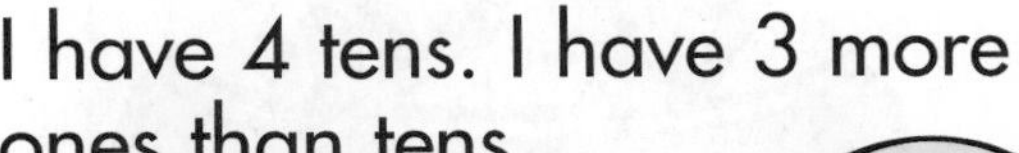

What number am I?

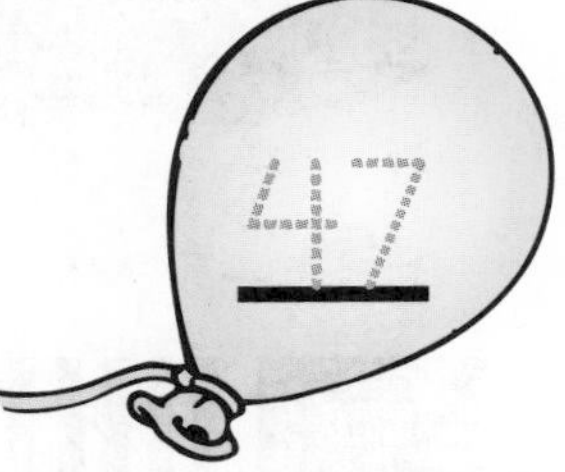

I have 6 tens. I have 1 fewer one than tens.

What number am I?

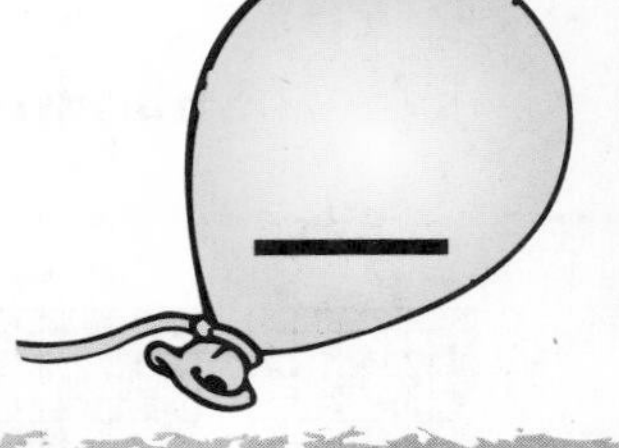

I have 1 one. I have 7 more tens than ones.

What number am I?

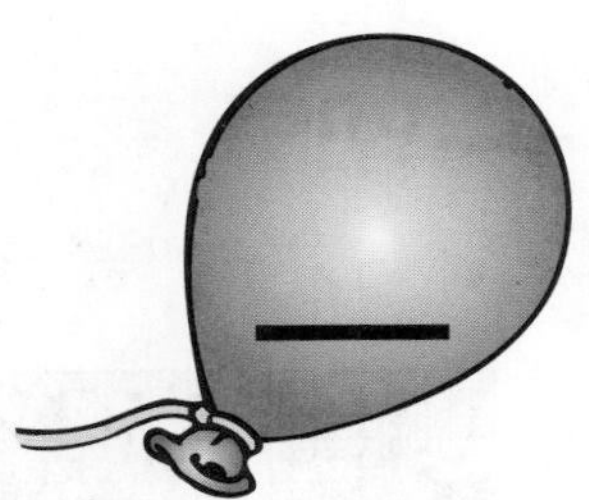

I have 9 ones. I have 2 fewer tens than ones.

What number am I?

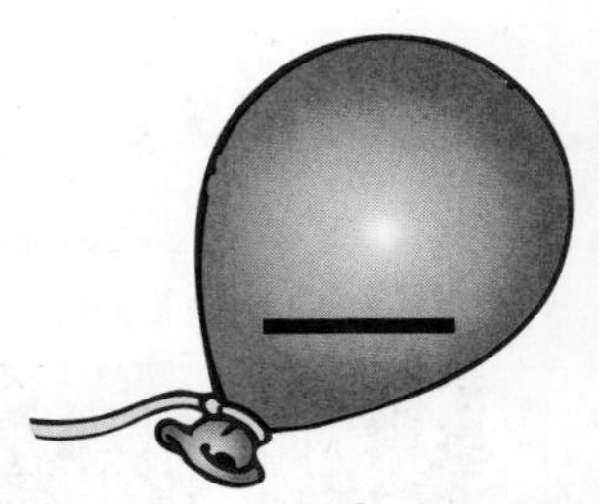

I have the same number of tens and ones. I am between 40 and 50.

What number am I?

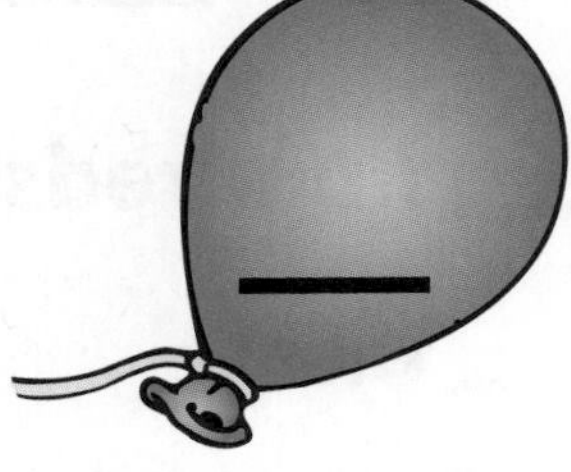

I have the same number of tens and ones. I am between 10 and 20.

What number am I?

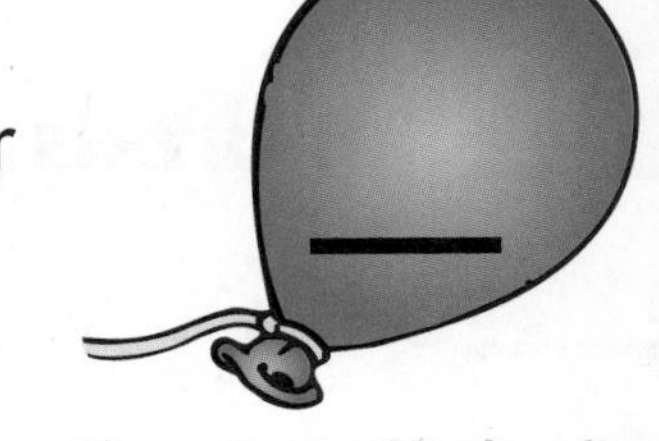

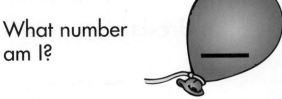

I have 1 fewer ten than ones. I am between 80 and 90.

What number am I?

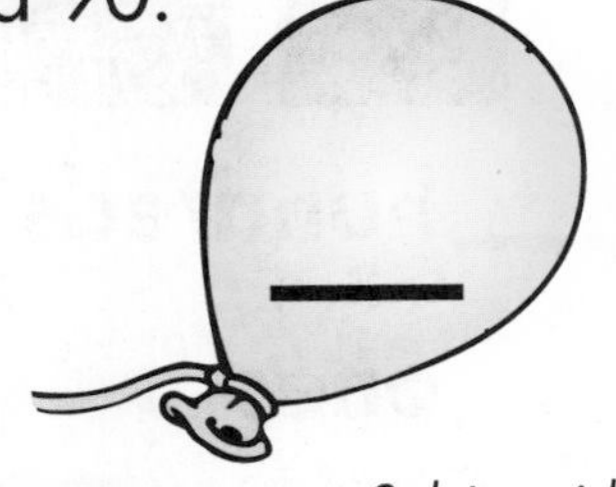

I have 1 more ten than ones. I am between 30 and 40.

What number am I?

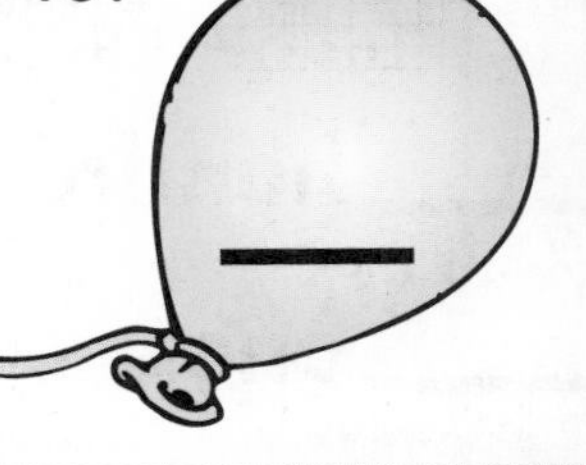

NUMBERS

Hundreds, Tens, and Ones

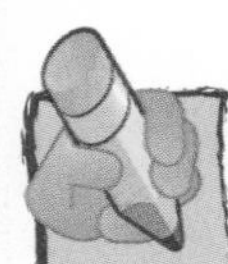

Write how many hundreds, tens, and ones. Then, write the whole number.

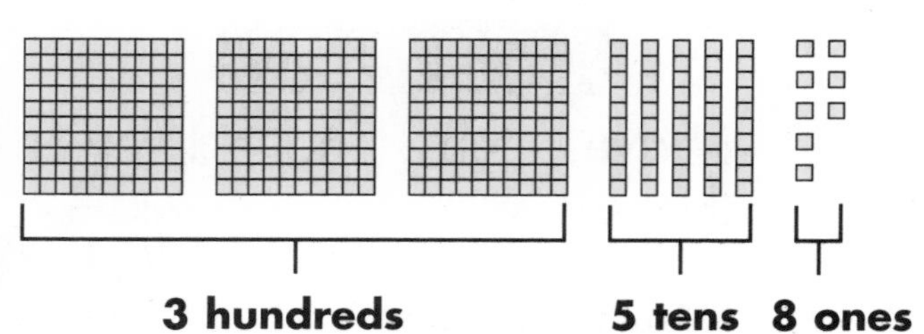

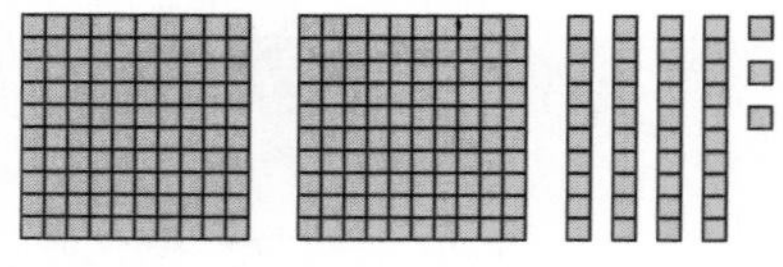

_____ hundreds _____ tens

_____ ones _________

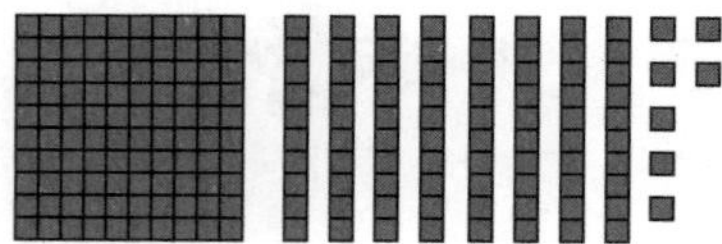

_____ hundreds _____ tens

_____ ones _________

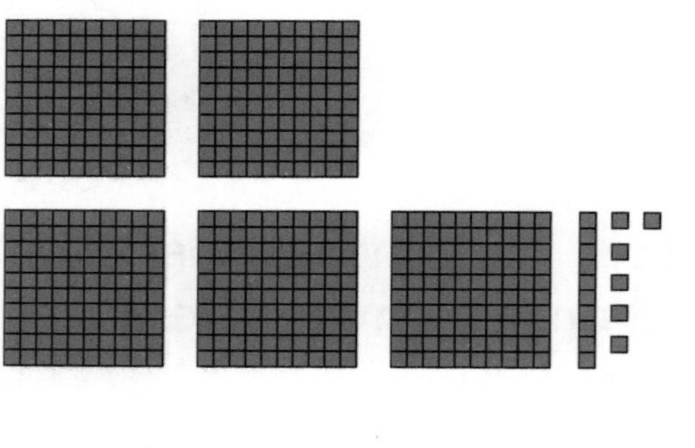

_____ hundreds _____ tens

_____ ones _________

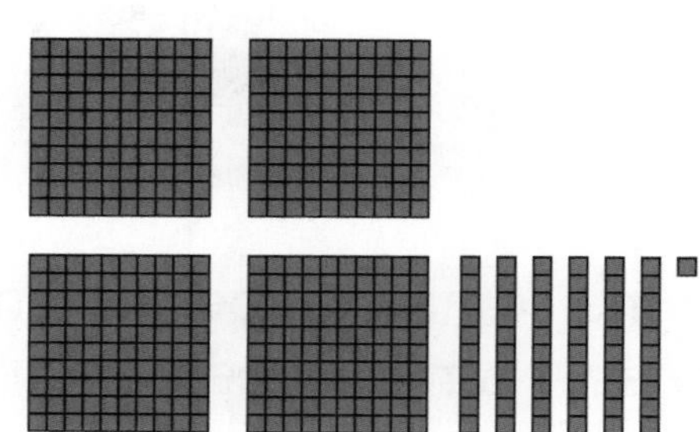

_____ hundreds _____ tens

_____ ones _________

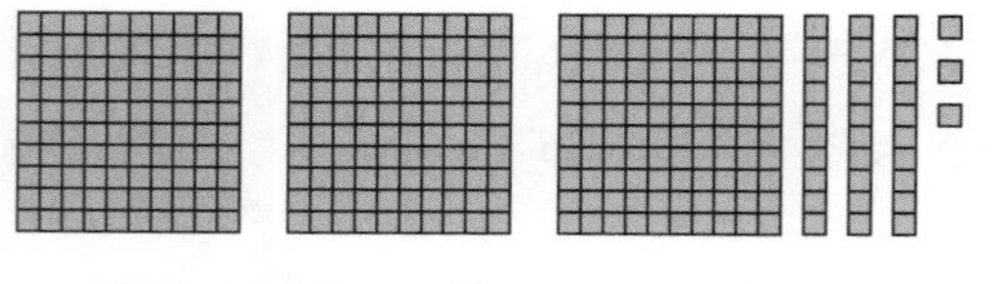

_____ hundreds _____ tens

_____ ones _________

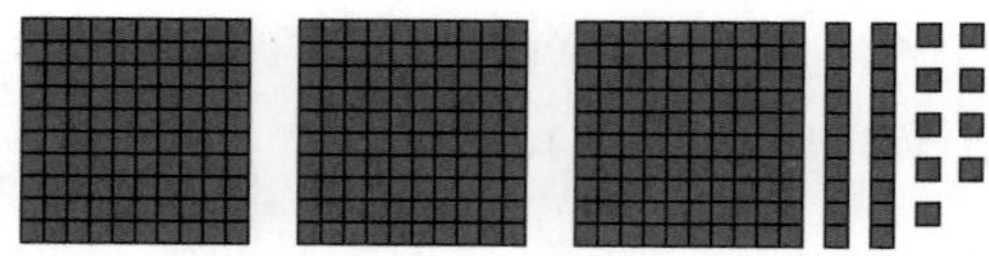

_____ hundreds _____ tens

_____ ones _________

Circle the number of hundreds, tens, and ones. Then, write the whole number.

300 + 40 + 2	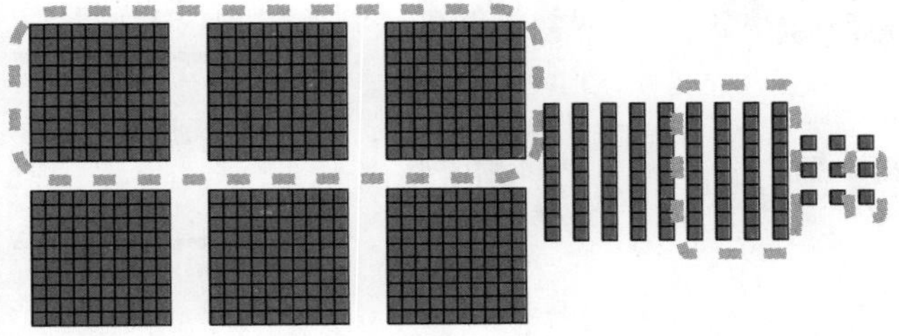	342
500 + 60 + 7	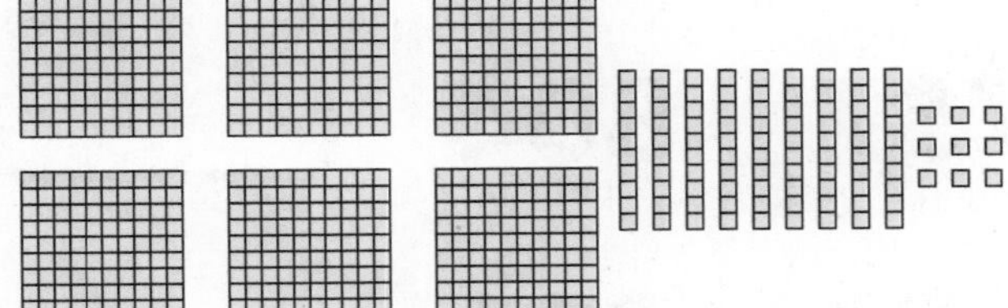	
200 + 10 + 9		
100 + 90 + 6	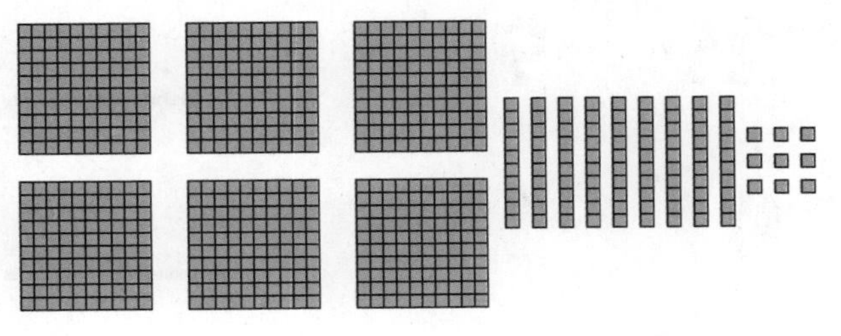	

NUMBERS

The Bear Family

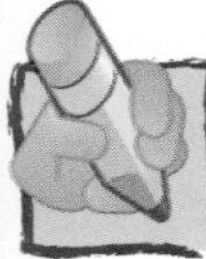

Write the numbers in order from greatest to least.

312	123	231	____	____	____
743	634	467	____	____	____
190	214	349	____	____	____
497	528	479	____	____	____
821	757	804	____	____	____
312	321	320	____	____	____
880	816	900	____	____	____
617	600	599	____	____	____
930	929	931	____	____	____
111	101	110	____	____	____

Match Game

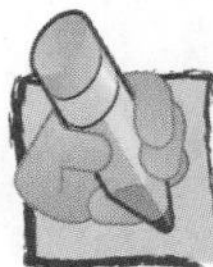

Match each word with the correct number.

Four hundred twenty-three	517
Five hundred seventeen	809
Seven hundred thirty-four	423
Eight hundred nine	342
Three hundred forty-two	290
Nine hundred sixty-one	734
Two hundred ninety	209
One hundred seventy-five	900
Six hundred fifty-seven	961
Nine hundred	432
Four hundred thirty-two	657
Two hundred nine	175

Cross-Number Puzzle

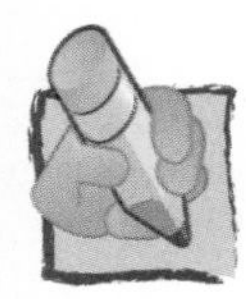

Write the numbers for each clue.

Across

A. 4 hundreds 2 tens 6 ones
B. Eight hundred five
D. 200 + 70 + 8
F. Five hundred thirty-seven
G. 7 hundreds 2 tens 9 ones
I. Four hundred seventy-six
K. 800 + 10 + 2
L. Four hundred

Down

A. 400 + 90 + 2
C. 5 hundreds 1 ten 7 ones
E. Eight hundred sixty-nine
F. 500 + 70 + 4
H. 2 hundreds 3 tens 1 one
J. Seven hundred ninety

A.				B.		C.
D.		E.		F.		
G.	H.			I.	J.	
K.				L.		

Number Sleuth

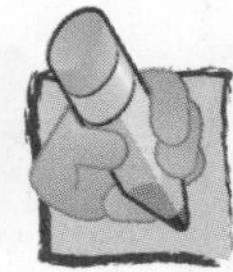

Read the riddles. Write the number. Match the number with a letter to find the answer to this riddle:

What goes through a door, but never goes in or out?

___	___	___	___	___	___	___	___
746	**614**	**923**	**593**	**111**	**278**	**539**	**444**

I have 4 tens, 7 hundreds, and 6 ones. What number am I?

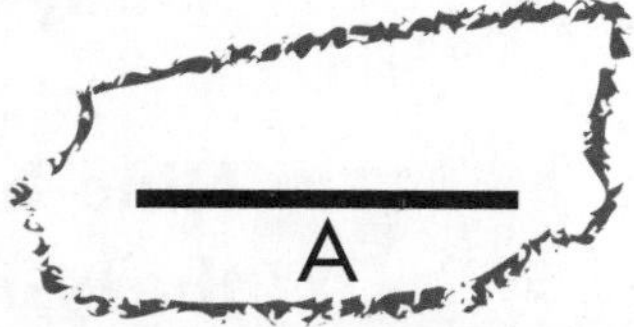

______ A

I have 3 ones, 9 hundreds, and 2 tens. What number am I?

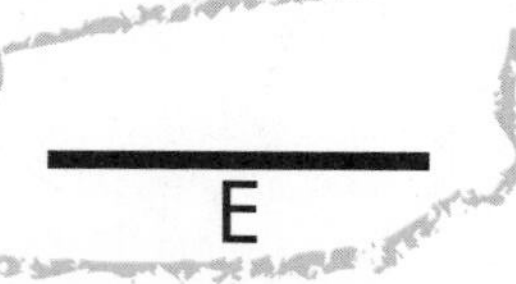

______ E

I have the same number of hundreds, tens, and ones. I have 4 tens. What number am I?

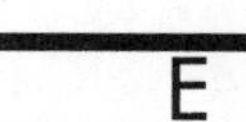

______ E

I have the same number of hundreds, tens, and ones. I have 1 one. What number am I?

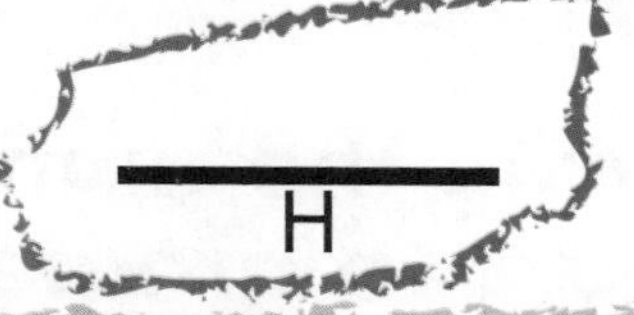

______ H

I have 4 ones and 1 ten. I am between 610 and 620. What number am I?

______ K

I have 3 tens and 9 ones. I am between 500 and 600. What number am I?

______ L

I have 8 ones and 2 hundreds. I am between 270 and 280. What number am I?

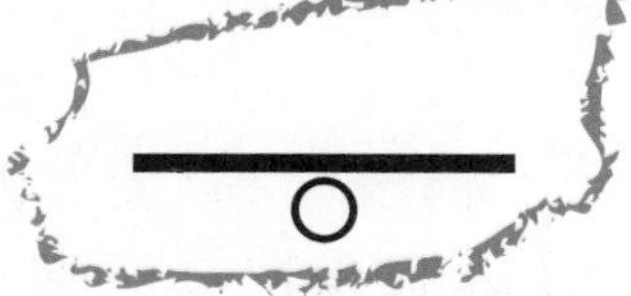

______ O

I have 5 hundreds and 3 ones. I am more than 590. What number am I?

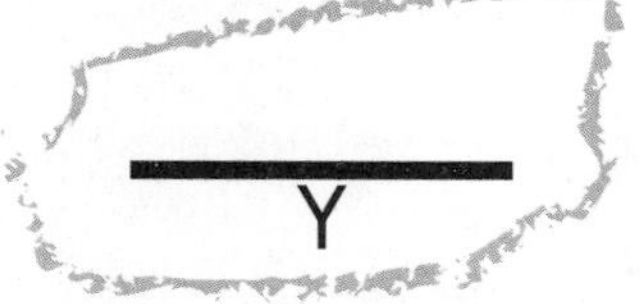

______ Y

Answer: A Keyhole

NUMBERS

Review

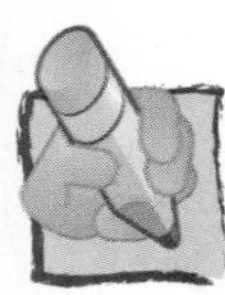

Match.

3 hundreds 9 tens 3 ones	900 + 3	Nine hundred thirty
9 hundreds 3 tens 9 ones	900 + 30 + 9	Nine hundred three
9 hundreds 3 ones	300 + 90 + 3	Nine hundred ninety-three
9 hundreds 3 tens	900 + 90 + 3	Nine hundred thirty-nine
9 hundreds 9 tens 3 ones	900 + 30	Three hundred ninety-three

Write the numbers in order from least to greatest.

87 98 91 ____ ____ ____ 78 75 77 ____ ____ ____

99 110 101 ____ ____ ____ 969 971 917 ____ ____ ____

380 400 394 ____ ____ ____ 809 812 800 ____ ____ ____

660 659 654 ____ ____ ____ 699 741 739 ____ ____ ____

Month 10 Checklist

Hands-on activities to help your child in school!

ADDITION

Adding Numbers to 18: pages 291-294
Adding 2-digit Numbers without Regrouping: pages 299-308

This month your child will work on committing addition facts up to 18 to memory; further understanding the place value of tens and ones; and using place value understanding to solve 2-digit addition problems.

❑ Complete the worksheets.

❑ Help your child learn a fact a day. Have him or her say it, sing it, make a poem for it, or write it in sand.

❑ Help your child learn two facts at a time using the concept of "turnaround facts." For example, your child can learn 1 + 9 = 10 by using the turnaround fact 9 + 1 = 10.

❑ Relate the idea of adding tens and ones to work with money. Use real dimes and pennies to create addition problems that do not require 10 pennies to be exchanged for a dime, or 1 dime to be exchanged for 10 pennies. For example, have your child add a group of 2 dimes and 3 pennies to another group of 4 dimes and 1 penny, for a sum of 6 dimes and 4 pennies or 64 cents. Repeat this activity several times with different amounts of dimes and pennies.

SUBTRACTION

Subtracting Numbers to 18: pages 295-298

Subtracting 2-digit Numbers without Regrouping: pages 309-314, 319-320

These pages will help your child practice subtraction facts with differences up to 18; continue to develop his or her understanding of the place value of tens and ones; and use this understanding to solve 2-digit subtraction problems.

- ❑ Complete the worksheets.
- ❑ Help your child learn a fact a day. Have him or her say it, sing it, make a poem for it, or write it in the sand.
- ❑ Use the ace through 9 of an ordinary deck of playing cards to create subtraction problems for your child to solve. Choose 2 pairs of cards, to form two 2-digit numbers. Make sure that the digits in the tens and ones places in the first pair are less than the digits in the tens and ones places in the second pair. For example, 12 and 43, 56 and 98, or 31 and 72. Ask your child to subtract the smaller number from the larger number. Remind him or her to subtract the ones first, then the tens.

T-Shirt Addition

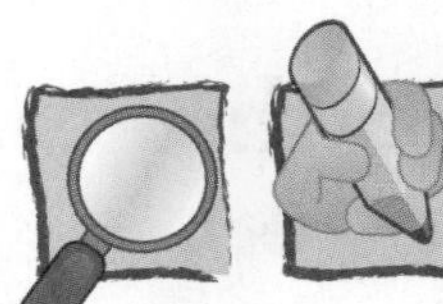

Look at the answer on each sleeve. Write the equations that equal that sum. Use the list below.

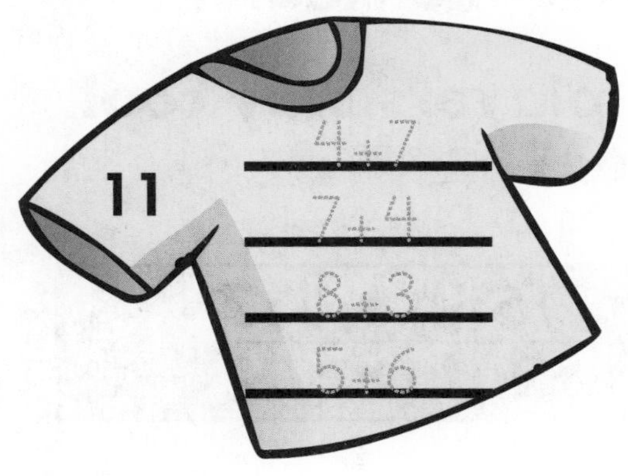

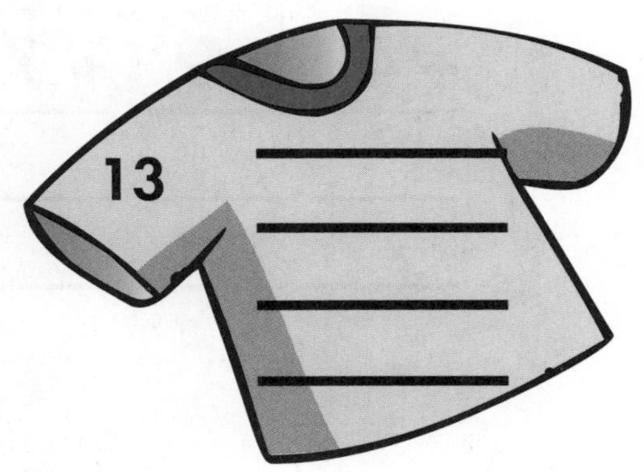

9 + 7	8 + 8	7 + 4	9 + 5	6 + 8
4 + 7	9 + 6	8 + 4	6 + 9	7 + 6
9 + 4	8 + 3	5 + 6	7 + 9	5 + 9
6 + 6	5 + 7	7 + 7	6 + 7	10 + 6
7 + 8	7 + 5	8 + 7	8 + 5	

Calling All Sports Fans

Add. Then, match your answers to the letters in the red box. Write the letters on the lines to answer the riddle.

How do basketball players stay cool at a basketball game?

9	10	11	12	13	14	15	16	17	18
A	F	S	E	L	T	R	O	H	N

$9 + 5 = 14$ (T) $8 + 9 =$ ___ $6 + 6 =$ ___ $7 + 8 =$ ___ $4 + 8 =$ ___

$5 + 4 =$ ___ $6 + 9 =$ ___ $5 + 7 =$ ___

$5 + 8 =$ ___ $7 + 9 =$ ___ $6 + 8 =$ ___ $4 + 7 =$ ___

$8 + 8 =$ ___ $6 + 4 =$ ___

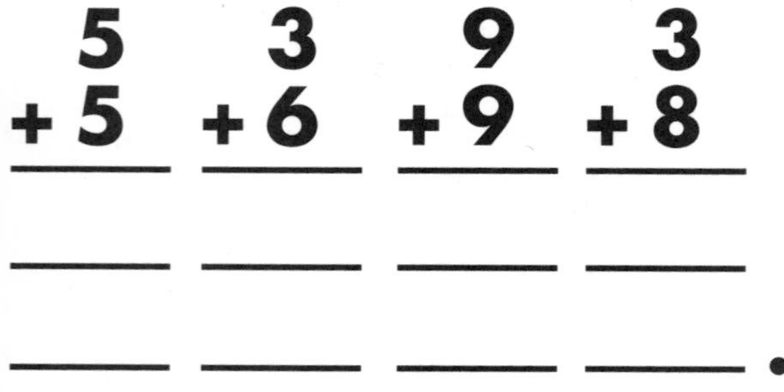

$5 + 5 =$ ___ $3 + 6 =$ ___ $9 + 9 =$ ___ $3 + 8 =$ ___ .

Answer: There are lots of fans.

Magic Squares

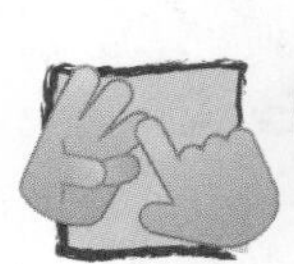
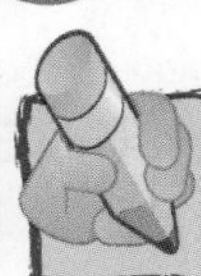

Add the numbers across and down. Write each answer. The number inside the star is magic!

8	0	
1	4	
		☆

2	7	
2	3	
		☆

0	9	
8	1	
		☆

ADDITION

Pet Stories

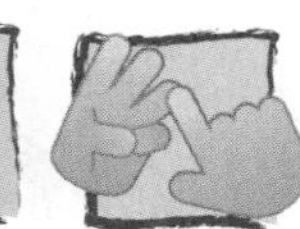

Read each story problem. Write a number sentence and solve.

1. There are 8 cats at the pet parade. Then, 7 more cats join the parade. How many cats are in the parade?

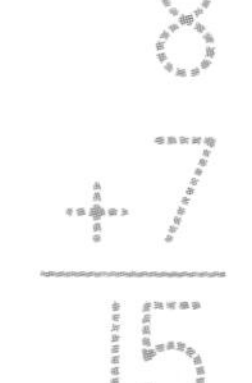

$$\begin{array}{r} 8 \\ +\ 7 \\ \hline 15 \end{array}$$

2. There are 9 dogs at the park. Then, 6 more dogs come. How many dogs are in the park?

3. Serina has 9 goldfish in her tank. Ray has 7 goldfish in his tank. How many goldfish are in both tanks?

4. Jeff had 4 guppies. His mother bought him 8 more guppies. How many guppies does Jeff have in all?

5. There are 6 horses in the barn. Then, 8 more horses are brought to the barn. How many horses are in the barn?

6. There are 9 cows grazing in the grass. Then, 8 more cows come along. How many cows are there?

Top to Bottom

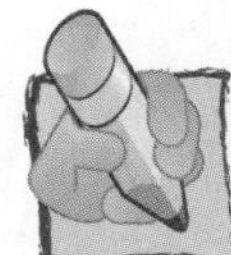

Subtract each number from the number in the center. Write the answers in the spaces.

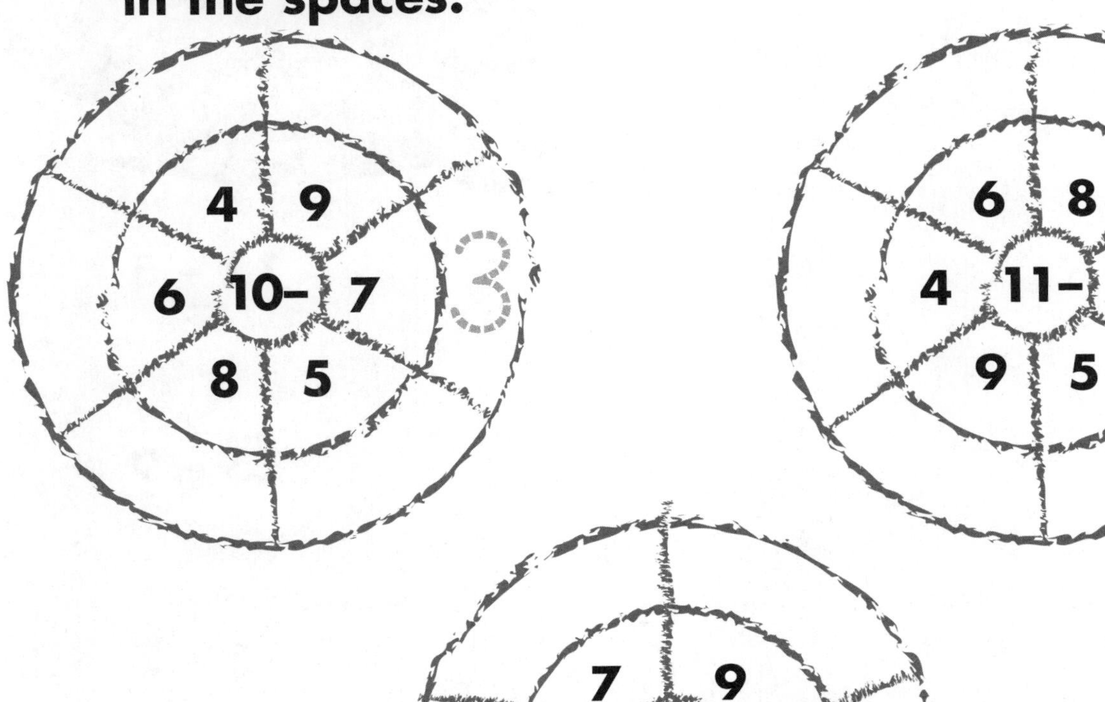

7 9
5 14– 6
8

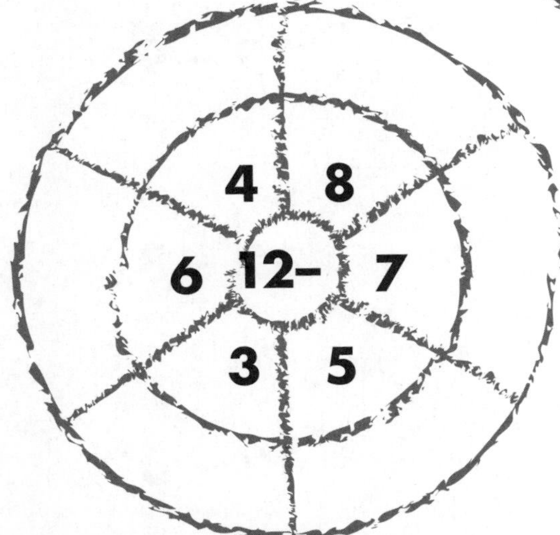

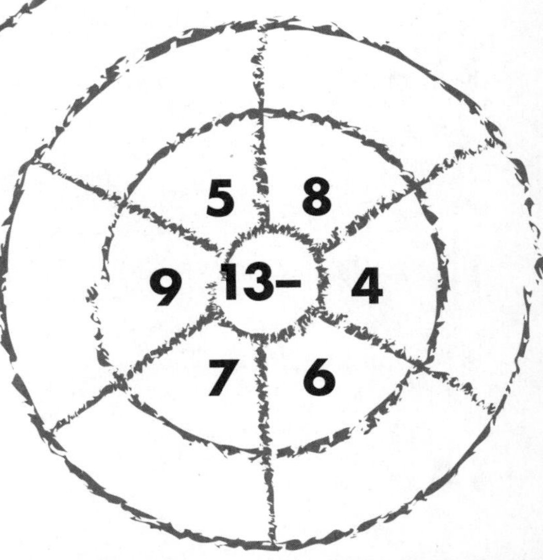

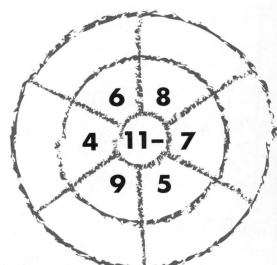

SUBTRACTION

Match the Differences

Draw lines to match the subtraction problems with their answers.

15 – 8	9	12 – 5
18 – 9	8	15 – 9
17 – 9	7	16 – 7
10 – 7	6	14 – 6
11 – 7	5	12 – 9
13 – 7	4	12 – 8
14 – 9	3	13 – 8

Patchwork Quilt

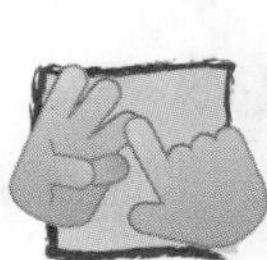 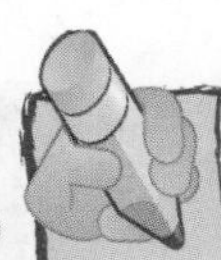 

Subtract and write each answer.
Use the code to color the quilt.

18 − 9 = 9	12 − 7		13 − 6	14 − 9	15 − 7	2, 3, 4
11 − 9	17 − 8	13 − 7	11 − 4	14 − 5	13 − 8	5, 6
16 − 7	14 − 6		13 − 9	12 − 3	13 − 5	7, 8, 9
	13 − 4	14 − 8	15 − 6	11 − 6		
11 − 2		11 − 3	12 − 5		11 − 7	12 − 9
11 − 5	17 − 9	16 − 8		14 − 7		11 − 8

How Does Your Garden Grow?

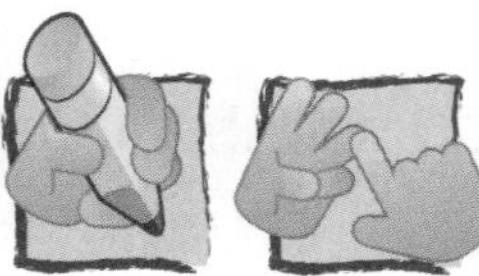

Read each story. Write a number sentence and solve.

1. Farmer Dan had 13 corn plants in the field. He harvested 6 of them. How many corn plants are left in the field?

13
−6
7

2. Tara bought 16 flowers. She bought 7 pansies and the rest were petunias. How many petunias did Tara buy?

3. Marci picked 15 flowers from the garden. She put 8 flowers in a vase and gave the rest away. How many flowers did Marci give away?

4. Keisha picked 12 tomatoes from the garden. She used 5 tomatoes for a sauce and saved the rest for salad. How many tomatoes did Keisha save?

5. Evan planted 14 green pepper plants and 9 red pepper plants. How many more green than red pepper plants did Evan plant?

6. Carlos picked 12 red apples and 9 green apples. How many more red than green apples did Carlos pick?

Lots of Bugs

13 + 5

18 in all

13

+ 5

18 in all

Count. Write how many.

in all

__7__ + __12__ = ______

in all

______ + ______ = ______

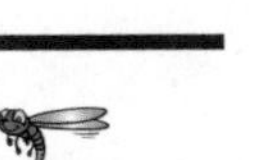

in all

______ + ______ = ______

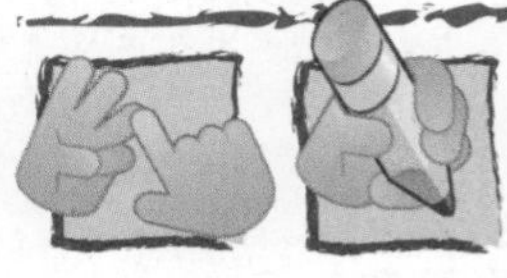

Count. Write how many in all.

14

+ 4

______ in all

15

+ 4

______ in all

Lots of Squares

23
+ 4
27 in all

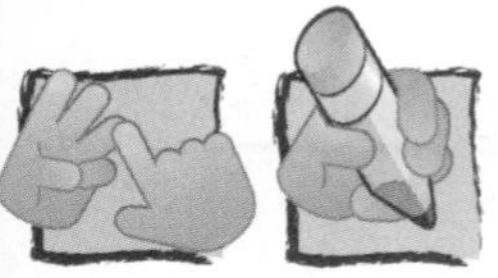

Count. Write how many in all.

13
+ 6
19 in all

24
+ 2
_____ in all

5
+ 22
_____ in all

40
+ 7
_____ in all

31
+ 4
_____ in all

33
+ 3
_____ in all

23
+ 4
_____ in all

18
+ 1
_____ in all

Fun in Tenstown

In Tenstown everything comes in packs of 10.

tens	ones
3	0
+2	0
5	0

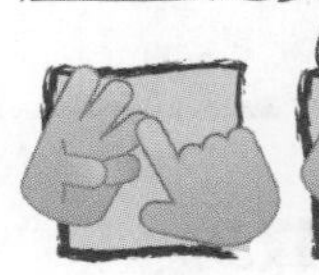
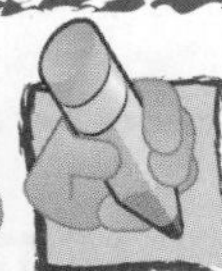

First, add the ones. Then, add the tens. Write the answers.

tens	ones
4	0
+1	0
5	0

tens	ones
7	0
+2	0

$$\begin{array}{r} 30 \\ +30 \\ \hline \end{array} \quad \begin{array}{r} 10 \\ +70 \\ \hline \end{array} \quad \begin{array}{r} 40 \\ +30 \\ \hline \end{array} \quad \begin{array}{r} 50 \\ +20 \\ \hline \end{array} \quad \begin{array}{r} 60 \\ +30 \\ \hline \end{array} \quad \begin{array}{r} 50 \\ +40 \\ \hline \end{array}$$

$$\begin{array}{r} 60 \\ +20 \\ \hline \end{array} \quad \begin{array}{r} 50 \\ +30 \\ \hline \end{array} \quad \begin{array}{r} 80 \\ +10 \\ \hline \end{array} \quad \begin{array}{r} 40 \\ +20 \\ \hline \end{array} \quad \begin{array}{r} 10 \\ +40 \\ \hline \end{array} \quad \begin{array}{r} 40 \\ +40 \\ \hline \end{array}$$

ADDITION

More Fun in Tenstown

Sometimes there are extra ones in Tenstown.

20 trees

+ 3 trees

23 trees

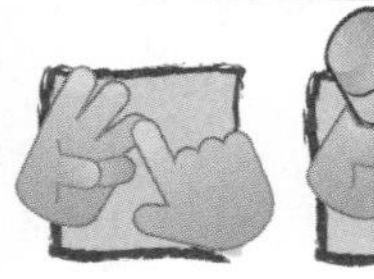

First add the ones. Then, add the tens. Write the answers.

tens	ones
3	4
+5	3
8	7

tens	ones
2	7
+3	0
6	7

$$\begin{array}{r} 51 \\ +38 \\ \hline \end{array} \quad \begin{array}{r} 62 \\ +25 \\ \hline \end{array} \quad \begin{array}{r} 31 \\ +\ 7 \\ \hline \end{array} \quad \begin{array}{r} 17 \\ +32 \\ \hline \end{array} \quad \begin{array}{r} 20 \\ +45 \\ \hline \end{array}$$

$$\begin{array}{r} 6 \\ +43 \\ \hline \end{array} \quad \begin{array}{r} 71 \\ +26 \\ \hline \end{array} \quad \begin{array}{r} 44 \\ +44 \\ \hline \end{array} \quad \begin{array}{r} 29 \\ +50 \\ \hline \end{array} \quad \begin{array}{r} 36 \\ +12 \\ \hline \end{array}$$

Pop the Balloons

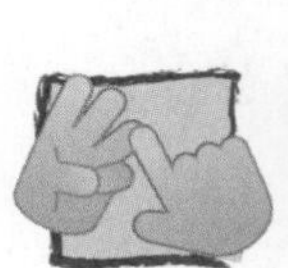
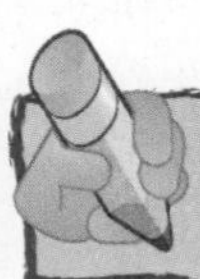

Add the ones, then the tens. Write the sum. Find and color the balloon with the same sum.

34 +15	21 +23	51 +15	5 +81
60 +29	43 +15	7 +70	21 +44
27 +12	32 +23	42 +50	21 +72
53 +26	62 +16	43 +44	91 + 7

49
44
92
86
79
93
89
58
65
78
39
55
66
98
87
77

ADDITION

Falling Leaves

Add. Write the answers.

$$\begin{array}{r} 12 \\ +27 \\ \hline \end{array} \quad \begin{array}{r} 16 \\ +42 \\ \hline \end{array} \quad \begin{array}{r} 62 \\ +21 \\ \hline \end{array} \quad \begin{array}{r} 32 \\ +43 \\ \hline \end{array}$$

$$\begin{array}{r} 35 \\ +14 \\ \hline \end{array} \quad \begin{array}{r} 17 \\ +11 \\ \hline \end{array} \quad \begin{array}{r} 10 \\ +61 \\ \hline \end{array} \quad \begin{array}{r} 11 \\ +44 \\ \hline \end{array}$$

$$\begin{array}{r} 56 \\ +32 \\ \hline \end{array} \quad \begin{array}{r} 8 \\ +90 \\ \hline \end{array} \quad \begin{array}{r} 42 \\ +42 \\ \hline \end{array} \quad \begin{array}{r} 22 \\ +16 \\ \hline \end{array}$$

Adding 2-digit numbers without regrouping

Soccer Practice

Don't forget!
Add the ones,
then the tens.

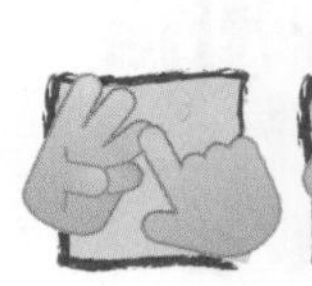
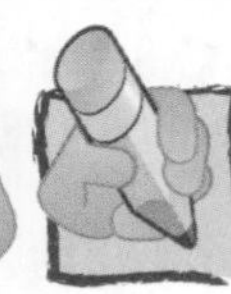

Add. Write the answers.

$$\begin{array}{r} 26 \\ +43 \\ \hline \end{array}$$

$$\begin{array}{r} 31 \\ +42 \\ \hline \end{array}$$

$$\begin{array}{r} 20 \\ +34 \\ \hline \end{array}$$

$$\begin{array}{r} 30 \\ +\ \ 9 \\ \hline \end{array}$$

$$\begin{array}{r} 41 \\ +57 \\ \hline \end{array}$$

$$\begin{array}{r} 52 \\ +32 \\ \hline \end{array}$$

$$\begin{array}{r} 64 \\ +11 \\ \hline \end{array}$$

$$\begin{array}{r} 7 \\ +52 \\ \hline \end{array}$$

$$\begin{array}{r} 26 \\ +43 \\ \hline \end{array}$$

$$\begin{array}{r} 31 \\ +42 \\ \hline \end{array}$$

$$\begin{array}{r} 20 \\ +34 \\ \hline \end{array}$$

$$\begin{array}{r} 30 \\ +\ \ 9 \\ \hline \end{array}$$

$$\begin{array}{r} 22 \\ +17 \\ \hline \end{array}$$

$$\begin{array}{r} 30 \\ +28 \\ \hline \end{array}$$

$$\begin{array}{r} 33 \\ +14 \\ \hline \end{array}$$

$$\begin{array}{r} 24 \\ +13 \\ \hline \end{array}$$

ADDIT

Add and write each sum. Color the box below with the answer. When you have colored 5 numbers in a row, you have won ADDIT!

11 13 + 43	21 30 + 32	10 35 + 34	12 21 + 5	23 32 + 13
13 62 + 24	31 41 + 20	64 20 + 3	7 12 + 50	30 12 + 54
20 30 + 41	50 12 + 13	27 12 + 50	40 31 + 14	75 11 + 12

A	D	D	I	T
67	49	79	85	99
30	83	90	50	91
96	98	75	38	89
40	68	20	80	92
81	60	69	87	70

Review

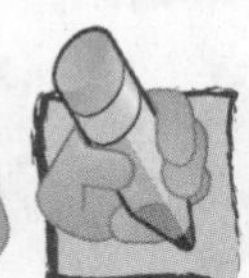

Add.
Write the answers.

6	4
+ 9	+ 7

8	5
+ 5	+ 6

50	70	60	20	30
+10	+20	+30	+40	+30

22	80	35	24	72
+30	+14	+41	+52	+26

43	19	27	36	35
+56	+40	+32	+52	+44

Practice Test

  11
+ 3
14

○ 12
○ 13
● 14

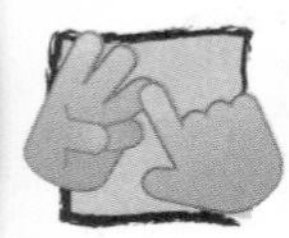

Add. Write the answers. Fill in the circle next to the correct answer.

A.

  23
+ 1

○ 23
○ 24
○ 25

E.

  40
+30

○ 7
○ 70
○ 77

B.

  65
+ 2

○ 60
○ 66
○ 67

F.

  23
+41

○ 22
○ 46
○ 64

C.

  34
+24

○ 38
○ 58
○ 54

G.

  82
+16

○ 98
○ 99
○ 88

D.

  60
+10

○ 7
○ 60
○ 70

H.

  55
+21

○ 65
○ 76
○ 56

Tens Take Away

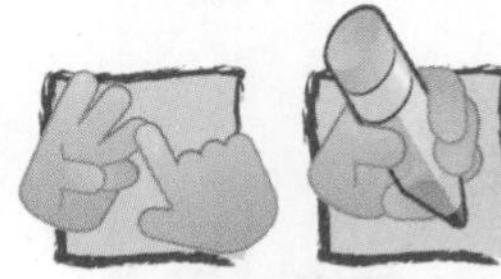

X out tens. Subtract.
Write how many are left.

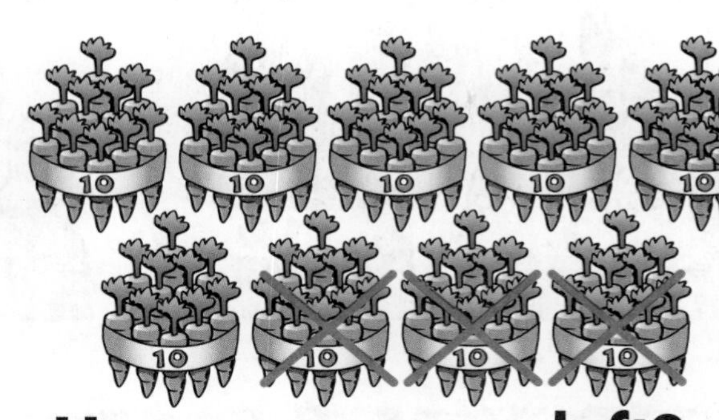

$$\begin{array}{r} 90 \\ -30 \\ \hline \end{array}$$

How many are left? 60

$$\begin{array}{r} 80 \\ -40 \\ \hline \end{array}$$

$$\begin{array}{r} 70 \\ -50 \\ \hline \end{array}$$

$$\begin{array}{r} 60 \\ -20 \\ \hline \end{array} \quad \begin{array}{r} 80 \\ -60 \\ \hline \end{array} \quad \begin{array}{r} 50 \\ -40 \\ \hline \end{array} \quad \begin{array}{r} 70 \\ -20 \\ \hline \end{array} \quad \begin{array}{r} 90 \\ -60 \\ \hline \end{array}$$

$$\begin{array}{r} 40 \\ -10 \\ \hline \end{array} \quad \begin{array}{r} 60 \\ -30 \\ \hline \end{array} \quad \begin{array}{r} 90 \\ -80 \\ \hline \end{array} \quad \begin{array}{r} 30 \\ -20 \\ \hline \end{array} \quad \begin{array}{r} 50 \\ -20 \\ \hline \end{array}$$

Brush Off

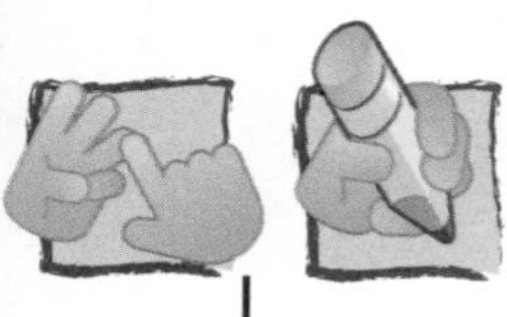

Subtract. Write how many are left.

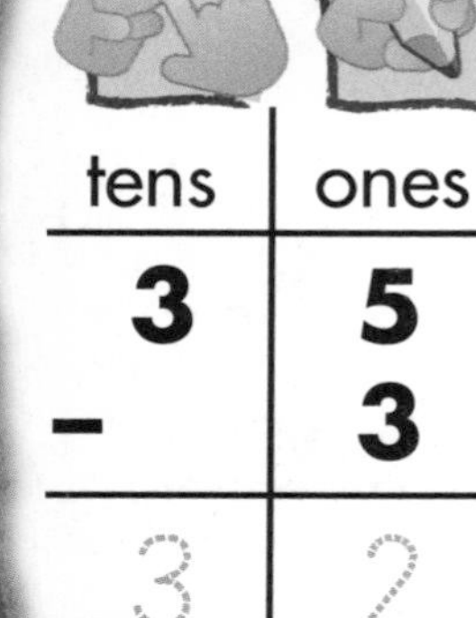

	tens	ones
	3	5
−		3
	3	2

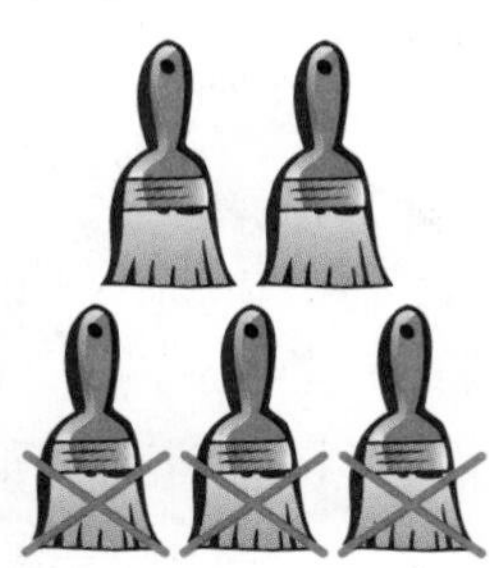

	tens	ones
	2	6
−		4

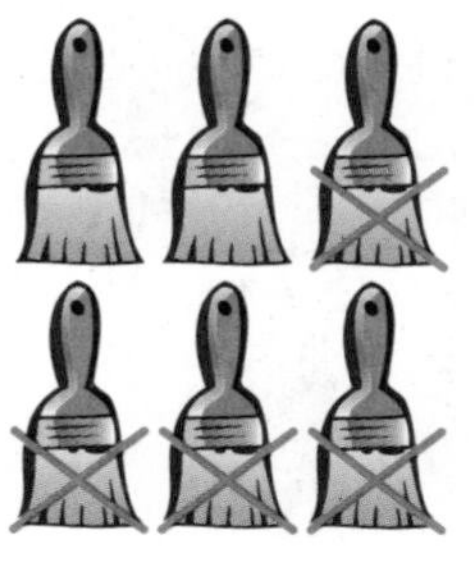

	tens	ones
	4	8
−		2

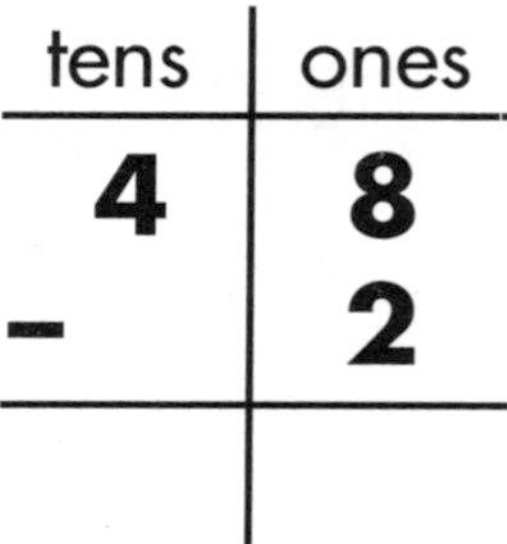

$$\begin{array}{r} 87 \\ -\ 6 \\ \hline \end{array} \quad \begin{array}{r} 54 \\ -\ 1 \\ \hline \end{array} \quad \begin{array}{r} 63 \\ -\ 3 \\ \hline \end{array} \quad \begin{array}{r} 99 \\ -\ 4 \\ \hline \end{array} \quad \begin{array}{r} 75 \\ -\ 2 \\ \hline \end{array}$$

$$\begin{array}{r} 49 \\ -\ 7 \\ \hline \end{array} \quad \begin{array}{r} 68 \\ -\ 4 \\ \hline \end{array} \quad \begin{array}{r} 96 \\ -\ 2 \\ \hline \end{array} \quad \begin{array}{r} 36 \\ -\ 5 \\ \hline \end{array} \quad \begin{array}{r} 55 \\ -\ 3 \\ \hline \end{array}$$

Subtract a Lot

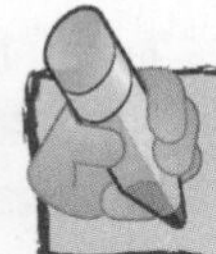

**Subtract the ones, then the tens.
Write the answers.**

tens	ones
3	8
− 2	3
1	5

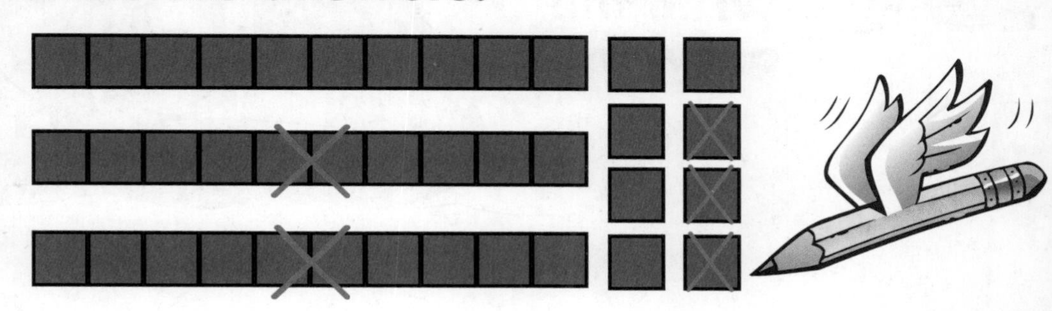

tens	ones
5	6
− 2	5

tens	ones
4	7
− 1	4

$$\begin{array}{r} 39 \\ -28 \\ \hline \end{array} \quad \begin{array}{r} 65 \\ -21 \\ \hline \end{array} \quad \begin{array}{r} 98 \\ -40 \\ \hline \end{array} \quad \begin{array}{r} 73 \\ -43 \\ \hline \end{array} \quad \begin{array}{r} 84 \\ -72 \\ \hline \end{array}$$

$$\begin{array}{r} 95 \\ -62 \\ \hline \end{array} \quad \begin{array}{r} 67 \\ -44 \\ \hline \end{array} \quad \begin{array}{r} 82 \\ -51 \\ \hline \end{array} \quad \begin{array}{r} 24 \\ -12 \\ \hline \end{array} \quad \begin{array}{r} 96 \\ -32 \\ \hline \end{array}$$

Sail Away

Subtract. Write the answers.

Don't forget! Subtract the ones, then the tens.

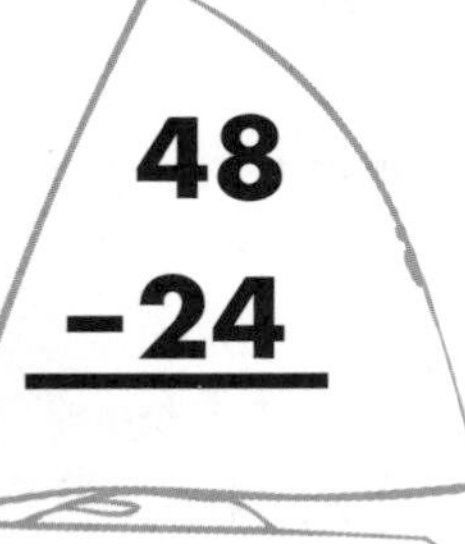

$\begin{array}{r} 48 \\ -24 \\ \hline \end{array}$

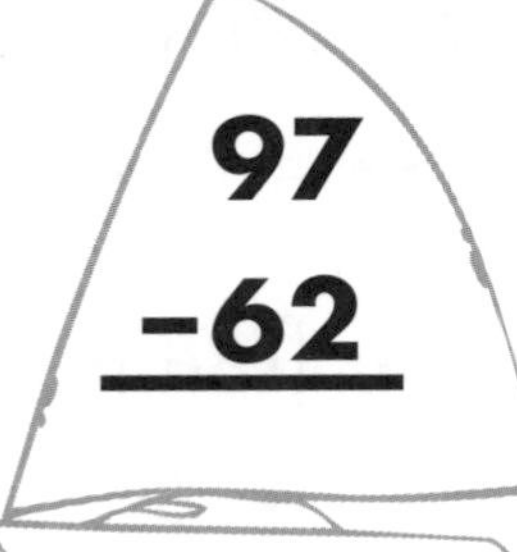

$\begin{array}{r} 97 \\ -62 \\ \hline \end{array}$

$\begin{array}{r} 99 \\ -81 \\ \hline \end{array}$

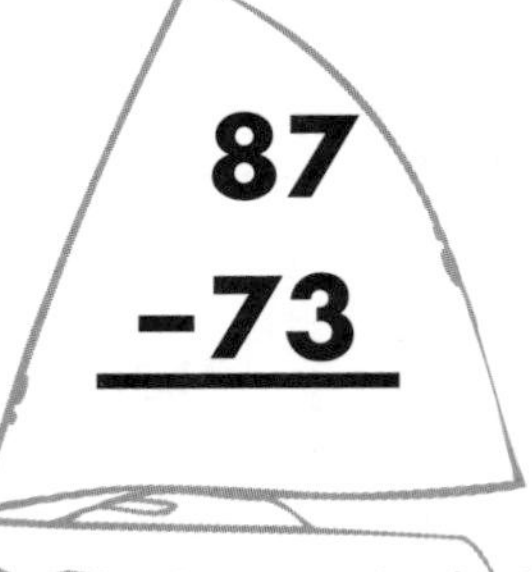

$\begin{array}{r} 87 \\ -73 \\ \hline \end{array}$

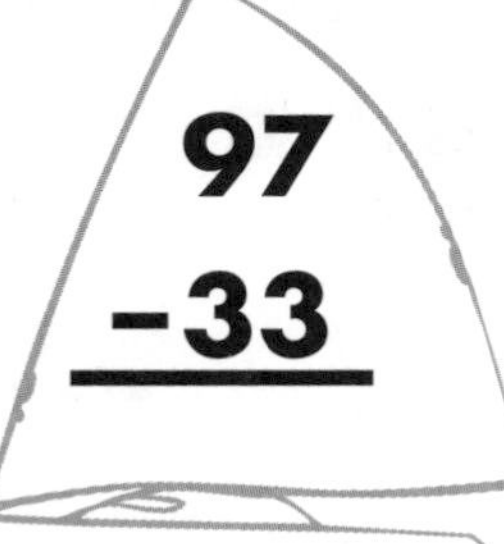

$\begin{array}{r} 97 \\ -33 \\ \hline \end{array}$

$\begin{array}{r} 45 \\ -14 \\ \hline \end{array}$

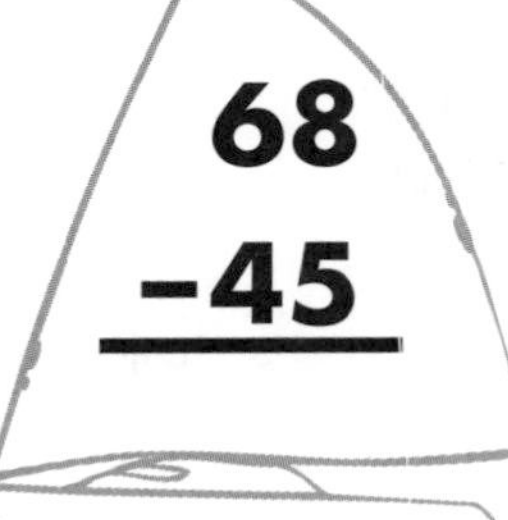

$\begin{array}{r} 68 \\ -45 \\ \hline \end{array}$

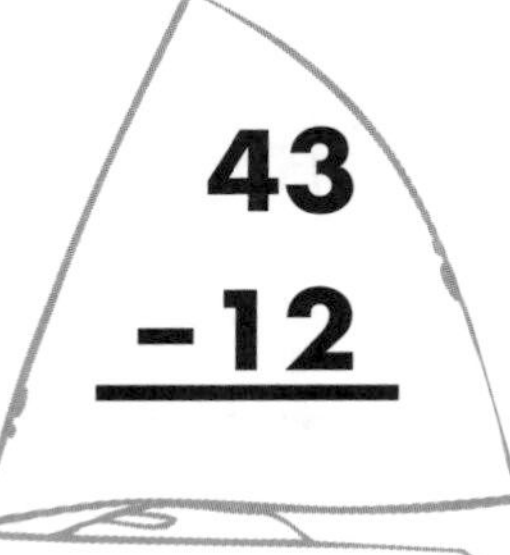

$\begin{array}{r} 43 \\ -12 \\ \hline \end{array}$

$\begin{array}{r} 67 \\ -35 \\ \hline \end{array}$

$\begin{array}{r} 66 \\ -24 \\ \hline \end{array}$

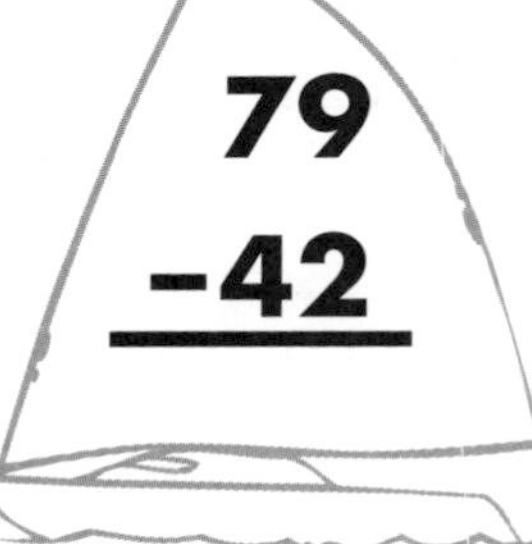

$\begin{array}{r} 79 \\ -42 \\ \hline \end{array}$

$\begin{array}{r} 98 \\ -56 \\ \hline \end{array}$

$\begin{array}{r} 39 \\ -13 \\ \hline \end{array}$

$\begin{array}{r} 27 \\ -16 \\ \hline \end{array}$

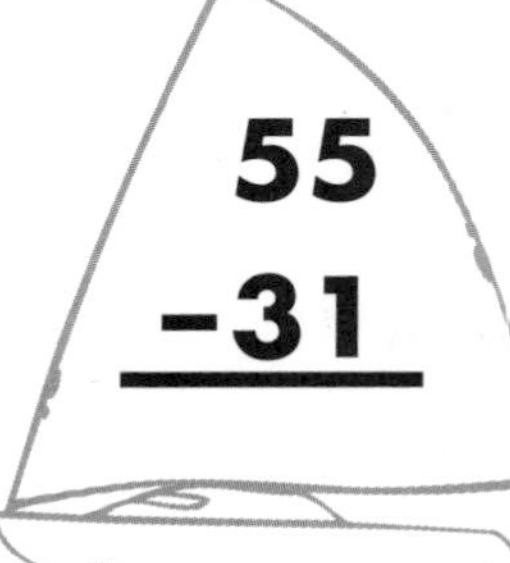

$\begin{array}{r} 55 \\ -31 \\ \hline \end{array}$

$\begin{array}{r} 79 \\ -22 \\ \hline \end{array}$

A Rainy Riddle

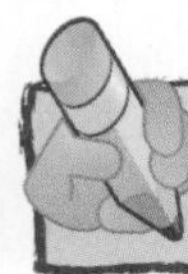

Subtract. Write each matching letter from the green box to answer the riddle.

What goes up when the rain comes down?

10	61	62	25	32	30	23	22	11
A	L	E	R	B	U	M	O	Y

52 − 41 = ___ ___

45 − 23 = ___ ___

67 − 37 = ___ ___

75 − 50 = ___ ___

89 − 59 = ___ ___

58 − 35 = ___ ___

79 − 47 = ___ ___

76 − 51 = ___ ___

85 − 23 = ___ ___

98 − 37 = ___ ___

78 − 17 = ___ ___

91 − 81 = ___ ___

Answer: Your umbrella

Under the Big Top

Subtract. Write the answers.

64	16	32	45	64
−23	− 6	−11	−13	−23
81	93	78	49	59
−70	−61	−56	−27	−18
36	68	95	87	74
− 3	−34	−14	−43	−63
	58	47	60	
	−30	−21	−40	

98	89
−33	−52

Lucky for them, a tailor came along. He sewed the beans together with his thread.

And that is why to this day all beans have seams.

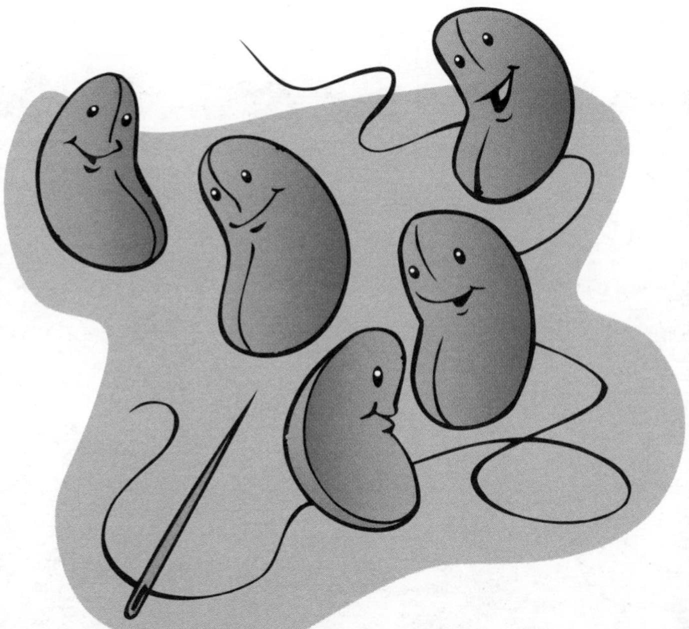

The Straw, the Coals, and the Beans

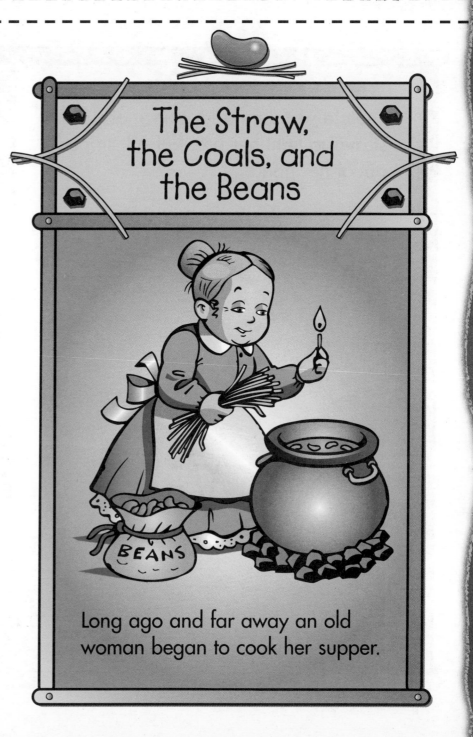

Long ago and far away an old woman began to cook her supper.

The old woman had a bunch of 35 dry straws to light her fire, but 13 slipped out of her hand.

$$\begin{array}{r} 35 \\ -\ 13 \\ \hline 22 \end{array}\ \text{straws}$$

The poor straws began to burn, and soon broke in two. All the coals and all the straws tumbled into the rushing water.

The beans who had stayed on the riverbank watched it all happen. They laughed until they split their sides.

The straws threw themselves across the river. And the hot coals began to cross on the backs of the straws.

But when they got to the middle, the coals became so scared of the rushing water they could not move.

Soon the woman had 27 glowing coals to warm her pot.

But 13 jumped out of her fire.

$$\begin{array}{r} 27 \\ -\ 13 \\ \hline 14 \end{array}$$ coals left

The woman put 19 fat beans in the pot, but 5 of these slipped away.

$$\begin{array}{r} 19 \\ -\ 5 \\ \hline 14 \end{array}$$ beans left

The straws, coals, and beans that got away went off to seek their fortunes. Along the way they came to a river with no bridge.

Review

Subtract and write each answer.
Color the spaces to match the answers.

8 = **12 =** **24 =** **30 =**

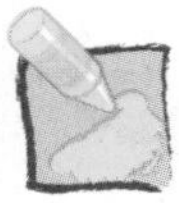

50
− 20

99
− 75

40
− 10

89
− 65

78
− 66

80
− 50

29
− 17

16
− 8

59
− 47

64
− 52

22
− 10

39
− 15

90
− 60

SUBTRACTION

Practice Test

40
−20
20

○ 30
● 20
○ 10

Subtract. Write each answer. Fill in the circle next to the correct answer.

A.

60
−20

○ 60
○ 50
○ 40

E.

89
−43

○ 47
○ 46
○ 45

B.

37
− 5

○ 32
○ 31
○ 30

F.

64
−14

○ 50
○ 40
○ 30

C.

54
− 3

○ 52
○ 51
○ 50

G.

32
−11

○ 22
○ 21
○ 20

D.

78
−53

○ 26
○ 25
○ 24

H.

45
−22

○ 13
○ 23
○ 22

Month 11 Checklist

Hands-on activities to help your child in school!

ADDITION

Add 2-digit Numbers: pages 323-327, 332-334
Add 3-digit Numbers with and without Regrouping: pages 328-334

In this month, the concepts learned in Months 9 and 10 are extended as your child practices adding 2- and 3-digit numbers with and without regrouping.

❑ Complete the worksheets.

❑ Play "Regroup or Not." Write a problem such as 63 + 28, and have your child show *thumbs up* if regrouping is needed to solve and *thumbs down* if it is not needed. Calculation at this point is not necessary. Repeat the process several times.

❑ Play "Roll a Problem." Your child rolls a pair of dice and records the largest of the two numbers, repeats the process to find another number, and then finds the sum of the two added together. Provide three dice and proceed similarly to adjust the game for work with 3-digit numbers.

❑ Apply the concepts of adding 2- and 3-digit numbers to adding money. Have your child compute the total cost of the two items at the grocery store, at a fast-food restaurant, or at an amusement park. Provide pencil and paper for sure calculations!

❑ Provide a problem such as 89 + 142 and challenge your child to make up a story problem using the number pair, for example: *I have 89 rubber bands. My friend gave me 142 rubber bands.* Then, have your child find the solution.

Introduction to Simple Multiplication
Concept of Multiplication: pages 346-348, 351-352
Multiples of 2 and 3: pages 349-352

In this month, your child will begin to work on simple multiplication. Use these activities to help him or her see how multiplication is a fast way to add.

❑ Complete the worksheets.

❑ Have your child find examples of equal groups, such as socks, shoes, juice boxes, packages of batteries, and so forth. Encourage him or her to discuss all the possible ways to find the total number of each item.

❑ Make up a jingle, song, or rhyme to practice multiples of two or three. Then practice it several times a day. For example: 2 groups of 3 sticks— 2 x 3 is 6.

❑ Have your child arrange items in equal groups. For example, 3 buttons and 3 buttons or 2 paperclips and 2 paperclips. Discuss how to find the totals by adding or multiplying.

SUBTRACTION

Subtracting 2-digit Numbers: pages 335-338, 343-345
Subtracting 3-digit Numbers with and without Regrouping: pages 339-345

In this month, your child will continue to practice subtraction, but now some of the problems wll involve regrouping.

❑ Complete the worksheets.
❑ Play "Regroup or Not" as described in the Addition section above.
❑ Play "Roll a Problem" as described in the Addition section above, but have your child write both numbers and then *rewrite* if needed to subtract the lesser number from the greater number.

Elephant Sums

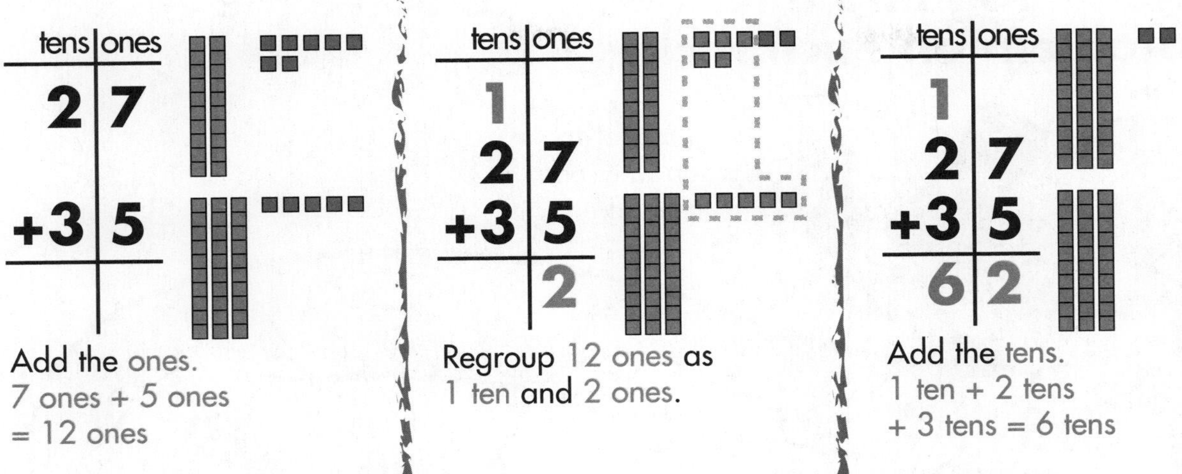

tens | ones
2 | 7
+3 | 5
Add the ones.
7 ones + 5 ones
= 12 ones
tens | ones
1
2 | 7
+3 | 5
| 2
Regroup 12 ones as
1 ten and 2 ones.
tens | ones
1
2 | 7
+3 | 5
6 | 2
Add the tens.
1 ten + 2 tens
+ 3 tens = 6 tens

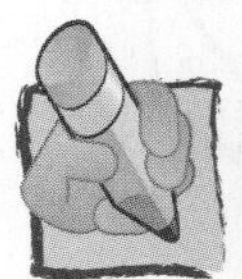 

Write the sum. Circle it if you regrouped.

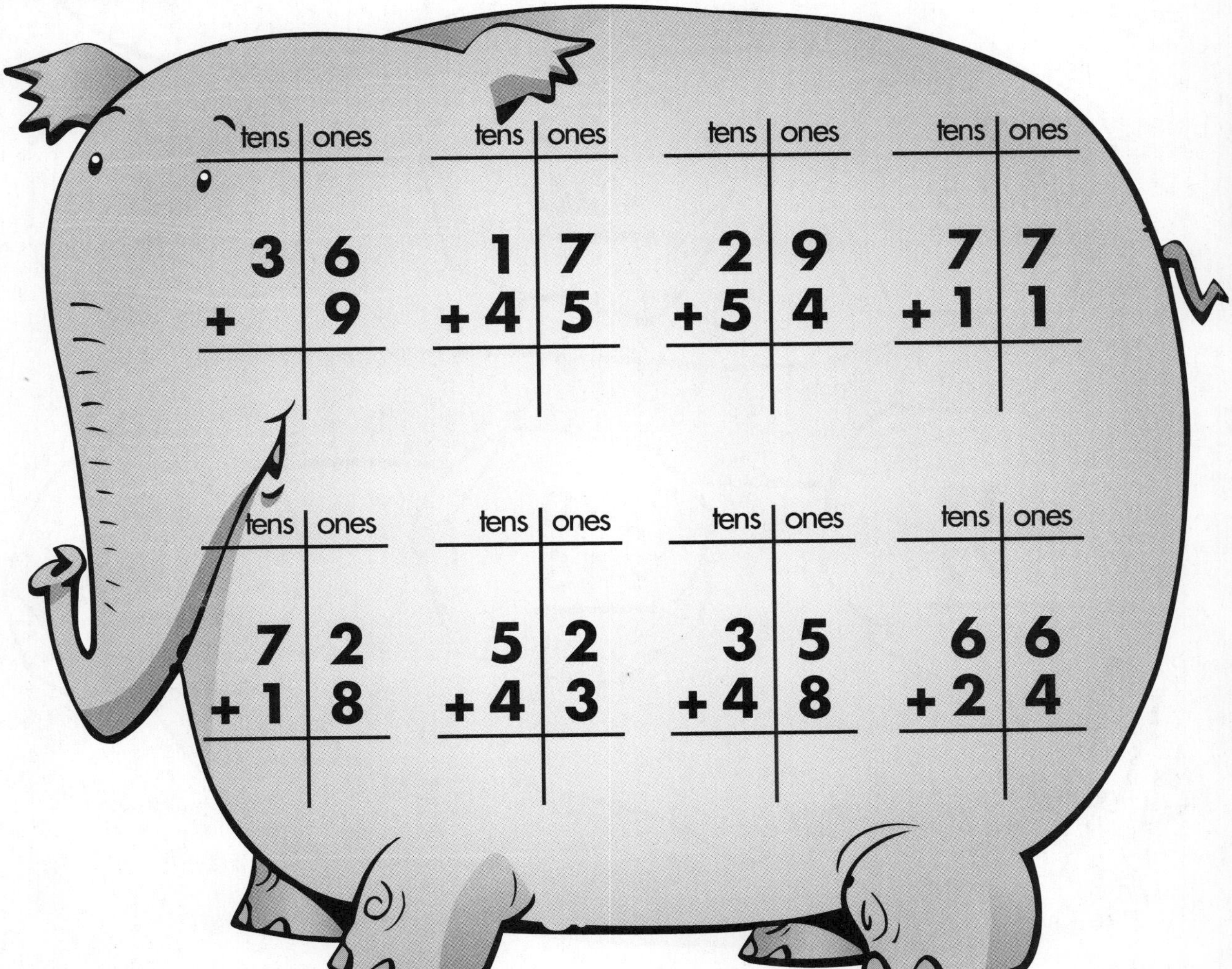

tens	ones
3	6
+	9

tens	ones
1	7
+4	5

tens	ones
2	9
+5	4

tens	ones
7	7
+1	1

tens	ones
7	2
+1	8

tens	ones
5	2
+4	3

tens	ones
3	5
+4	8

tens	ones
6	6
+2	4

ADDITION

Addition Hop

Help Frog hop into the pond. Solve the problem on each rock.

Don't forget to regroup when you need to.

38 + 5 = 43	27 + 17 =	19 + 34 =
73 + 15 =	39 + 26 =	44 + 6 =
12 + 72 =	20 + 45 =	19 + 19 =

Touchdown!

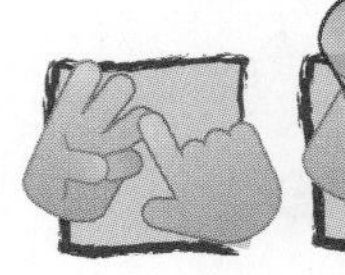
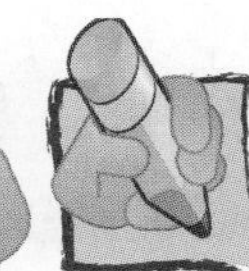

Add to find the total score in each game.

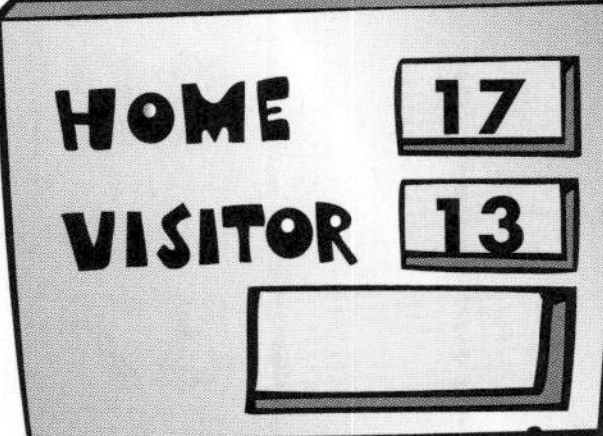

HOME 7
VISITOR 21

HOME 10
VISITOR 14

HOME 18
VISITOR 14

HOME 25
VISITOR 38

HOME 27
VISITOR 19

HOME 18
VISITOR 23

HOME 16
VISITOR 26

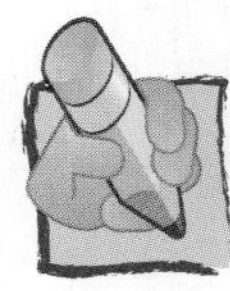

What was the highest total? __________

What was the lowest total? __________

Blue Ribbon Sums

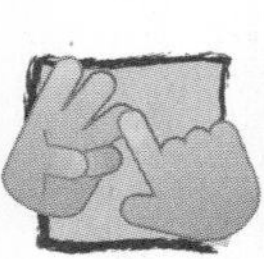
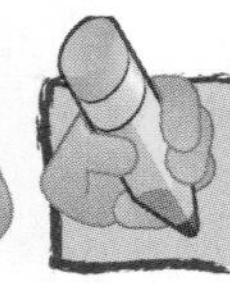

Add the numbers across and down. Find out why the blue ribbon square is magic!

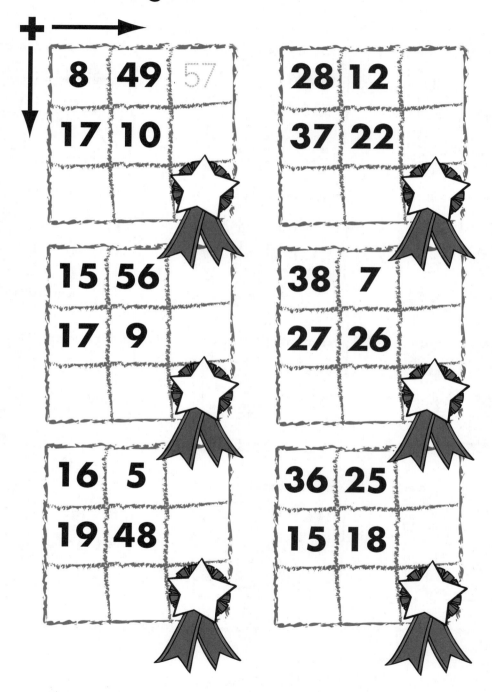

+ → ↓

8	49	57
17	10	

28	12	
37	22	

15	56	
17	9	

38	7	
27	26	

16	5	
19	48	

36	25	
15	18	

What is magic about the magic square?

Answer: The sum is the same whether you add across or down to the ribbon.

In the Deep Blue Sea

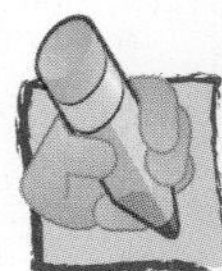

Write the answer. Use the code to color the sea animals.

If the sum is between	40-54	55-69	70-84	85-99
Color the creature	Red	Orange	Green	Yellow

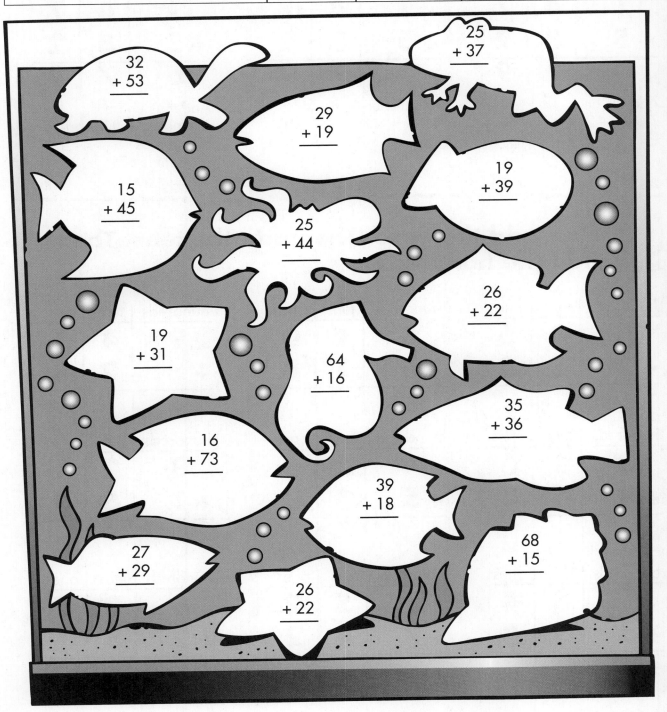

32 + 53 =

25 + 37 =

29 + 19 =

15 + 45 =

19 + 39 =

25 + 44 =

26 + 22 =

19 + 31 =

64 + 16 =

35 + 36 =

16 + 73 =

39 + 18 =

27 + 29 =

68 + 15 =

26 + 22 =

ADDITION

Diving for Treasure

hundreds	tens	ones
1	4	7
+ 5	3	2
		9

Add the ones.
7 ones + 2 ones = 9 ones

hundreds	tens	ones
1	4	7
+ 5	3	2
	7	9

Add the tens.
4 tens + 3 tens = 7 tens

hundreds	tens	ones
1	4	7
+ 5	3	2
6	7	9

Add the hundreds.
1 hundred + 5 hundreds = 6 hundreds.
The sum is 679.

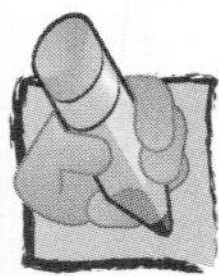

First add the ones. Then add the tens. Then add the hundreds.

hundreds	tens	ones
5	1	6
+ 2	8	0

hundreds	tens	ones
3	4	0
+ 5	1	8

hundreds	tens	ones
9	4	1
+	2	8

hundreds	tens	ones
3	2	6
+ 4	5	3

hundreds	tens	ones
4	3	6
+ 5	3	0

hundreds	tens	ones
8	2	1
+ 1	6	3

hundreds	tens	ones
	3	4
+ 8	5	4

hundreds	tens	ones
1	5	2
+ 7	4	2

hundreds	tens	ones
6	0	7
+ 2	5	1

Patterned Sums

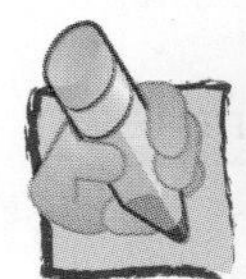

Write the sums. Circle the sums that are greater than 599.

200 + 400 600	279 + 110	412 + 213
240 + 410	353 + 322	152 + 345

509 + 50	400 + 300	620 + 105	321 + 123	230 + 520
327 + 261	316 + 282	443 + 332	400 + 400	258 + 341

Read and say the numbers you circled. What pattern do you see?

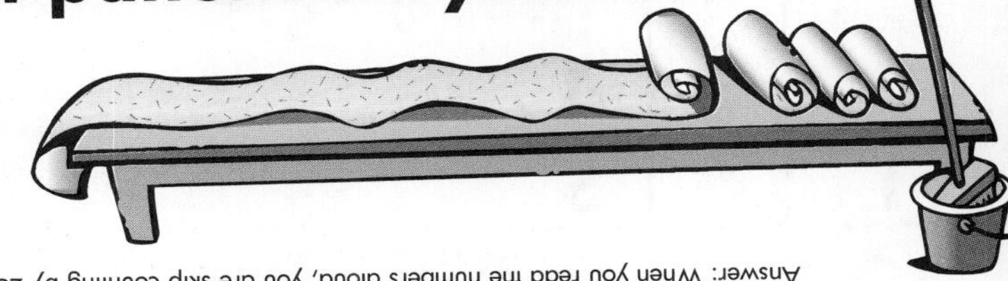

Answer: When you read the numbers aloud, you are skip-counting by 25's.

ADDITION

Hula Hoops

hundreds	tens	ones
	1	
2	5	8
+ 3	9	4
		2

Add the ones.
There are 12 ones.
Regroup 10 ones for 1 ten.

hundreds	tens	ones
1	1	
2	5	8
+ 3	9	4
	5	2

Add the tens.
There are 15 tens.
Regroup 10 tens for 1 hundred.

hundreds	tens	ones
1	1	
2	5	8
+ 3	9	4
6	5	2

Add the hundreds.
There are 6 hundreds.
The sum is 652.

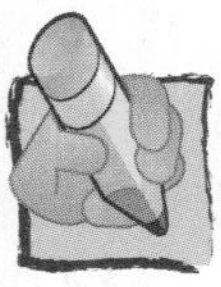

Add. Use the example above to help you.

hundreds	tens	ones
4	3	2
+ 2	8	3

hundreds	tens	ones
2	4	8
+ 3	4	6

hundreds	tens	ones
2	5	6
+ 3	3	3

hundreds	tens	ones
3	6	5
+ 3	7	9

hundreds	tens	ones
1	2	5
+	4	9

hundreds	tens	ones
7	8	4
+ 1	6	5

Sum Puzzle

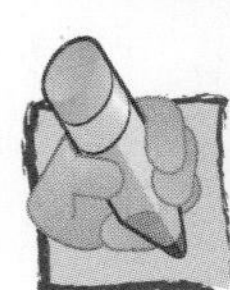

Write the sum for each clue.

Across

A. 227 + 96

F. 47 + 110

J. 518 + 342

C. 470 + 219

H. 169 + 379

K. 494 + 459

E. 86 + 148

Down

A. 198 + 163

C. 318 + 327

I. 336 + 89

B. 225 + 102

D. 381 + 547

J. 59 + 28

G. 257 + 249

A. 3	2	B. 3		C.		D.
		E.				
F.	G.			H.	I.	
J.				K.		

Sticker Shop

Read each story problem.
Write a number sentence and solve.

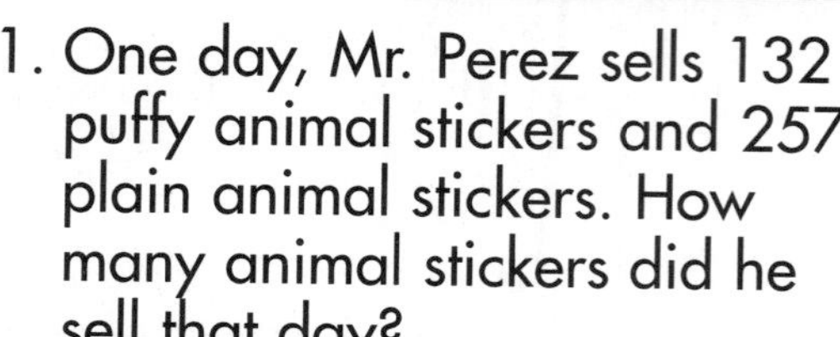

1. One day, Mr. Perez sells 132 puffy animal stickers and 257 plain animal stickers. How many animal stickers did he sell that day?

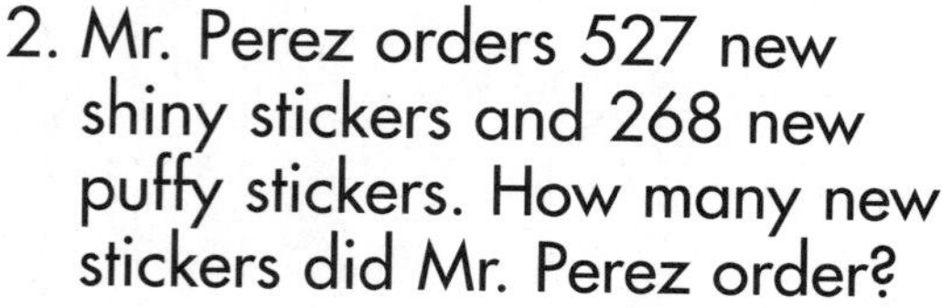

2. Mr. Perez orders 527 new shiny stickers and 268 new puffy stickers. How many new stickers did Mr. Perez order?

______________________ ______________________

3. Ms. Ross buys 87 car stickers and 125 happy face stickers. How many stickers did Ms. Ross buy?

4. Julie's scout troop buys 328 puffy stickers and 480 shiny stickers. How many stickers did the troop buy?

______________________ ______________________

5. Mrs. Patel buys 249 "Good Work" stickers and 518 star stickers. How many stickers did Mrs. Patel buy?

6. The Sticker Club buys 375 animal stickers and 297 animal stickers. How many stickers did the club buy?

______________________ ______________________

Token Trade In

Read each story problem. Write a number sentence and solve.

1. Manuel bought a truck and markers. How many tokens did he spend?

2. Hunter bought two coloring books. How many tokens did he spend?

3. Kameisha bought a doll and stickers. How many tokens did she spend?

4. Nick bought stickers and a sticker book. How many tokens did he spend?

5. Liz bought a coloring book and markers. How many tokens did she spend?

6. Mai bought a stuffed bear and a coloring book. How many tokens did she spend?

7. Seth bought two trucks. How many tokens did he spend?

8. Jenna bought a doll and a sticker book. How many tokens did she spend?

Who spent the most tokens?

Who spent the fewest tokens?

ADDITION

Review

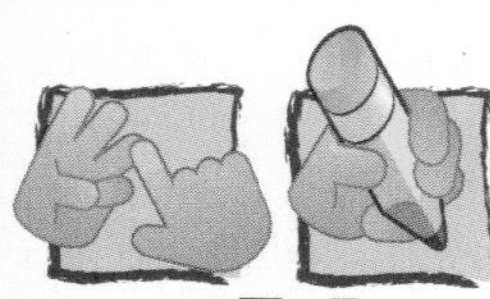

Add. Write each sum.

54 + 36	39 + 52	28 + 44	51 + 29	46 + 25
63 + 24	50 + 75	84 + 11	7 + 89	16 + 67
236 + 143	310 + 425	200 + 354	738 + 290	359 + 427
563 + 167	704 + 298	353 + 194	624 + 319	168 + 586

Read each story problem.
Write a number sentence and solve.

At a garage sale, Arta's family sold 197 paperback books and 84 hardback books. How many books did they sell in all?

____

Mr. Green's class read 243 books in April and 328 books in May. How many books did they read in the two-month period?

____

Flying High

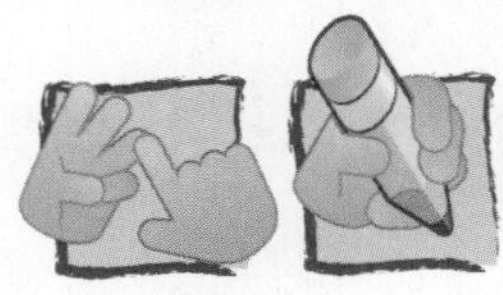

Subtract. Write each answer.

tens	ones
4	5
−2	8

You cannot subtract 8 ones from 5 ones.
Regroup 1 ten for 10 ones.

tens	ones
3	15
4	5
−2	8
	7

Subtract the ones.
15 ones − 8 ones = 7 ones

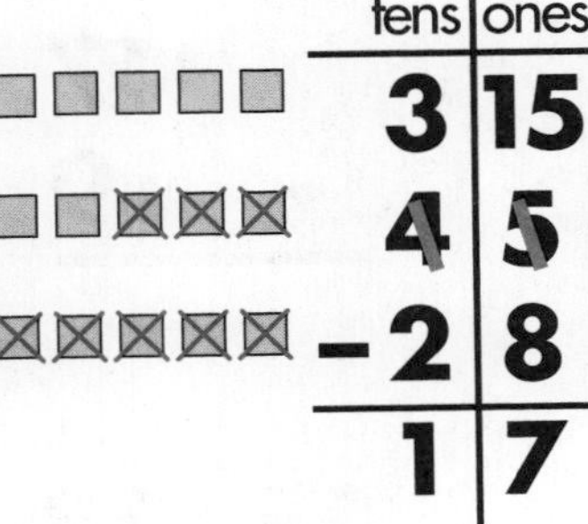

tens	ones
3	15
4	5
−2	8
1	7

Subtract the tens.
3 tens − 2 tens = 1 ten
45 − 28 = 17

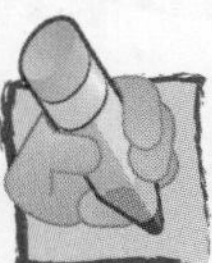

Subtract and write the difference. Circle it if you regrouped.

tens	ones
3	6
−	9

tens	ones
6	8
−4	5

tens	ones
7	2
−5	4

tens	ones
5	7
−1	8

tens	ones
3	2
−1	8

tens	ones
5	2
−4	7

tens	ones
9	8
−4	8

tens	ones
6	0
−2	4

SUBTRACTION

Detect the Difference

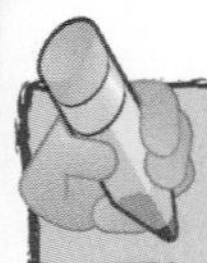 

Subtract. Circle the number that matches your answer.

52 − 7	47 − 19
59 45	28 38

91 − 56	65 − 16
35 45	49 59

73 − 67	34 − 14	83 − 66	56 − 28
16 6	10 20	17 27	28 38

90 − 41	81 − 35	37 − 29	70 − 34
49 51	46 56	8 18	34 36

Subtracting 2-digit numbers with and without regrouping

Winning Scores

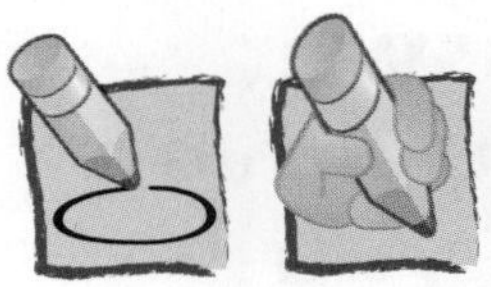

Circle the greater score. Then, subtract to find out the point difference in the scores.

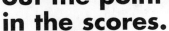

HOME 94
VISITOR 79

HOME 83
VISITOR 67

HOME 78
VISITOR 76

SUBTRACTION

Subtraction BINGO

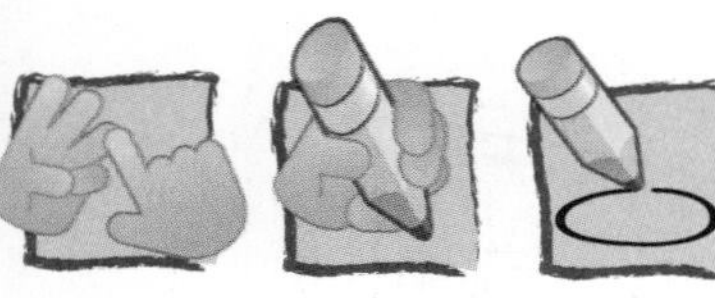

Subtract. Then, circle the answer in the box below. When you have circled 5 numbers in a row, you have won BINGO!

$$\begin{array}{r} 52 \\ -\ 37 \\ \hline \end{array} \quad \begin{array}{r} 83 \\ -\ 51 \\ \hline \end{array} \quad \begin{array}{r} 64 \\ -\ 39 \\ \hline \end{array} \quad \begin{array}{r} 60 \\ -\ 13 \\ \hline \end{array}$$

$$\begin{array}{r} 85 \\ -\ 20 \\ \hline \end{array} \quad \begin{array}{r} 42 \\ -\ 19 \\ \hline \end{array} \quad \begin{array}{r} 83 \\ -\ 24 \\ \hline \end{array} \quad \begin{array}{r} 60 \\ -\ 40 \\ \hline \end{array}$$

$$\begin{array}{r} 39 \\ -\ 12 \\ \hline \end{array} \quad \begin{array}{r} 57 \\ -\ 38 \\ \hline \end{array} \quad \begin{array}{r} 70 \\ -\ 63 \\ \hline \end{array} \quad \begin{array}{r} 46 \\ -\ 25 \\ \hline \end{array}$$

$$\begin{array}{r} 50 \\ -\ 35 \\ \hline \end{array} \quad \begin{array}{r} 37 \\ -\ 13 \\ \hline \end{array} \quad \begin{array}{r} 56 \\ -\ 47 \\ \hline \end{array} \quad \begin{array}{r} 70 \\ -\ 21 \\ \hline \end{array}$$

B	I	N	G	O
15	90	7	9	23
10	32	15	25	81
27	60	49	76	21
80	20	47	4	12
65	19	24	70	59

Dive In

hundreds	tens	ones
8	4	9
− 5	1	2
		7

Subtract the ones.
9 ones − 2 ones = 7 ones

hundreds	tens	ones
8	4	9
− 5	1	2
	3	7

Subtract the tens.
4 tens − 1 ten = 3 tens

hundreds	tens	ones
8	4	9
− 5	1	2
3	3	7

Subtract the hundreds.
8 hundreds − 5 hundreds = 3 hundreds
The difference is 337.

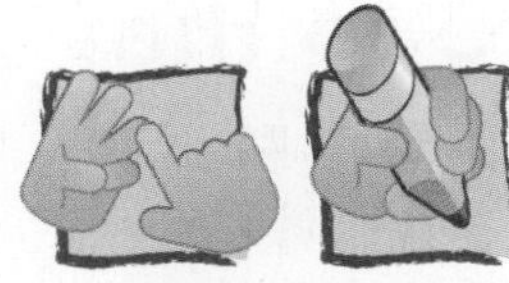

Subtract. Write the answers.

hundreds	tens	ones
9	7	6
− 3	5	3

hundreds	tens	ones
7	8	5
− 4	8	1

hundreds	tens	ones
5	8	6
− 2	5	4

hundreds	tens	ones
8	3	6
− 5	2	0

hundreds	tens	ones
4	9	8
− 2	5	1

hundreds	tens	ones
3	9	2
−	9	2

Subtraction Scales

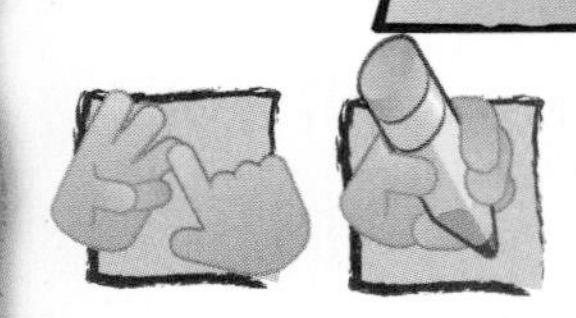

Subtract. Compare the difference to the number on the right. Write <, >, or = to complete the sentence.

475 − 341 475 − 341 134 (<) 150	684 − 312 ◯ 325	497 − 265 ◯ 254
837 − 512 ◯ 325	479 − 355 ◯ 100	173 − 52 ◯ 140
286 − 43 ◯ 222	975 − 602 ◯ 334	528 − 427 ◯ 81
745 − 234 ◯ 500	386 − 62 ◯ 324	942 − 641 ◯ 300

All Aboard

hundreds	tens	ones
7	3	9
− 4	5	3
		6

Subtract the ones.
9 ones − 3 ones = 6 ones

hundreds	tens	ones
6	13	
~~7~~	~~3~~	9
− 4	5	3
	8	6

You cannot subtract 5 tens from 3 tens. Regroup 1 hundred for 10 tens.
Subtract the tens.
13 tens − 5 tens = 8 tens

hundreds	tens	ones
6	13	
~~7~~	~~3~~	9
− 4	5	3
2	8	6

Subtract the hundreds.
6 hundreds − 4 hundreds = 2 hundreds.
The difference is 286.

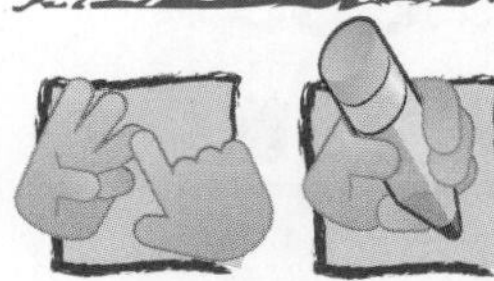

Subtract and write the answers. Regroup if you need to.

hundreds	tens	ones
8	6	5
− 3	7	1

hundreds	tens	ones
7	9	7
− 6	4	7

hundreds	tens	ones
6	8	4
− 1	6	5

SUBTRACTION

A Riddle For You

What is black and white and read all over?

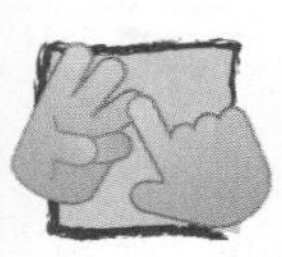
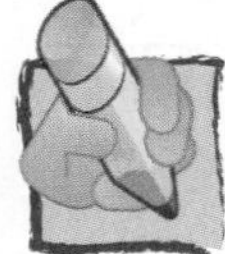

Subtract. To solve the riddle, write the letter above the number that matches your answer.

387 − 216	781 − 669	197 − 149	863 − 256
T	N	E	P

795 − 348	845 − 631	729 − 483	461 − 253
E	A	W	R

537 − 319	721 − 414	529 − 261	645 − 218
H	P	S	E

___ ___ ___   ___ ___ ___ ___ ___ ___ ___ ___ ___

171 218 48   112 427 246 268 607 214 307 447 208

Answer: The newspaper

Subtracting 3-digit numbers with and without regrouping

Take Me Out to the Ball Game

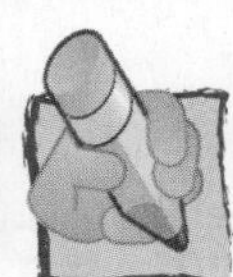

Read each story problem.
Write a number sentence and solve.

1. There are 387 boys and 410 girls at the *Stars* game. How many more girls than boys are at the game?

   ____

2. There are 797 children and 912 adults at the *Stars* game. How many more adults than children are at the game?

   ____

3. Manny sells 425 sodas and 670 bottled waters. How many more bottled waters than sodas are sold?

   ____

4. Jane sells 459 bags of peanuts and 953 hot dogs. How many more hot dogs than peanuts are sold?

   ____

5. The *Stars* sell 564 pennants. Of those, 181 are small pennants and the rest are large pennants. How many large pennants are sold?

   ____

6. The *Stars* give away 175 t-shirts. All but 38 of them are given to children. How many t-shirts are given to children?

   ____

7. Mr. Patel has 800 *Stars* baseball caps to sell. He sells all but 282 of them. How many caps does Mr. Patel sell?

   ____

8. The *Stars* play 65 games at home out of a total of 123 games. How many games are played away from home?

   ____

School Fair

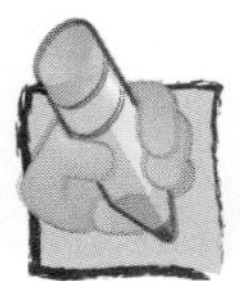
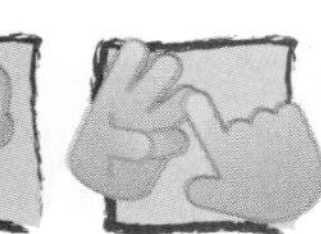

Read each story problem.
Write a number sentence and solve.

1. Of a total of 612 children at the fair, 386 are girls. How many boys are at the fair?

2. There are 612 children and 475 adults at the fair. How many more children than adults are at the fair?

3. Mr. Brown prepares 275 hamburgers, but he only sells 158 of them. How many hamburgers are not sold?

4. Of 208 families that buy raffle tickets, only 47 of them win prizes. How many families do not win prizes?

5. Amy sells 502 bags of popcorn. Of those, 419 are regular-size bags, and the rest are super-size. How many super-size bags of popcorn are sold?

6. Mr. Chen had 385 school sweatshirts, but he sold 150 of them. How many school sweatshirts did Mr. Chen have left?

7. Jen has 567 tickets. She trades in 450 of them for a pencil case. How many tickets does Jen have now?

8. Justin has 85 tickets. He needs 110 to buy a toy car. How many more tickets does Justin need?

Review

Subtract. Write the answers.

64 - 37	89 - 54	98 - 39	41 - 27	76 - 55
61 - 54	50 - 36	31 - 17	73 - 55	90 - 67
336 - 143	425 - 370	863 - 354	738 - 390	559 - 427
463 - 127	764 - 228	375 - 194	624 - 319	968 - 586

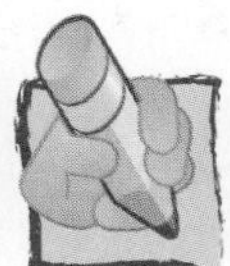
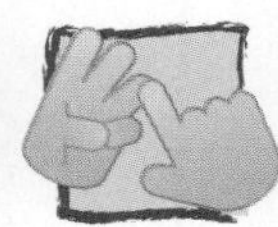

**Read each story problem.
Write a number sentence and solve.**

Marci has 48 dolls and 75 stuffed animals. How many more stuffed animals than dolls does Marci have?

A total of 614 tickets are sold for a play. Of those, 341 are student tickets. How many tickets are not student tickets?

SUBTRACTION

ADDITION

Spots, Spots Everywhere

Each bug has the same number of spots. Count or multiply to find how many spots in all.

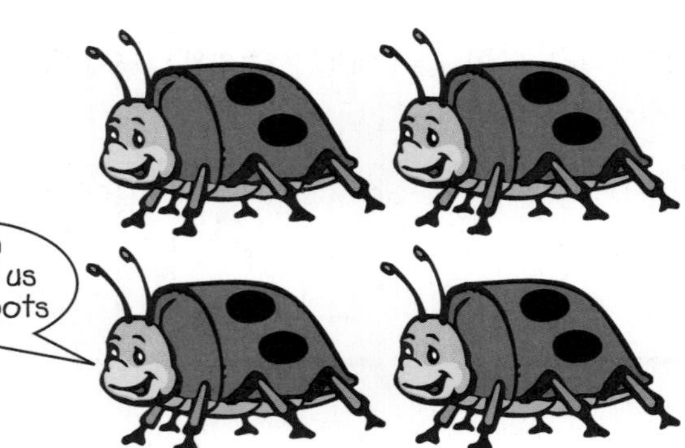
Each one of us has 2 spots

<u>4</u> ladybugs x <u>2</u> spots on each = 8 spots

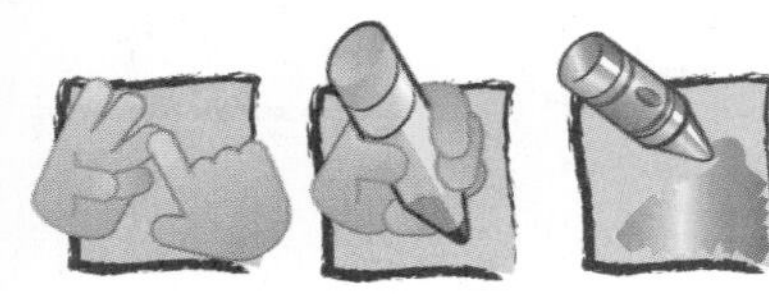

Count or multiply. Write how many things, spots on each, and spots in all. Color all the spots.

__3__ frogs

x __4__ spots on each

__12__ spots in all

_____ dogs

x _____ spots on each

_____ spots in all

_____ cats

x _____ spots on each

_____ spots in all

_____ mushrooms

x _____ spots on each

_____ spots in all

Flower Garden

There are 3 rows of daisies.
There are 5 daisies in each row.
There are 15 daisies in all.

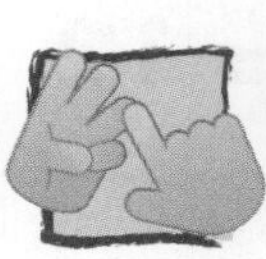
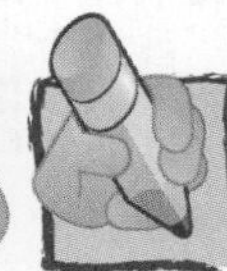

Count how many groups. Count how many in each group. Write the total.

2 rows of 4 = 8

2 x 4 = ______

3 rows of 3 = ______

3 x 3 = ______

3 rows of 4 = ______

3 x 4 = ______

2 rows of 5 = ______

2 x 5 = ______

3 rows of 6 = ______

3 x 6 = ______

4 rows of 5 = ______

4 x 5 = ______

Spots, Spots Everywhere

How many cherries?
Add or multiply to find out.

4 groups of 3
3 + 3 + 3 + 3 = 12
3 x 4 = 12

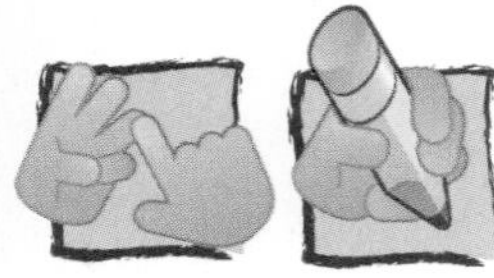

Add. Then, multiply. Write the answers.

2 groups of 3 **3 + 3 = 6** **2 x 3 = ____**

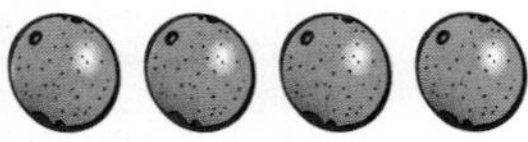 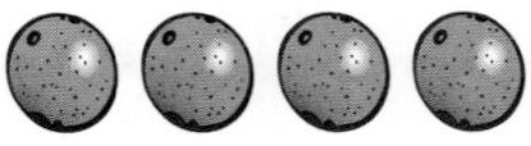 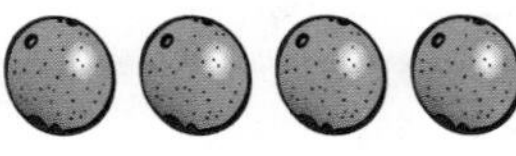 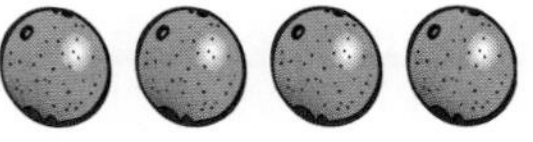

4 groups of 4 **4 + 4 + 4 + 4 = ____** **4 x 4 = ____**

2 groups of 5 **5 + 5 = ____** **2 x 5 = ____**

3 groups of 3 **3 + 3 + 3 = ____** **3 x 3 = ____**

3 groups of 4 **4 + 4 + 4 = ____** **3 x 4 = ____**

Domino Double Dots

The domino has two sides.
Each side has 3 dots.
How many dots in all?

2 groups of 3 dots

2 x 3 = 6

6 dots in all

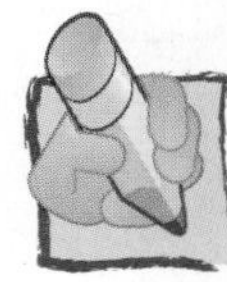

Multiply to find the total number of dots.

2 **groups of** 5 **dots**

2 **x** 5

10 **dots in all**

_____ **groups of** _____ **dots**

_____ **x** _____

_____ **dots in all**

_____ **groups of** _____ **dots**

_____ **x** _____

_____ **dots in all**

_____ **groups of** _____ **dots**

_____ **x** _____

_____ **dots in all**

_____ **groups of** _____ **dots**

_____ **x** _____

_____ **dots in all**

_____ **groups of** _____ **dots**

_____ **x** _____

_____ **dots in all**

Special Delivery

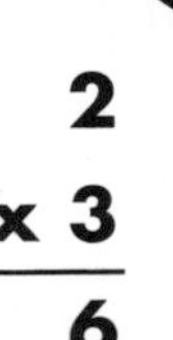

Remember, with equal groups
you can multiply.

On Monday, 3 bunnies got mail.
Each bunny got 2 letters.
How many letters in all?
3 groups of 2 $\quad 3 \times 2 = 6$
6 letters in all

$$\begin{array}{r} 2 \\ \times\ 3 \\ \hline 6 \end{array}$$

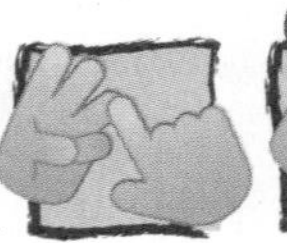
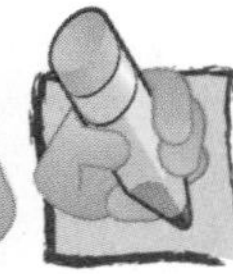

Read each story problem. Multiply. Write each answer.

1. **On Tuesday, 3 bunnies got mail.**
   Each bunny got 3 letters.
   How many letters in all? _____

2. **On Wednesday, 3 bunnies got mail.**
   Each bunny got 1 letter.
   How many letters in all? _____

3. **On Thursday, 2 bunnies got mail.**
   Each bunny got 2 letters.
   How many letters in all? _____

4. **On Friday, 2 bunnies got mail.**
   Each bunny got 3 letters.
   How many letters in all? _____

5. **On Saturday, 1 bunny got mail.**
   The bunny got 3 letters.
   How many letters in all? _____

Theme Park

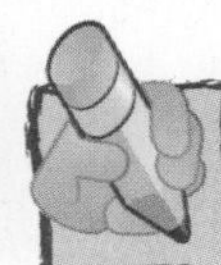
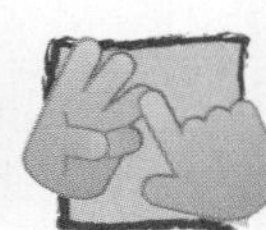

Read each story problem.
Write a number sentence and solve.

1. Each roller coaster car holds 3 people. How many people are seated in 2 cars?

____

2. A game has 3 fish in each fishbowl. How many fish in 4 fishbowls?

____

3. The Tilt-a-Whirl costs 5 tickets to ride. How many tickets for 3 people to ride?

____

4. Railroad cars hold 6 people each. How many people can ride in 2 railroad cars?

____

5. A theme park visor costs $6. Mary's family buys 3 visors. How much do they spend?

____

6. There are 2 clowns walking around the park. Each clown holds 4 balloons. How many balloons in all?

____

Review

Draw lines to match.

2 groups of 3	5 + 5	2 x 3	12
3 groups of 4	3 + 3	3 x 4	9
2 groups of 5	7 + 7	2 x 7	6
3 groups of 3	3 + 3 + 3	3 x 5	10
3 groups of 5	4 + 4 + 4	3 x 3	14
2 groups of 7	5 + 5 + 5	2 x 5	15

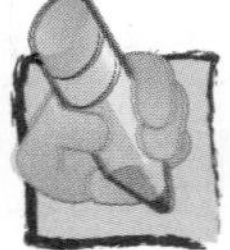
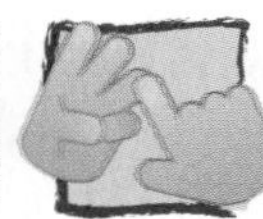

Read the story problem. Write a number sentence and solve.

There are 2 softballs in a pack. How many softballs in 8 packs?

Month 12 Checklist

Hands-on activities to help your child in school!

MEASUREMENT

Comparing Length: pages 355-356, 382
Measuring Length in Nonstandard Units, Inches, and Centimeters: pages 357-365, 373, 382
Comparing Capacity: pages 366-367, 373, 382
Comparing and Estimating Weight: pages 368-371, 373, 382
Identifying Measurement Tools and Units of Measurement: page 372

This month your child will learn concepts of measurement that include length (measuring in inches and centimeters), capacity (measuring with liters, cups, pints, and quarts), and weight (measuring in kilograms and pounds).

- ❑ Complete the worksheets.
- ❑ Provide nonstandard units such as pasta, straws, or paper clips that your child can use to measure the length of household objects. Compare the measurements. Discuss why, for example, it takes fewer straws than pieces of ziti to measure the same object.
- ❑ Ask your child to estimate and then measure the lengths of your arm, finger, foot, and so on using inches and centimeters.
- ❑ Draw a line that is 6 inches long. Ask your child to find something at home that is shorter, longer, and about the same length. Repeat, using different lengths.
- ❑ Collect several household objects whose length your child can measure, such as spoons, pencils, crayons, and small boxes. Invite your child to pick two items at a time and tell which is longer and which is shorter (or which is taller and which is shorter). Then, have your child estimate the length of each item in inches or centimeters. Help your child use a ruler to measure the item. Compare the estimate with the actual measurements.
- ❑ When you and your child are at the grocery store, help him or her estimate the weight of food items such as fruits and vegetables. Then, use a scale together to discover the actual weight. Compare it to the estimate.
- ❑ Ask your child to estimate the number of cups of water it will take to fill various containers. Then, see how many cups of water each container actually holds. Compare the estimates with your actual measurements.
- ❑ When you are cooking, let your child help measure some of the ingredients.
- ❑ Give your child a grocery item, such as a box of pasta, that weighs one pound. Let your child hold the item to get a feel for the weight. Then, ask your child to collect other unopened grocery items and sort them into three groups by weight: less than 1 pound, about 1 pound, and more than 1 pound. Use a scale or read the weights on the packages to check the estimates.

FRACTIONS

Recognizing Equal Parts: pages 374, 382
Recognizing Halves: pages 375-37, 379-382
Recognizing Thirds: pages 377, 379-382
Recognizing Fourths: pages 378-382

In this month, your child will learn to identify equal parts and recognize halves as two equal parts, thirds as three equal parts, and fourths as four equal parts.

❑ Complete the worksheets.

❑ On index cards or slips of paper, draw a half, third, or a fourth of a shape. Write corresponding fractions on other index cards or paper slips. Ask your child to match the cards.

❑ Fold pieces of paper into halves, thirds, and fourths. Ask your child to identify one half (1/2), one third (1/3), and one fourth (1/4).

❑ Provide your child with opportunities to divde food items into equal parts. Encourage your child to tell the fraction name for each part.

❑ When you make a sandwich for your child, cut it in half (or thirds or fourths) before serving. Challenge your child to name the fraction for each part.

❑ Give your child several paper squares. Ask him or her to fold (or draw lines on) each square to make 4 equal parts and color 1/4. Challenge your child to divide the square into fourths in as many ways as possible. You can repeat with paper rectangles.

❑ Play "Fraction Concentration." On index cards, draw pictures to illustrate 1/2, 1/3, and 1/4. Make two cards for each fraction. Prepare a second set of six cards on which you write the corresponding fraction symbols and words: *1/2, 1/3, 1/4, one half, one third, one fourth*. Shuffle the cards and arrange them face down in a 3 X 4 grid. To play, take turns turning over two cards. If the player turns over a picture and its matching fraction, he or she keeps the cards. If not, the player replaces the cards. When all the cards have been matched, the player with the most cards wins.

Shorter and Longer

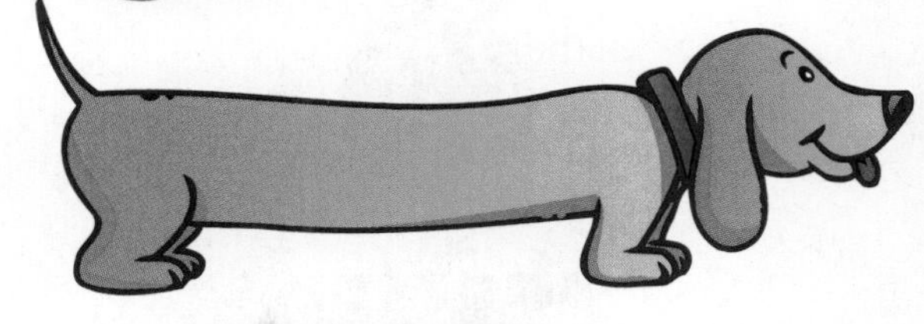

shorter **longer**

Circle the **longer** leash.

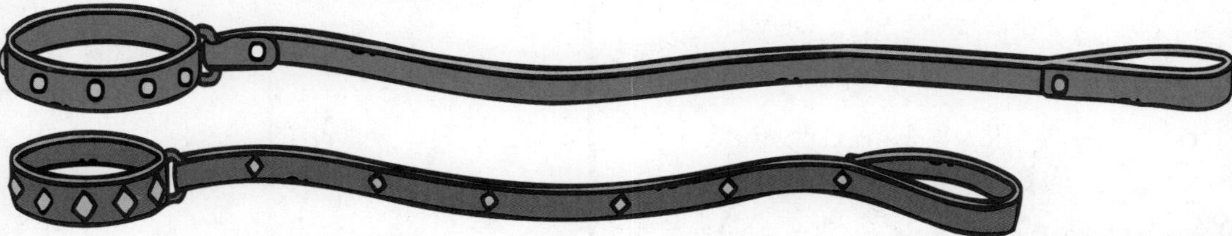

Color the **shorter** collar.

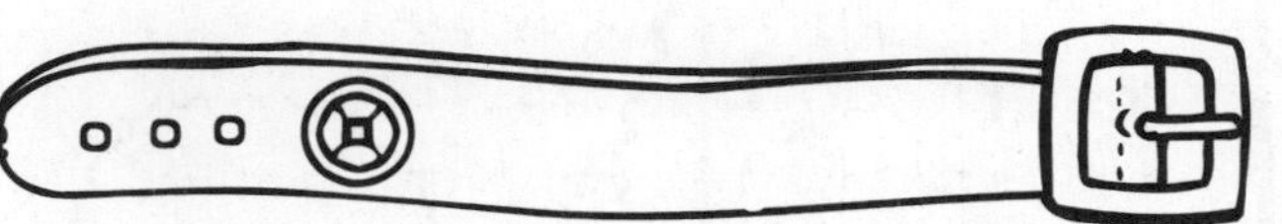

Color the dog with the **shorter** nose.

Color the **longer** tail.

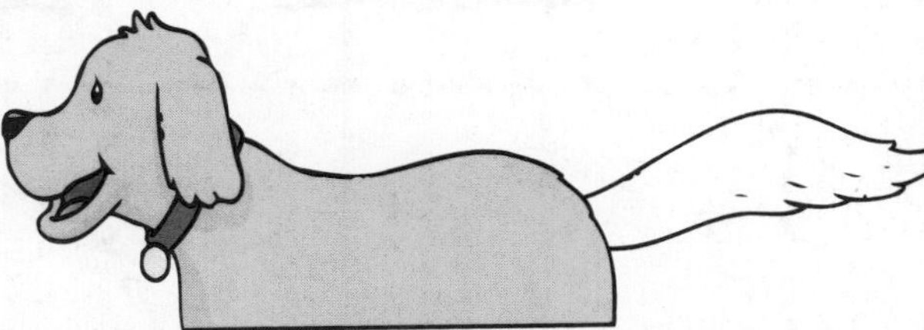
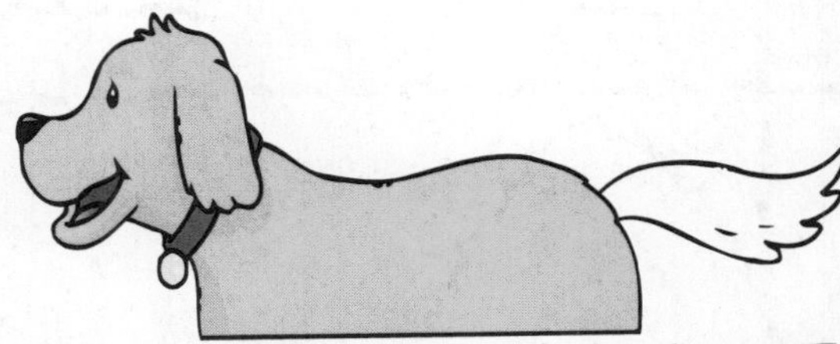

Circle about how many 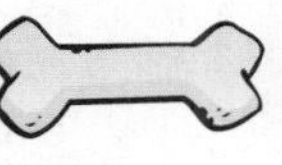 s fit in the box.

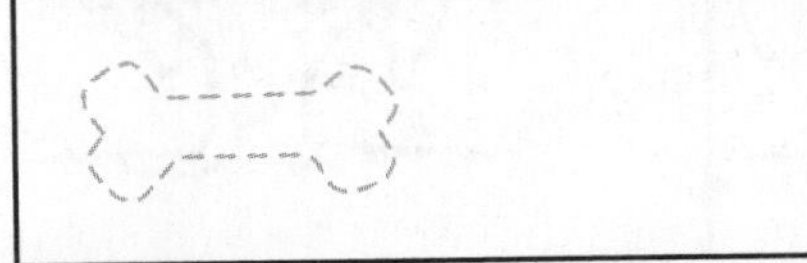

2 4 10

MEASUREMENT

Shorter and Taller

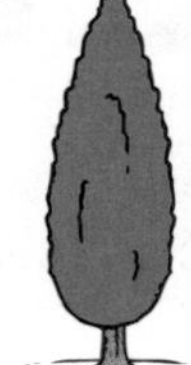

taller

Color the taller tree. Draw a line under the shorter tree.

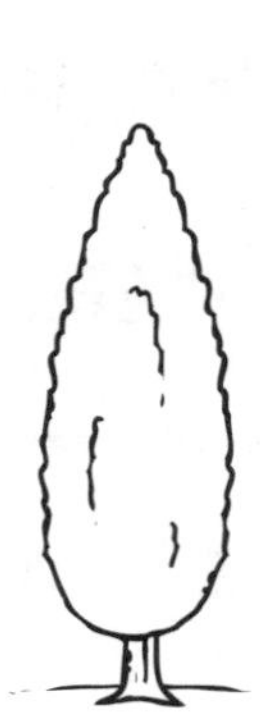 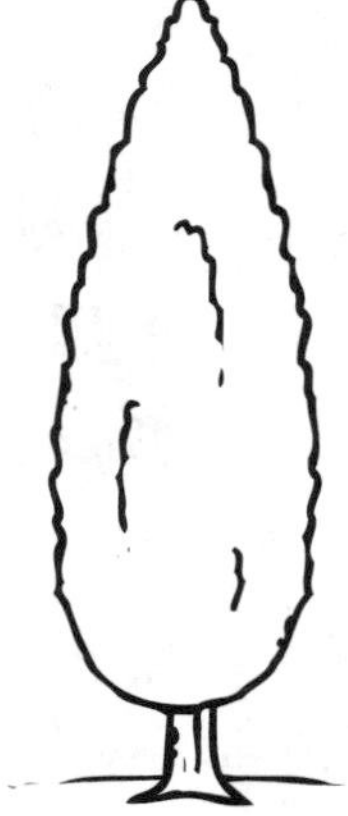

How Long Is It?

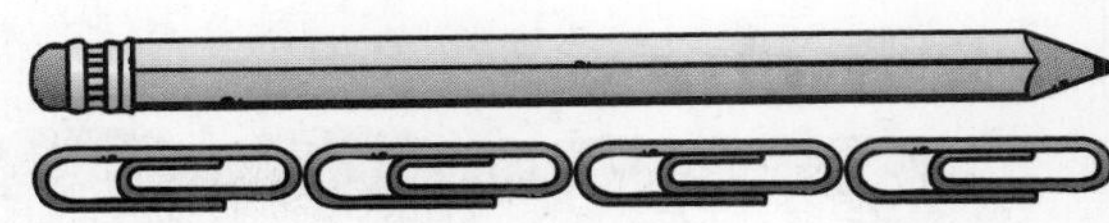

You can use [paper clip]s to measure.
This pencil is 4 [paper clip]s long.

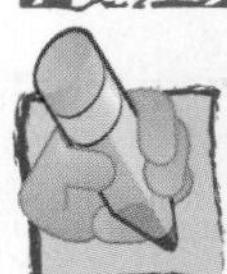

Use real [paper clip]s to measure each picture.
Write the numbers to tell how long.

_____ [paper clip]s

_____ [paper clip]s

_____ [paper clip]s

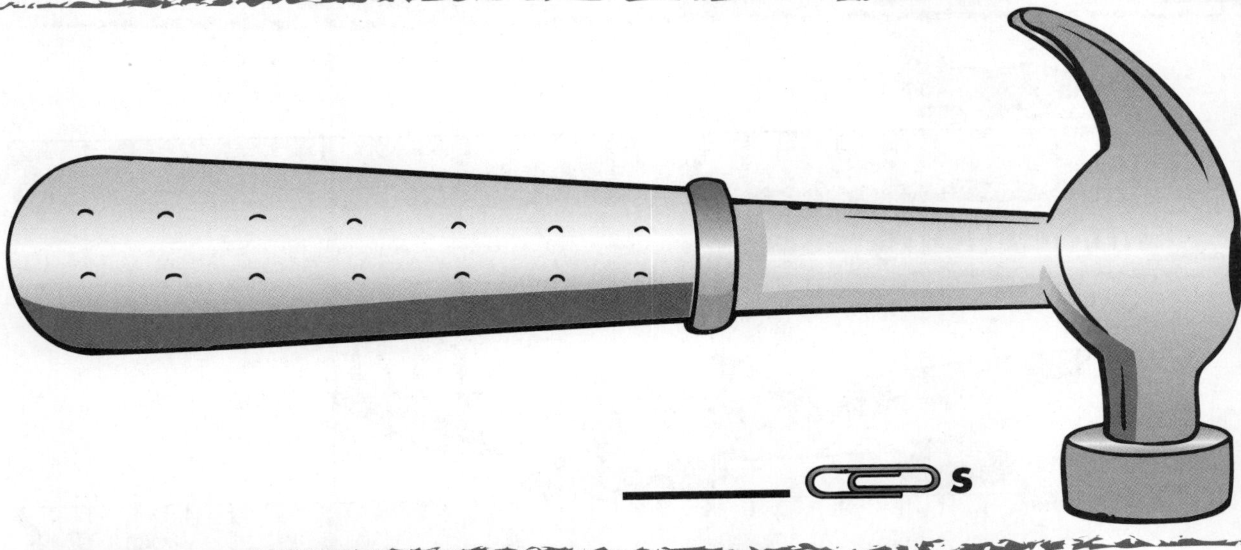

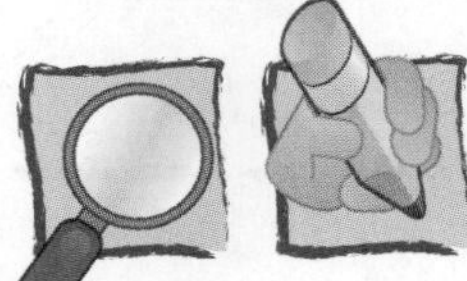

Find these objects in your house. Use real [paper clip]s to measure. Write how many.

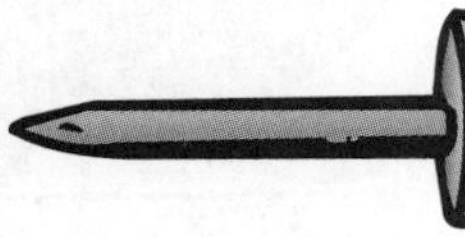

_____ [paper clip]s

_____ [paper clip]s

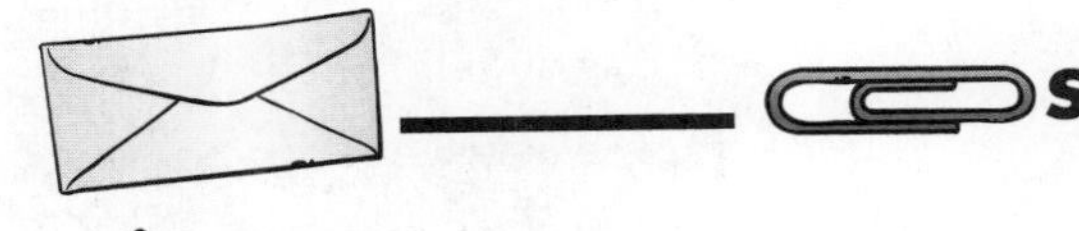

_____ [paper clip]s

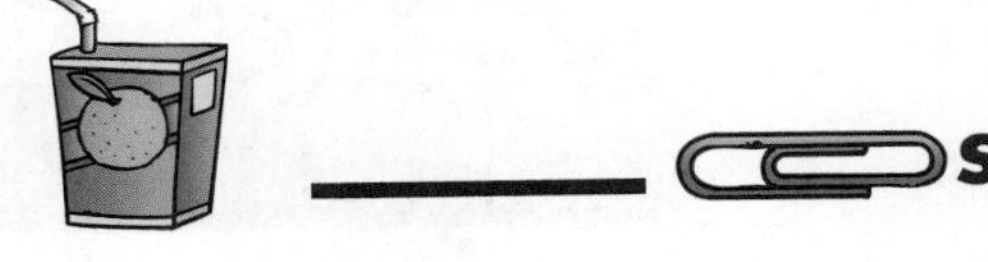

_____ [paper clip]s

MEASUREMENT

Inching Along

5 inches

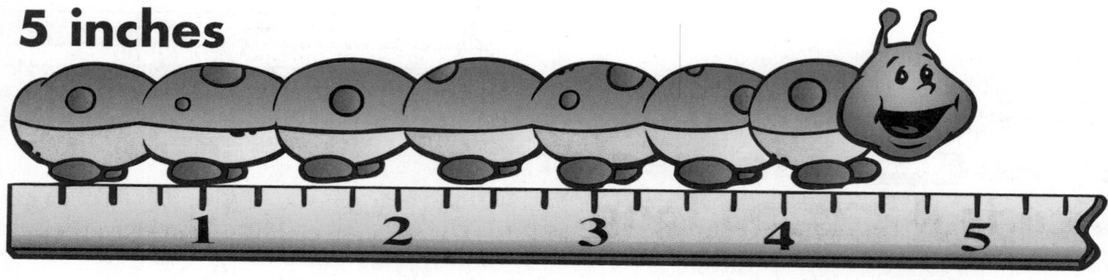

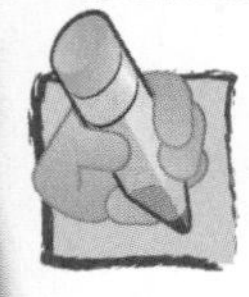

Write the number of inches.

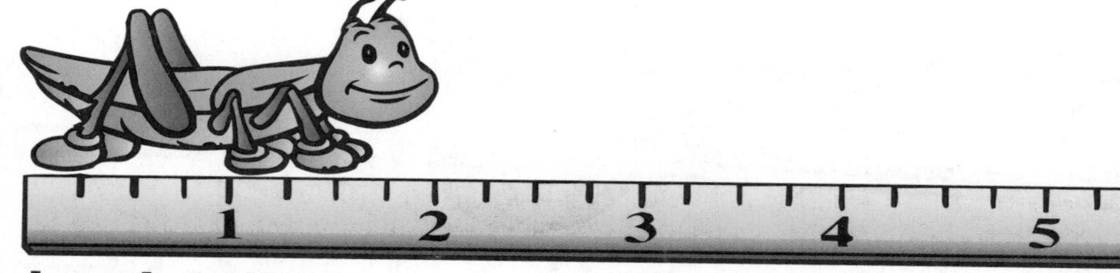

2 inches long

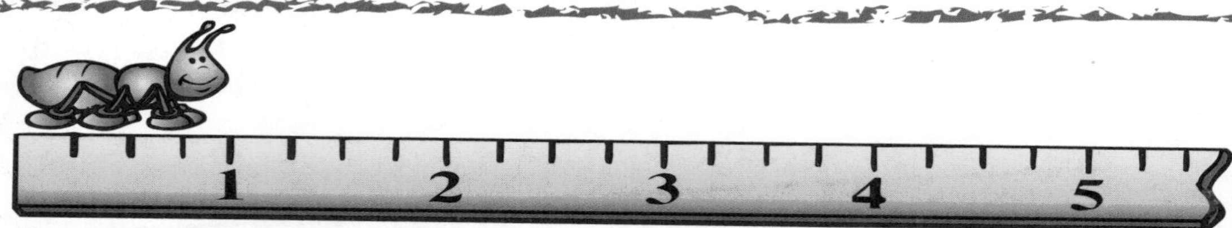

____ inches long

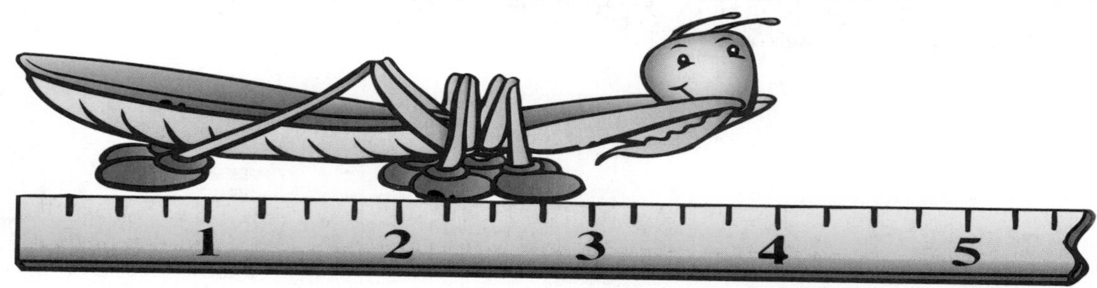

____ inches long

____ inches long

Inch by Inch

Cut out the inch ruler. Measure each worm to the nearest inch. Write how many inches.

about 4 inches

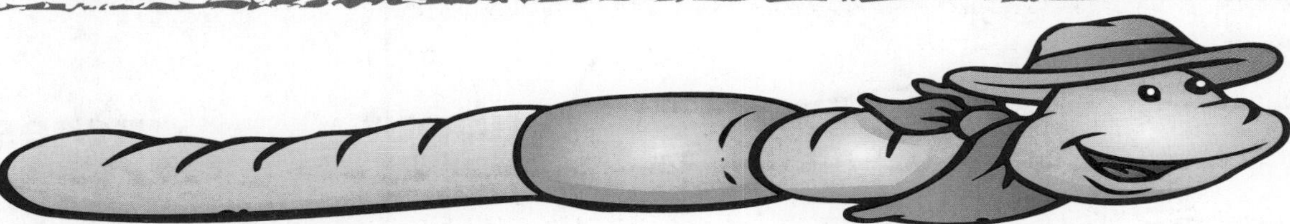

about ____ inches

about ____ inches

about ____ inches

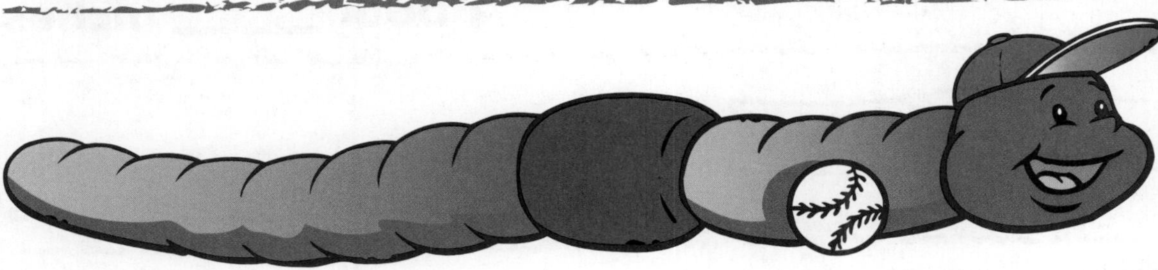

about ____ inches

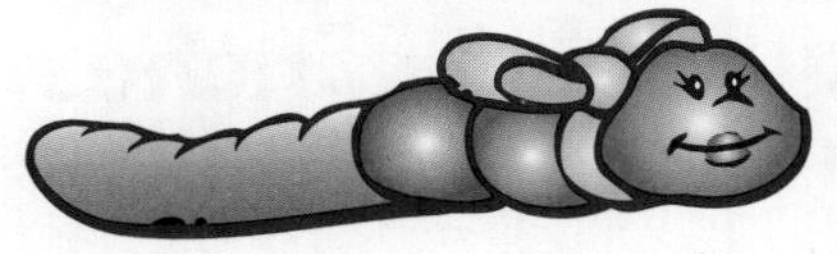

about ____ inches

MEASUREMENT

Pretty Ribbons

Measure each ribbon to the nearest inch. Write the number.

Color the longest ribbon red.

Color the shortest ribbon blue.

about ______ inches

about ___2___ inches

about ______ inches

about ______ inches

about ______ inches

about ______ inches

1 2 3 4 5 6

At the Zoo

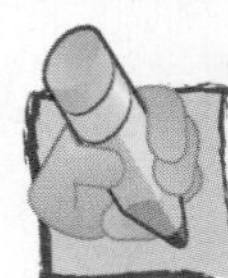

Use an inch ruler to measure each path on the map. Write about how many inches.

How long is the path:

1. From the Entrance to the Monkeys? ______ inches

2. From the Entrance to the Snakes? ______ inches

3. From the Monkeys to the Birds? ______ inches

4. From the Snack Bar to the Seals? ______ inches

5. From the Elephants to the Lions? ______ inches

6. From the Lions to the Snakes? ______ inches

MEASUREMENT

Gone Fishing

I estimate this fish is
3 inches long.

Estimate the length of each fish. Then, use an inch ruler to measure. Write your answers on the lines.

Estimate _____ inches **Measure _____ inches**

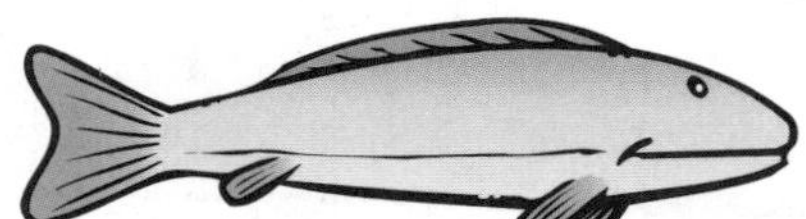

Estimate _____ inches **Measure _____ inches**

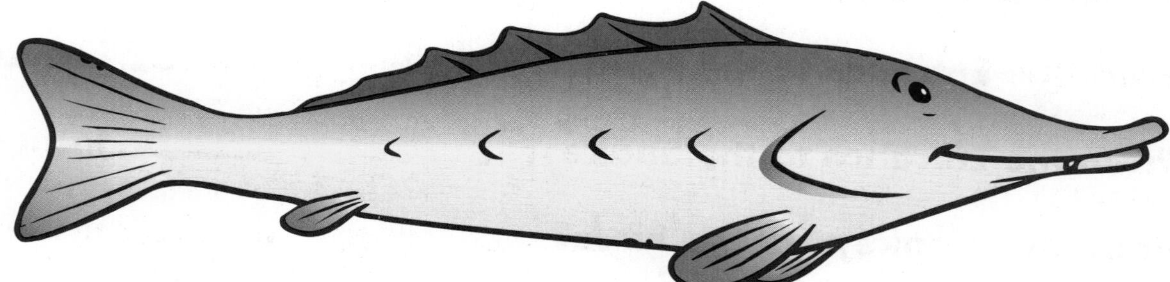

Estimate _____ inches **Measure _____ inches**

Estimate _____ inches **Measure _____ inches**

Art Fun

Cut out the centimeter ruler. Measure each object to the nearest centimeter. Write how many centimeters.

about _____ centimeters

about _____ centimeters

about _____ centimeters

about _____ centimeters

about _____ centimeters

about _____ centimeters

1 2 3 4 5 6 7 8 9 10 11 12 13 14 15

Find Sam's Sneaker

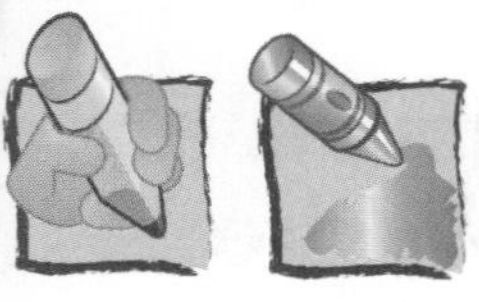

Use a centimeter ruler. Measure the length of each sneaker. Sam's sneaker is 9 centimeters long. Find and color Sam's sneaker.

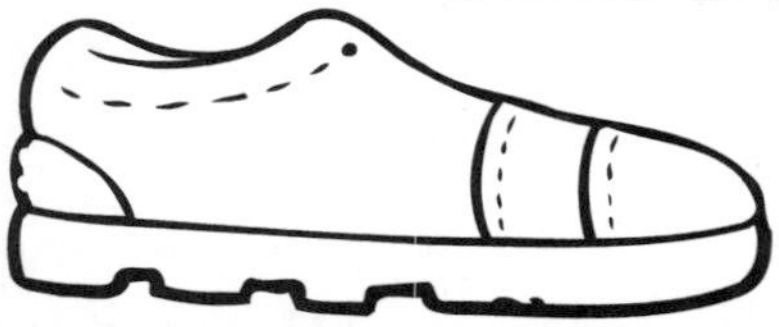

5 centimeters

____ centimeters

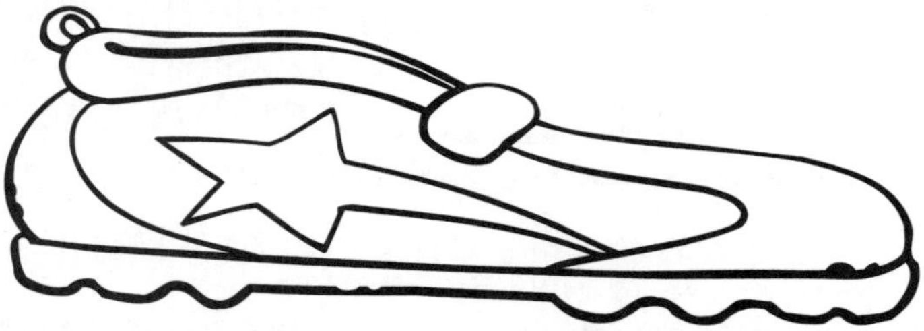

____ centimeters

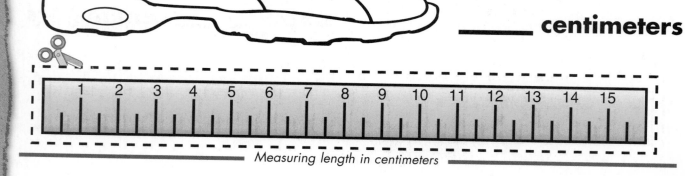

____ centimeters

____ centimeters

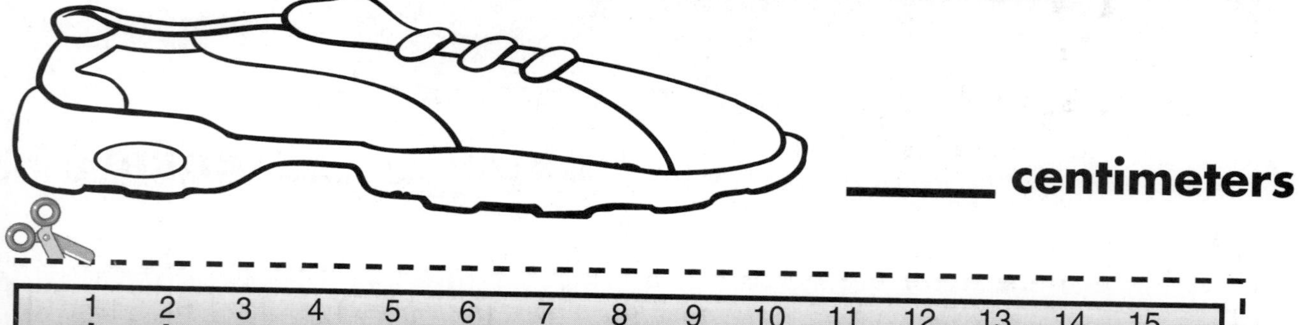

Measuring length in centimeters

Measure at Home

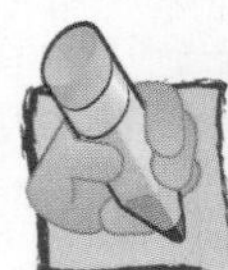

Use a centimeter ruler to measure these things around your house. Write the answer.

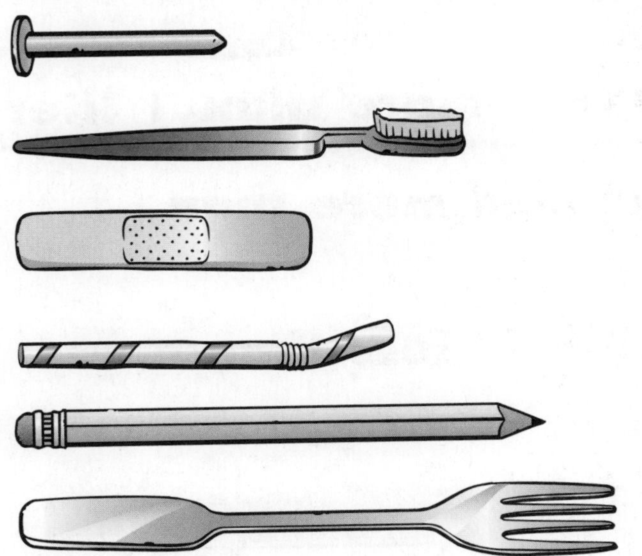

about _____ centimeters

about _____ centimeters

about _____ centimeters

about _____ centimeters

about _____ centimeters

about _____ centimeters

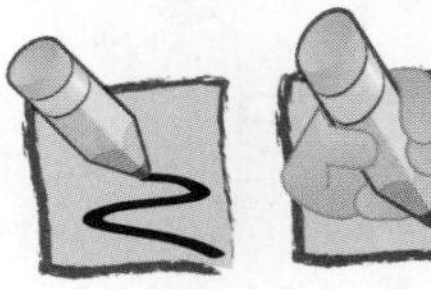

Look for more things to measure. Draw a picture. Write how many centimeters.

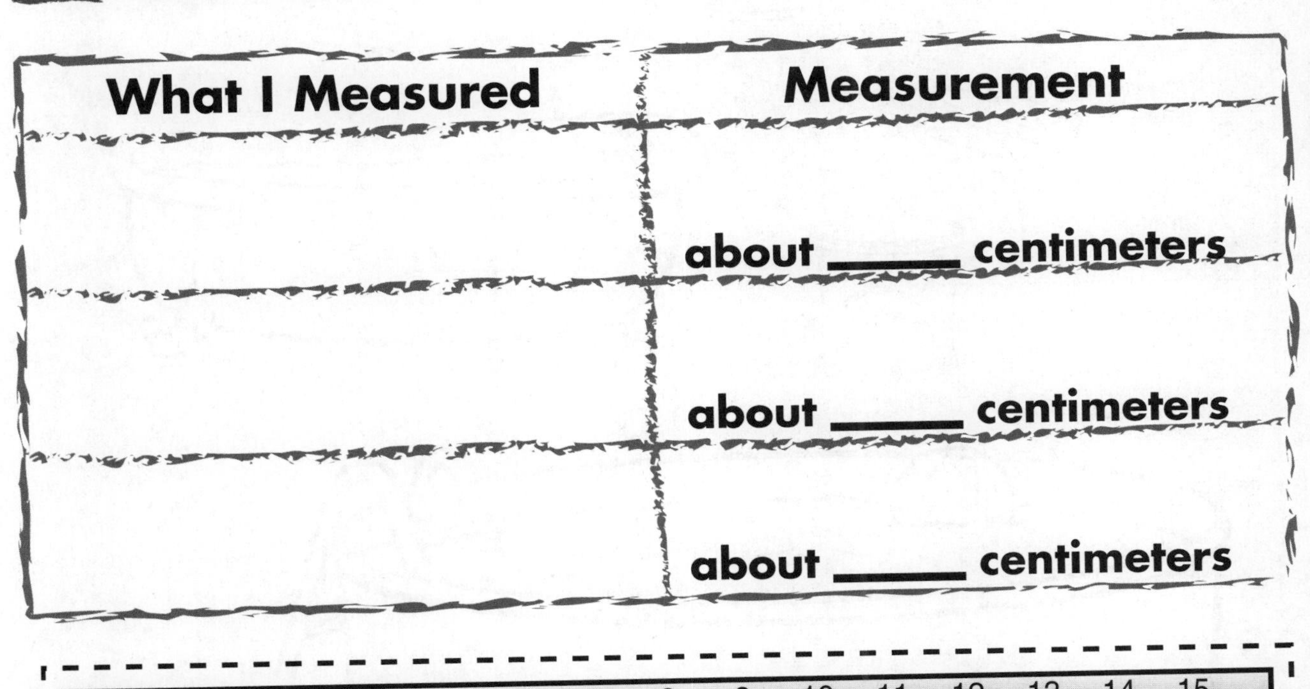

What I Measured	Measurement
	about _____ centimeters
	about _____ centimeters
	about _____ centimeters

MEASUREMENT

How Much Does It Hold?

less than 1 liter

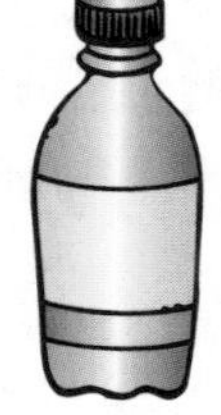

1 liter

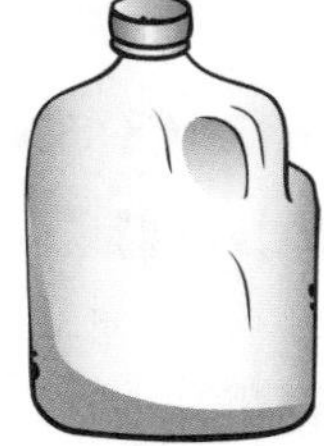

more than 1 liter

Color all the things that hold more than 1 liter.

Color all the things that hold less than 1 liter.

yogurt

Cups, Pints, and Quarts

1 cup **2 cups = 1 pint** **4 cups = 1 quart**

Color the cups to show the same amount.

 = 

 = 

 = 

 = 

 = 

Comparing the capacity of cups, pints, and quarts

MEASUREMENT

Heavier and Lighter

The [book] is **heavier.**

The [feather] is **lighter.**

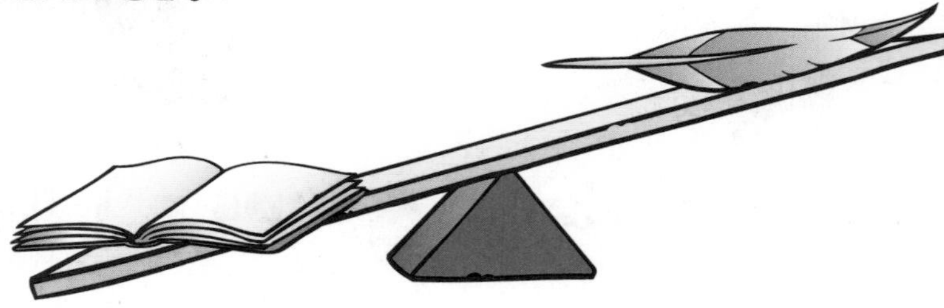

Circle the ones that are **heavier.**

Circle the ones that are **lighter.**

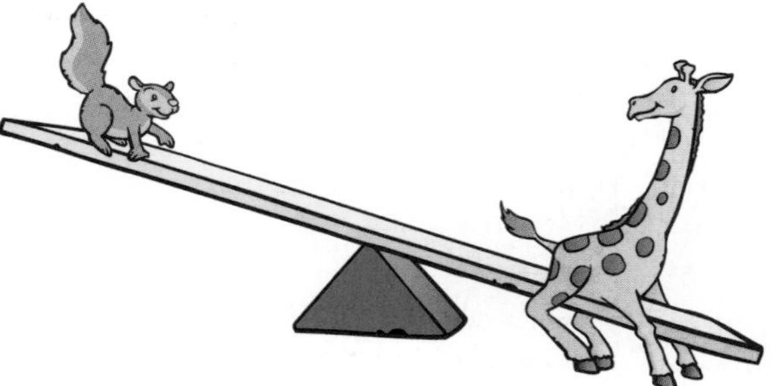

Color the animals that are **heavier** than a .

Weighing Kilograms

This weighs **less than 1 kilogram.**

These weigh **1 kilogram.**

This weighs **more than 1 kilogram.**

Draw lines to match.

lighter than 1 kilogram

about 1 kilogram

heavier than 1 kilogram

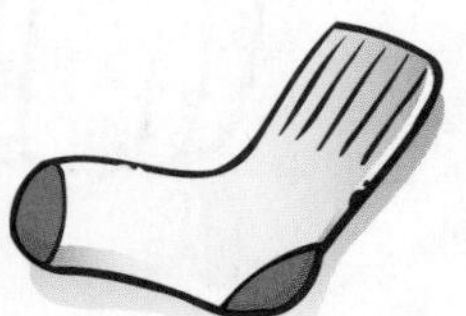

lighter than 1 kilogram

heavier than 1 kilogram

about 1 kilogram

Weighing Pounds

This spaghetti weighs 1 pound.

Color all the things that weigh more than  .

Color all the things that weight less than  .

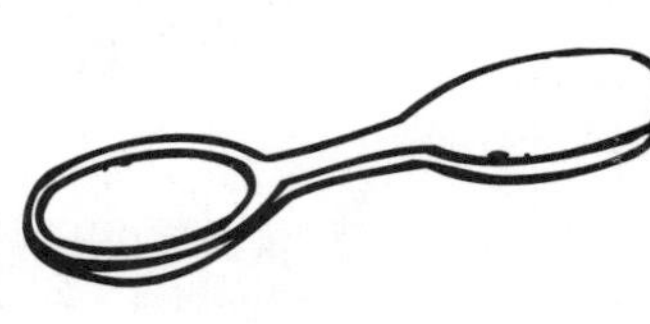

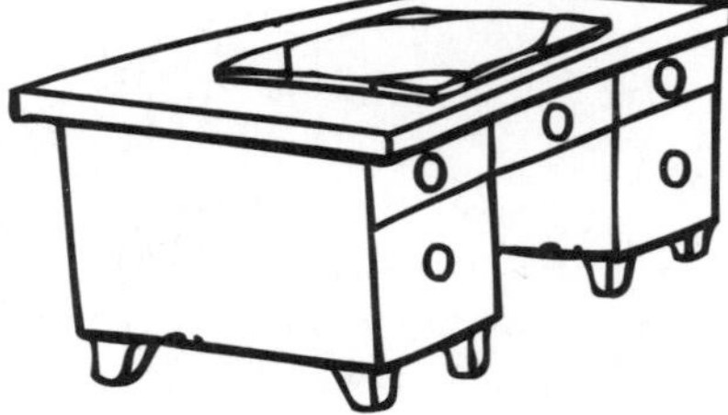

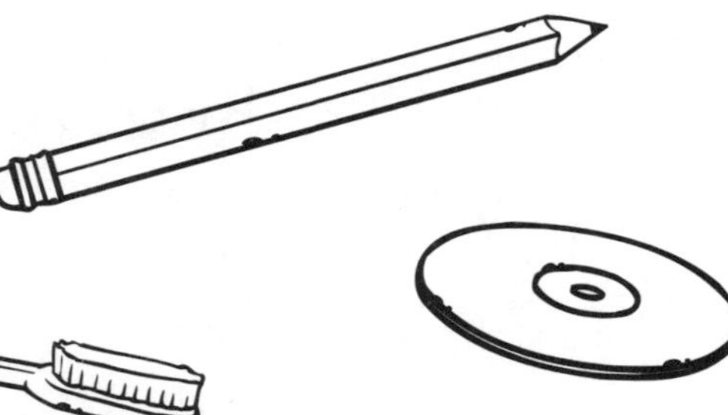

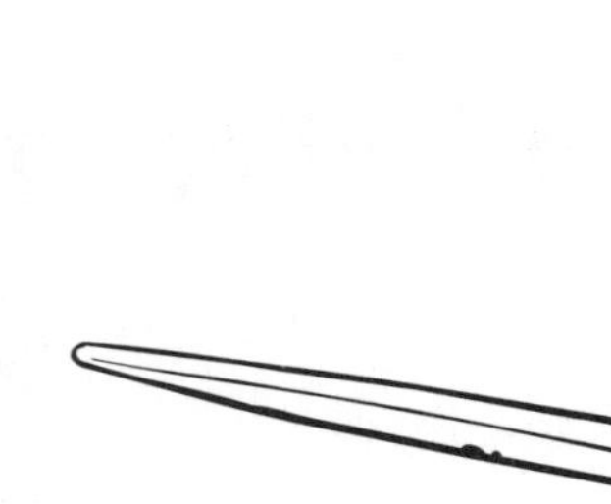

More or Less?

Circle the words that tell about how much each thing weighs.

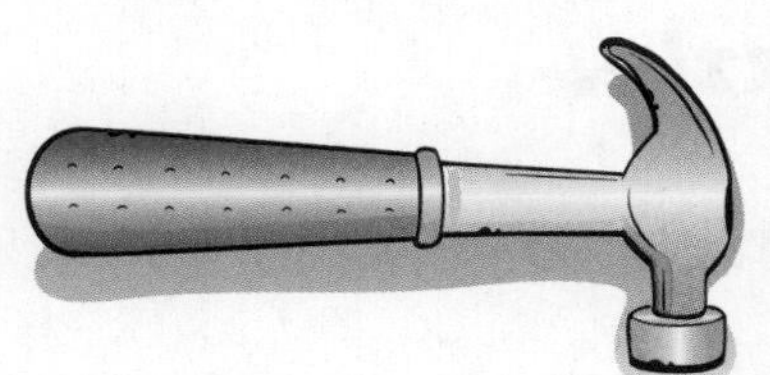 **less than 1 pound** **more than 1 pound**	 **less than 1 pound** **more than 1 pound**	 **less than 1 pound** **more than 1 pound**
 **less than 1 pound** **more than 1 pound**	 **less than 1 pound** **more than 1 pound**	 **less than 1 pound** **more than 1 pound**
 **less than 1 kilogram** **more than 1 kilogram**	 **less than 1 kilogram** **more than 1 kilogram**	 **less than 1 kilogram** **more than 1 kilogram**
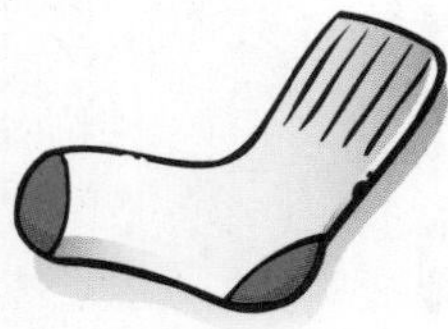 **less than 1 kilogram** **more than 1 kilogram**	 **less than 1 kilogram** **more than 1 kilogram**	 **less than 1 kilogram** **more than 1 kilogram**

Puzzle Fun

scale quart inches ruler cup pounds

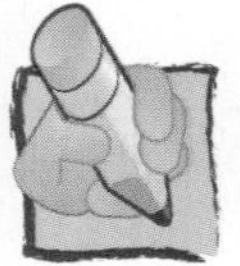

Write a word to complete each sentence. Circle the words in the puzzle.

1. A ____________ measures how long.
2. A ____________ measures how heavy.
3. A quart and a ____________ can measure how much something holds.
4. You can measure weight in ____________.
5. A ____________ is the same as 4 cups.
6. A ruler can measure ____________.

b	u	s	i	l	a	p
i	n	c	h	e	s	o
f	c	a	r	t	p	u
r	u	l	e	r	z	n
b	p	e	d	o	k	d
q	u	a	r	t	a	s

Review

Write the length.

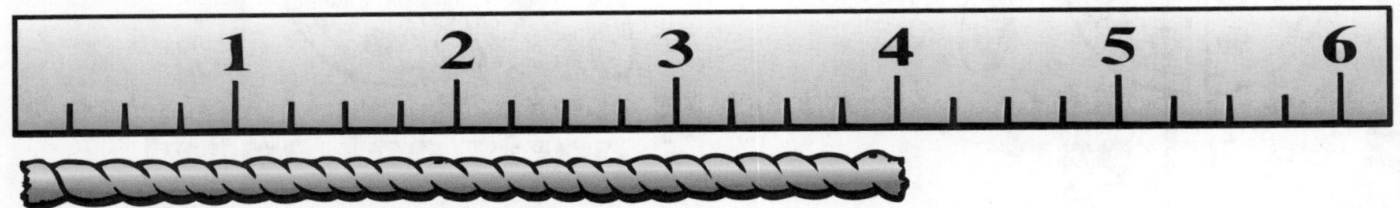

about _____ inches

about _____ centimeters

Color the cups to show the same amount.

=

Circle the words that tell about how much each thing weighs.

more than
1 pound

less than
1 pound

more than
1 kilogram

less than
1 kilogram

FRACTIONS

Equal Parts

2 equal parts

2 parts not equal

Circle the pictures that show 2 equal parts.

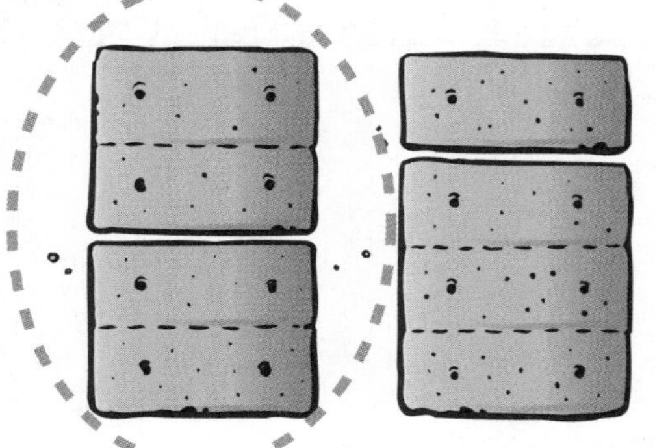

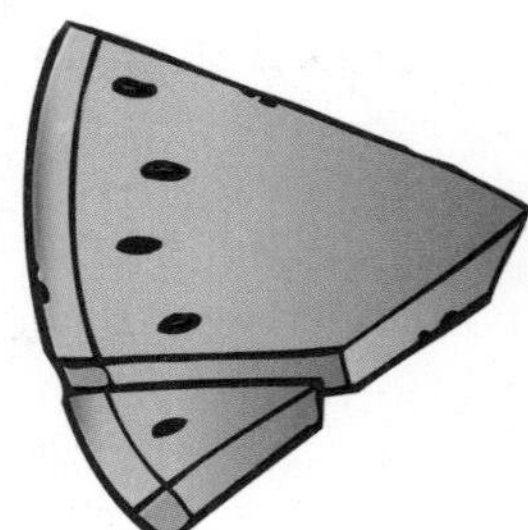

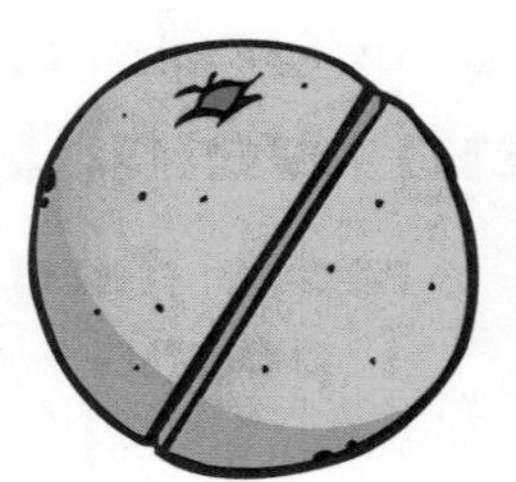

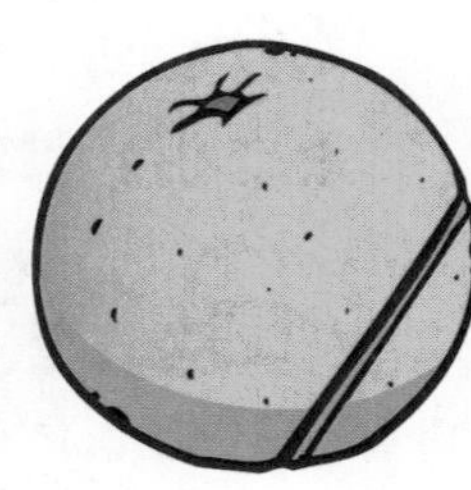

What Is a Half?

$\frac{\text{1 part shaded}}{\text{2 equal parts}}$

1/2 or **one half** is shaded.

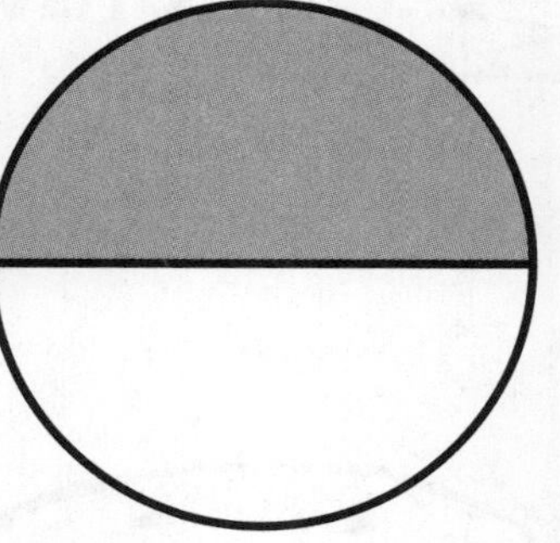

Two equal parts are **halves.**

Circle the shapes that show **halves.**
Color **1/2** of each shape.

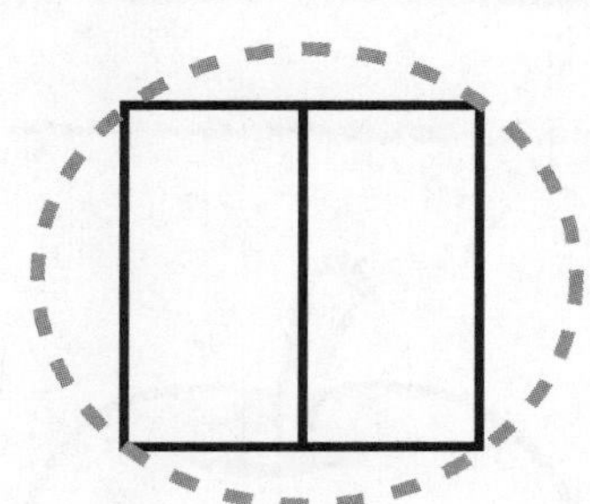

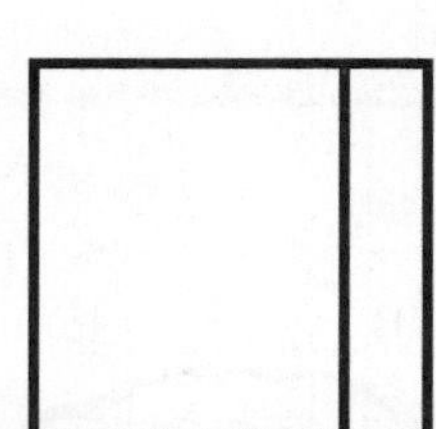

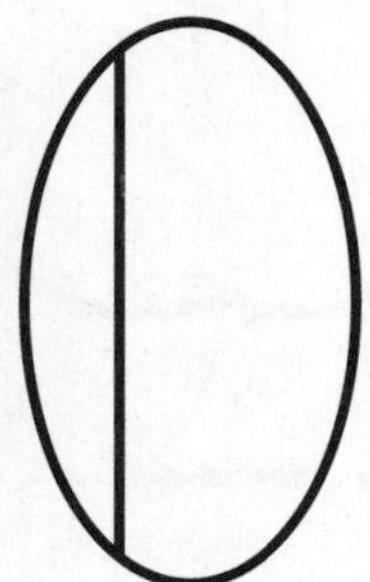
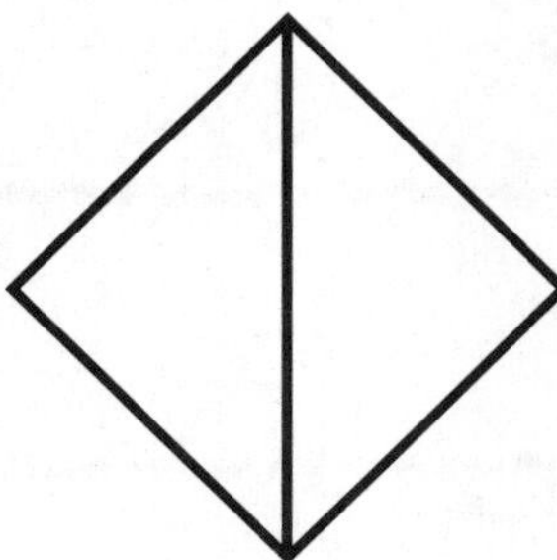
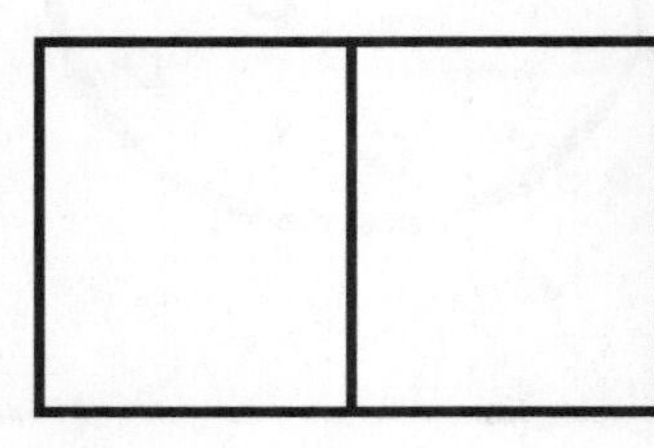

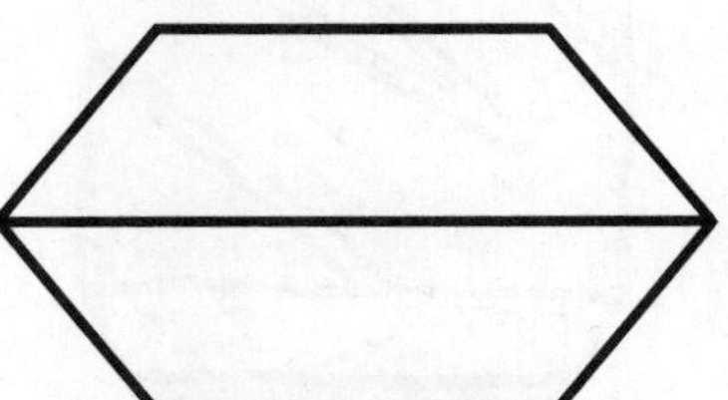

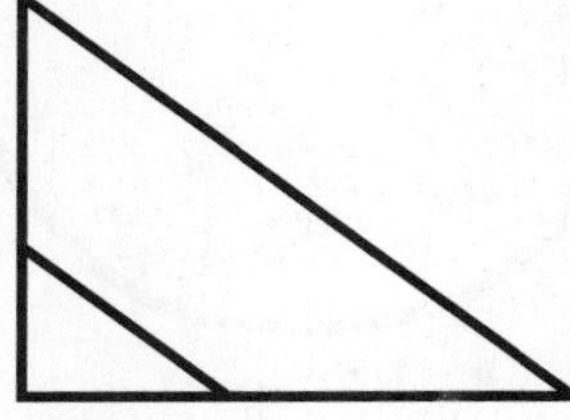

FRACTIONS

Sharing Snacks

Draw a line and color to show 1/2.

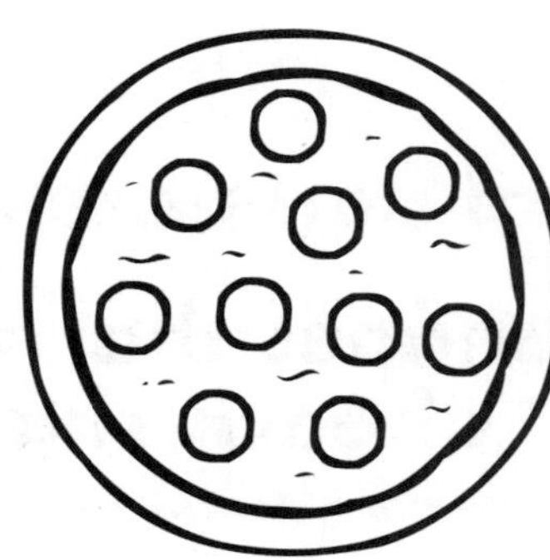

What Is a Third?

1 part shaded
3 equal parts

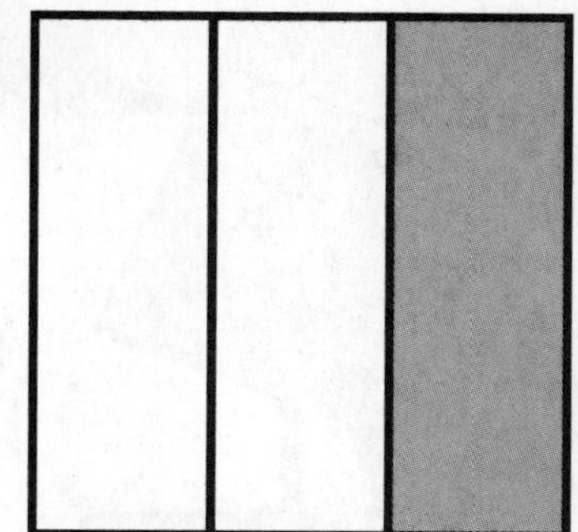

1/3 or one third is shaded.

Three equal parts are thirds.

Circle the shapes that show thirds.
Color 1/3 of each shape.

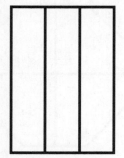

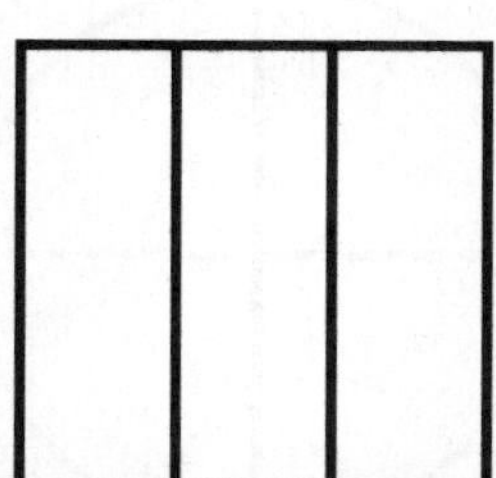

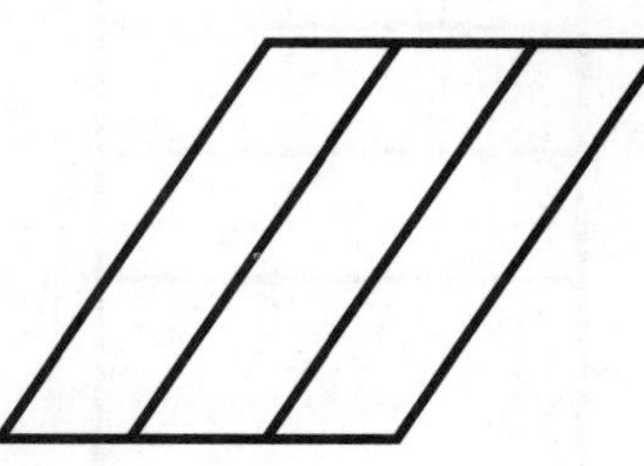
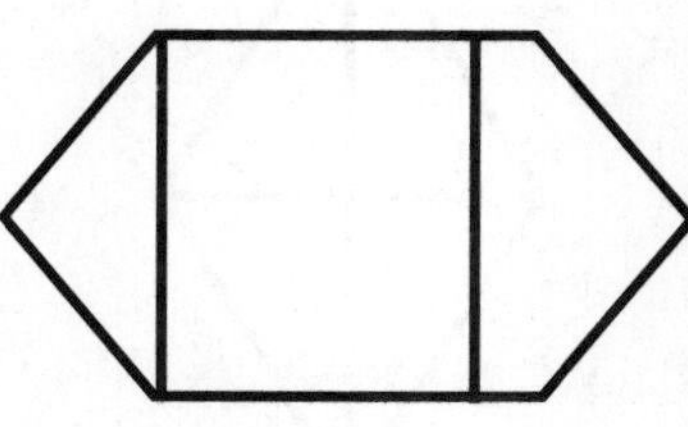

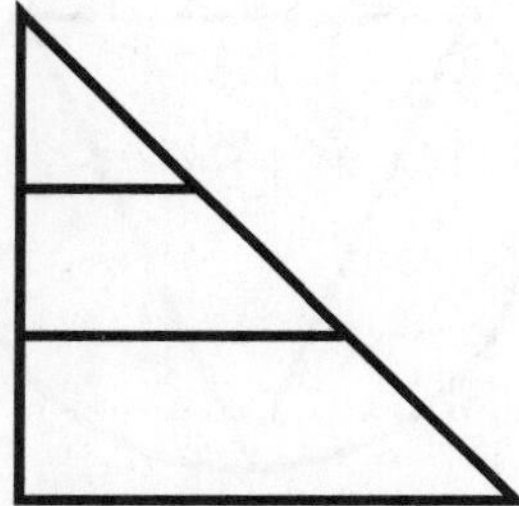
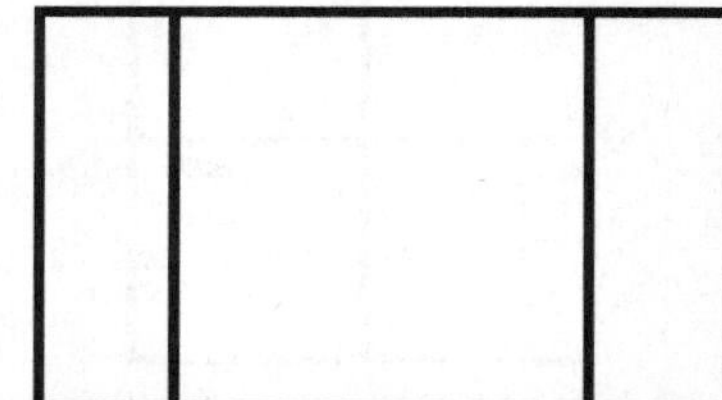
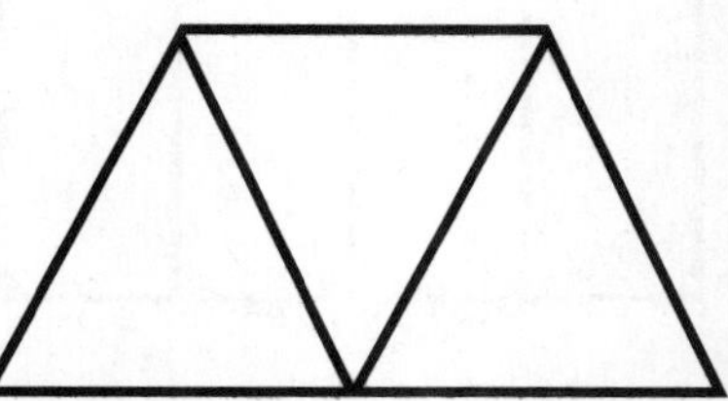

Recognizing thirds as three equal parts

FRACTIONS

What Is a Fourth?

1 part shaded
4 equal parts

1/4 or one fourth is shaded.

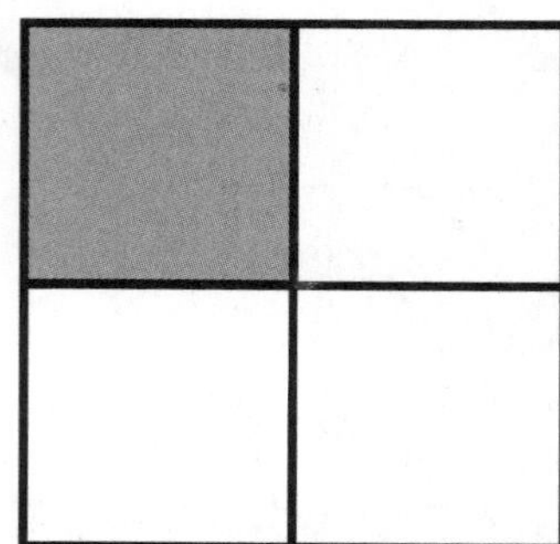

Four equal parts are fourths.

Circle the shapes that show fourths.
Color 1/4 of each shape.

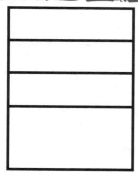

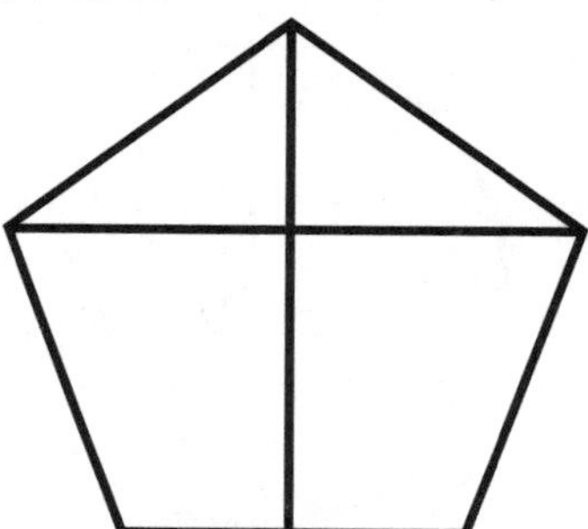

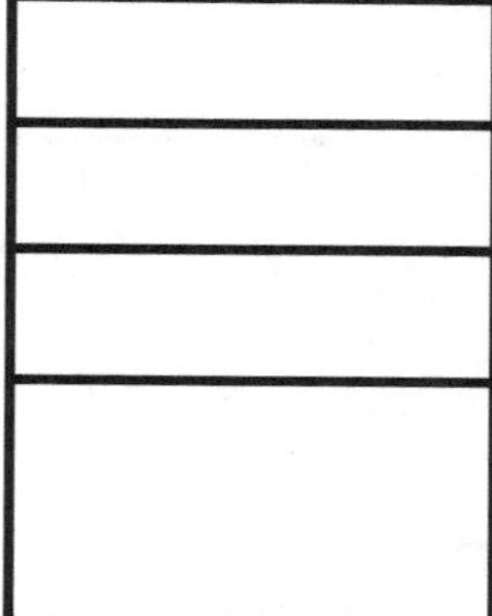
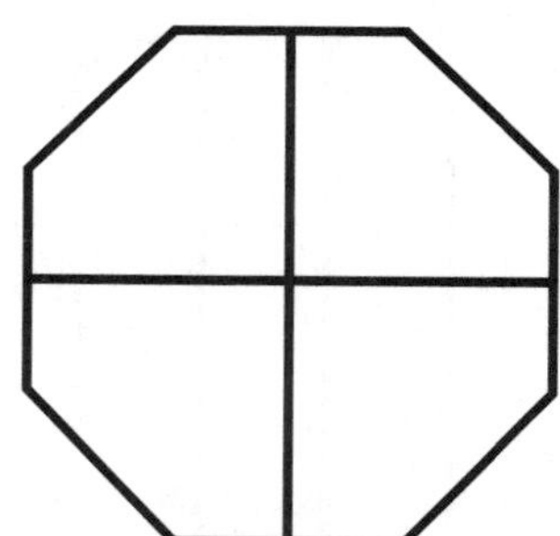

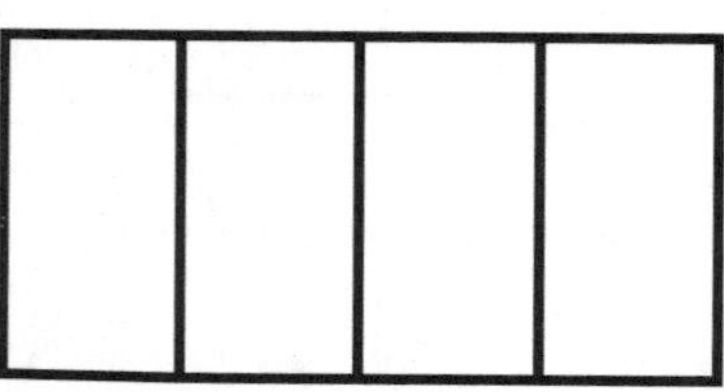
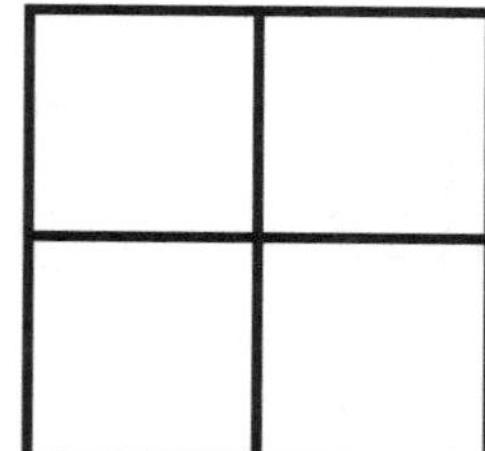
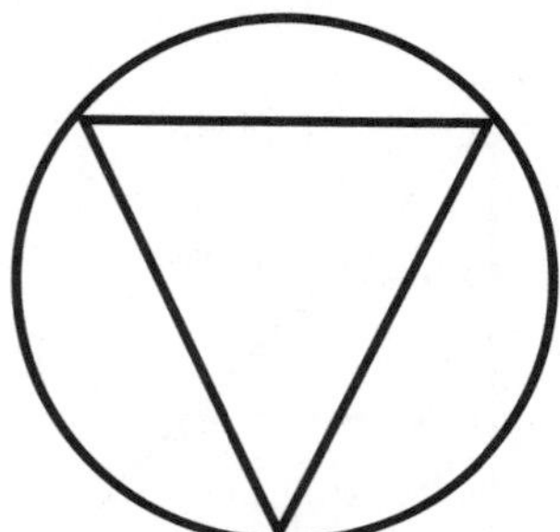

Food for you

Color 1/2 red.

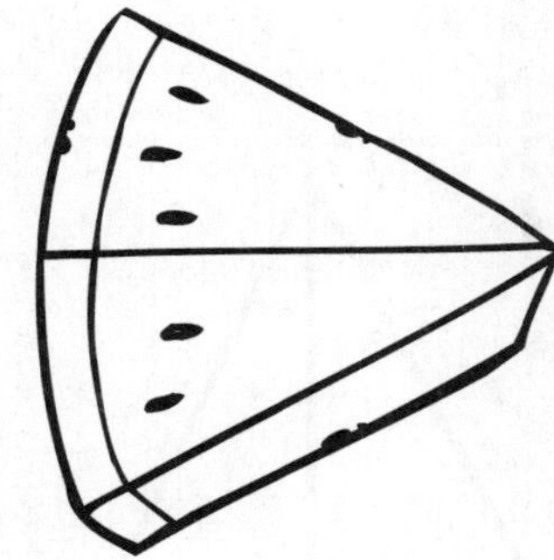

Color 1/3 green.

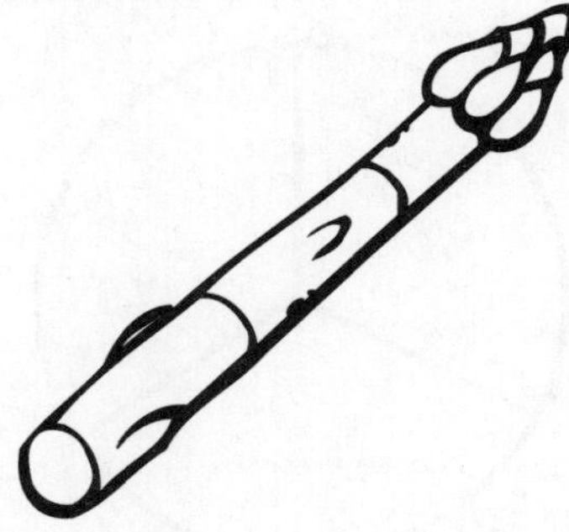

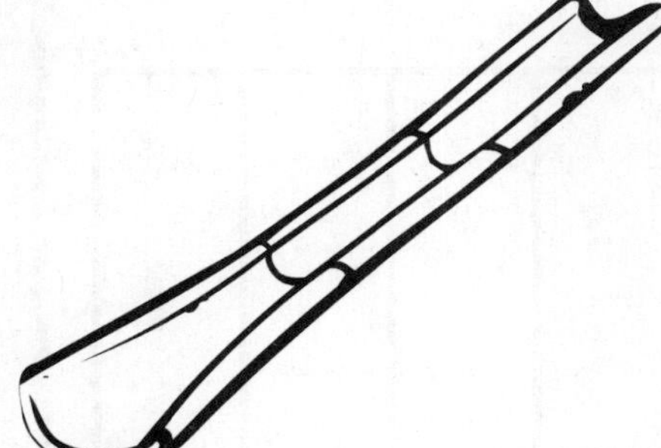

Color 1/4 orange.

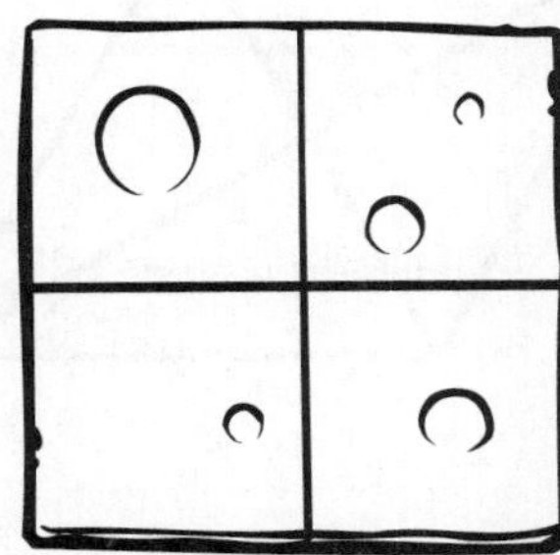

Fraction Fun

Color one part. Circle the fraction that names the colored part.

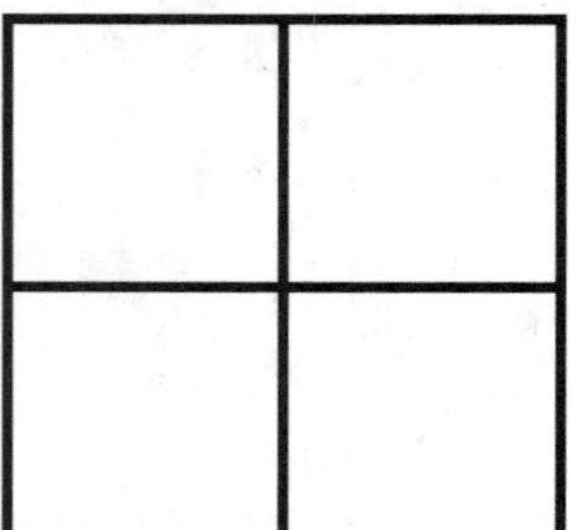

1/2 1/3 1/4

1/2 1/3 1/4

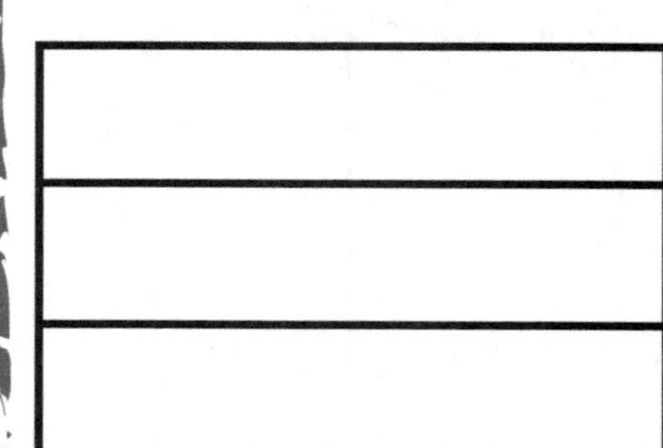

1/2 1/3 1/4

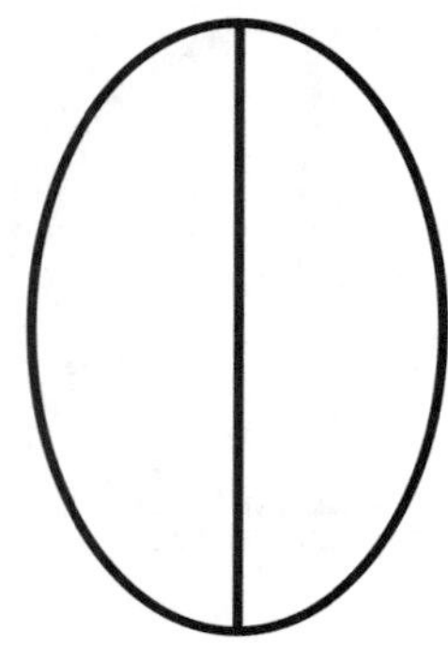

1/2 1/3 1/4

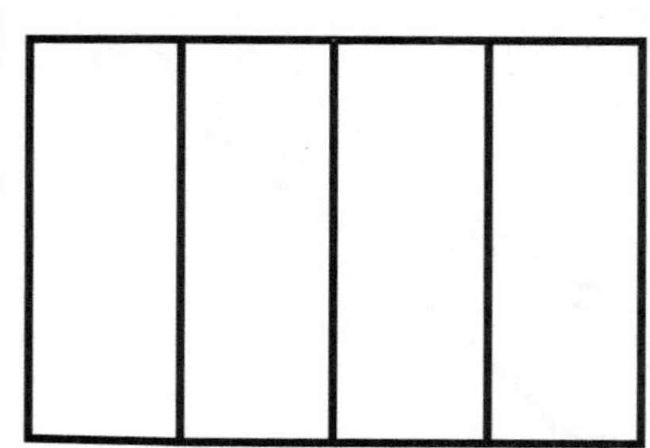

1/2 1/3 1/4

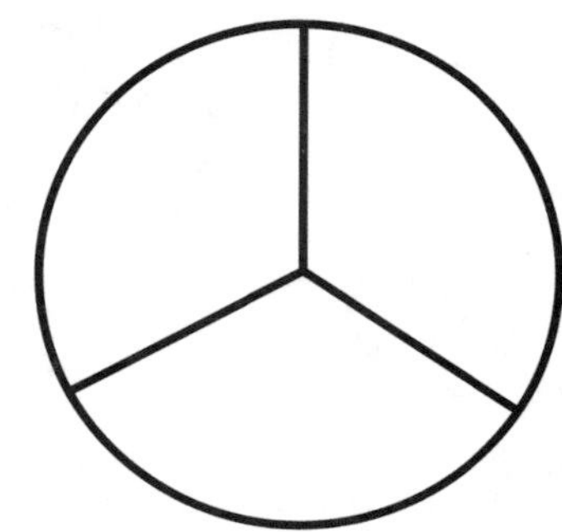

1/2 1/3 1/4

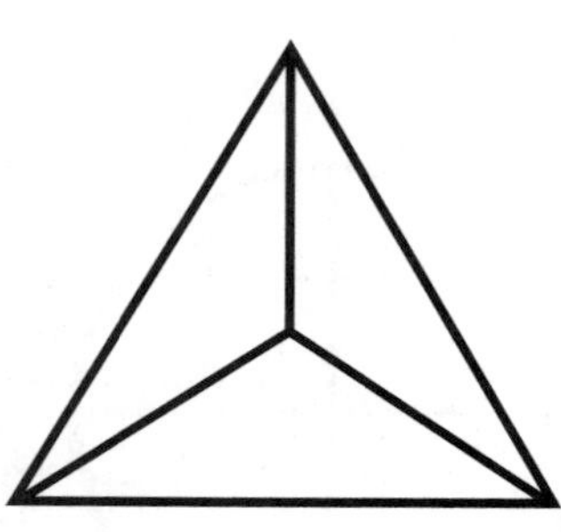

1/2 1/3 1/4

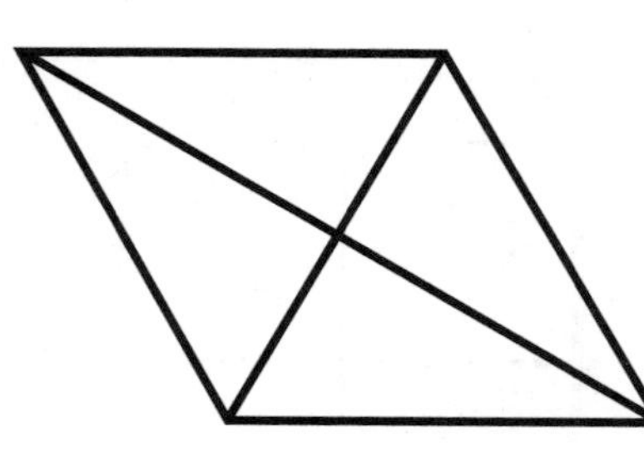

1/2 1/3 1/4

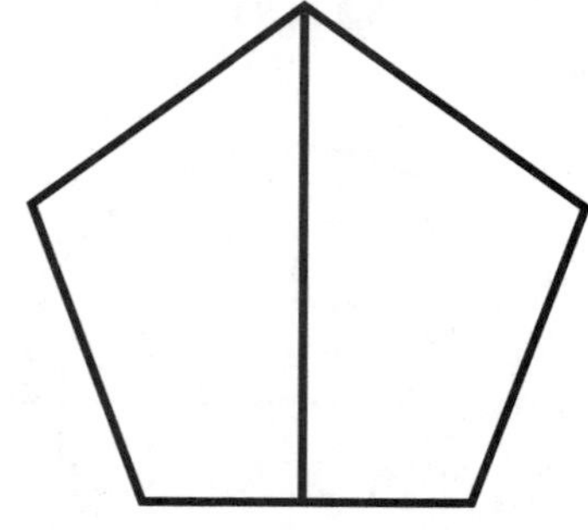

1/2 1/3 1/4

Review

Circle the pictures that show equal parts.

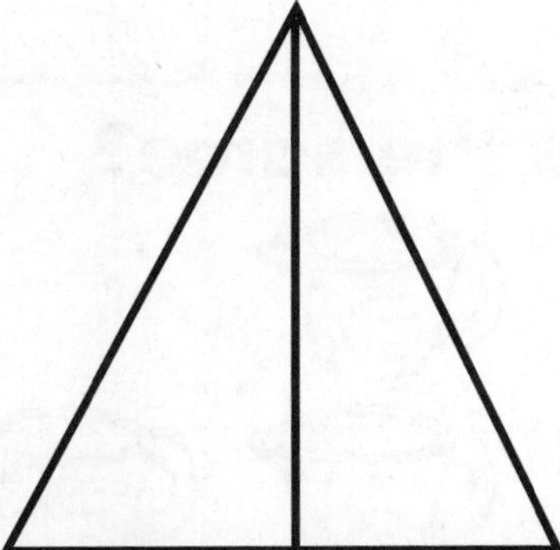 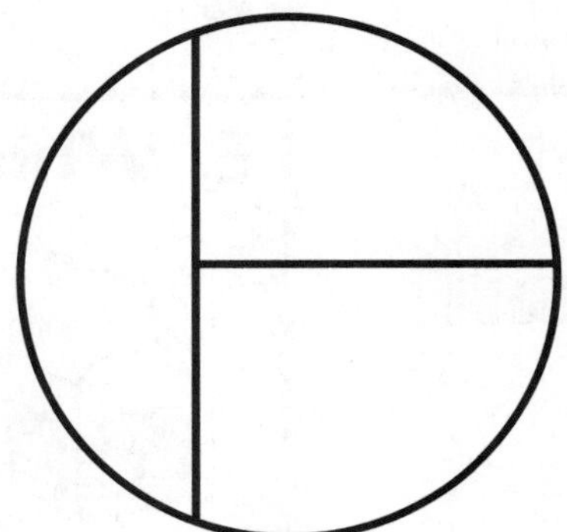 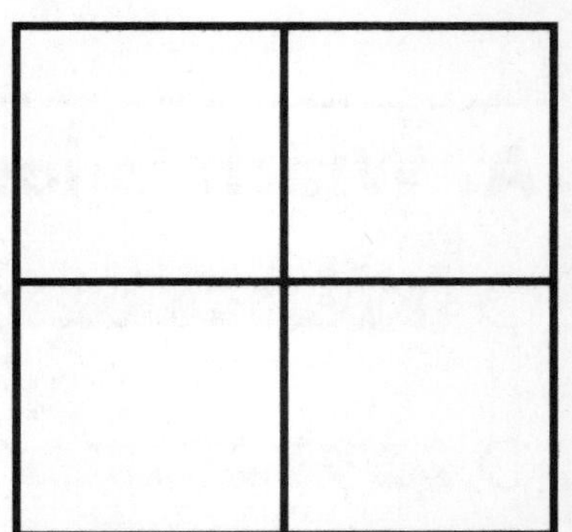

Circle the fraction.

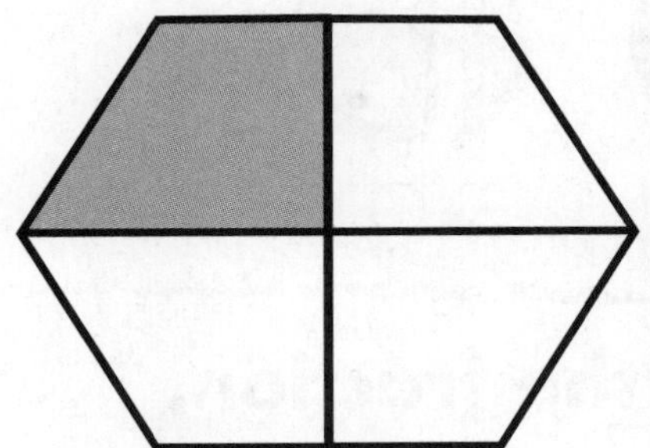

1/2 1/3 1/4

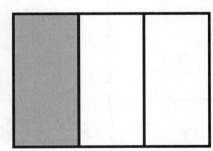

1/2 1/3 1/4

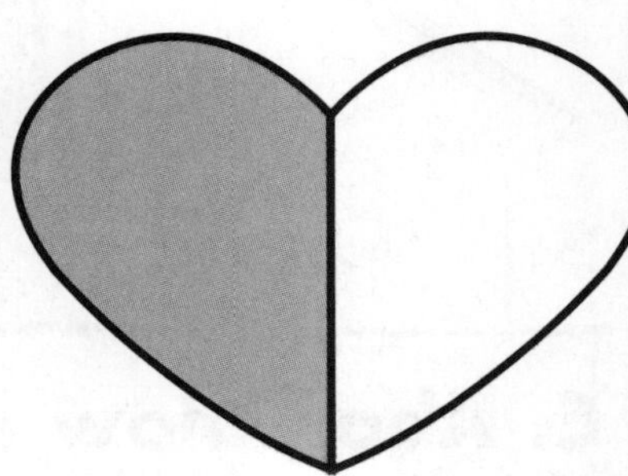

1/2 1/3 1/4

Color the fraction.

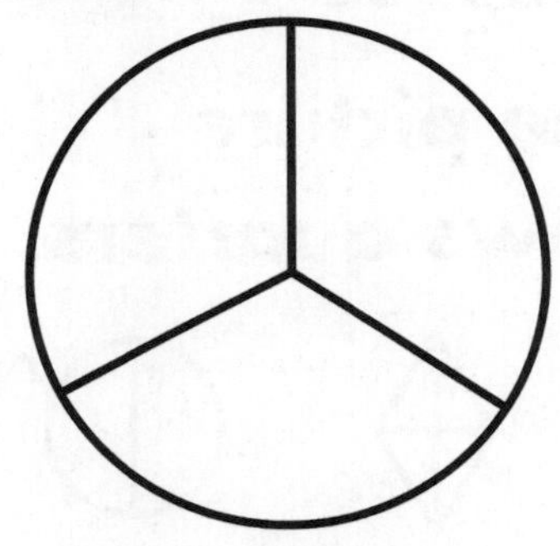

1/3

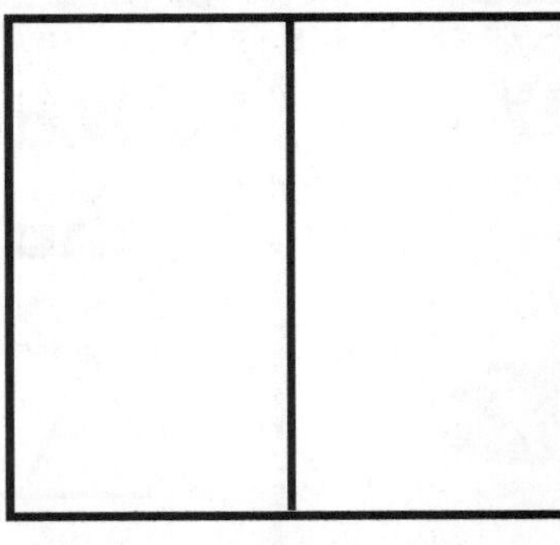

1/2

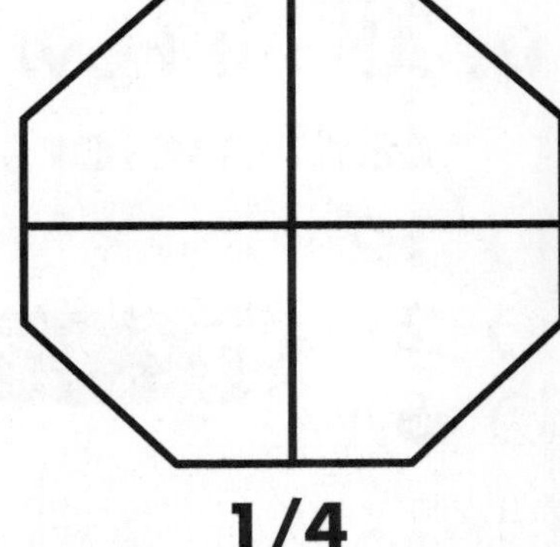

1/4

Practice Test

Which is shorter?

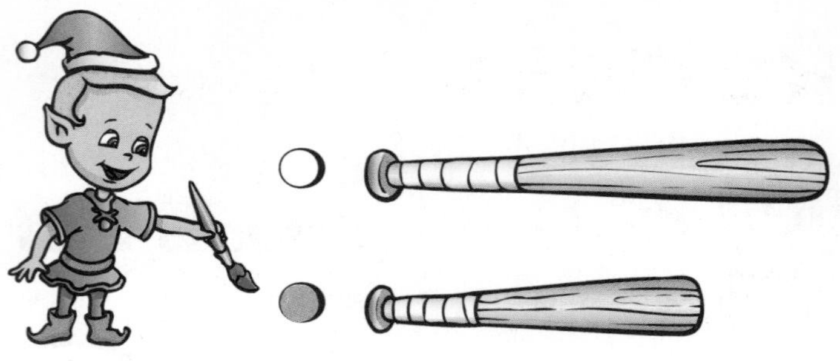

A. Which is longer?

❍

❍

E. Which is the same?

B. Which is heavier?

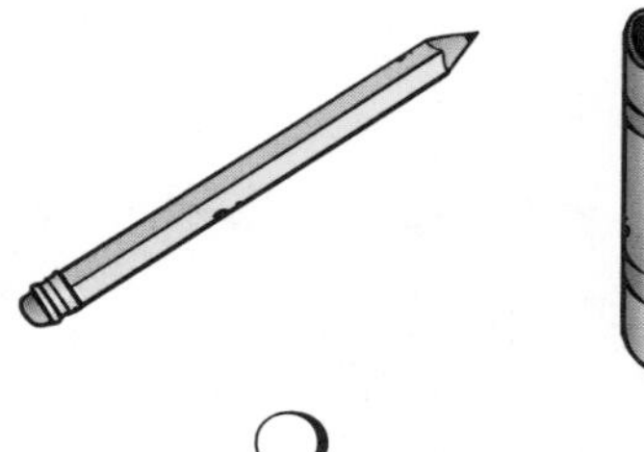

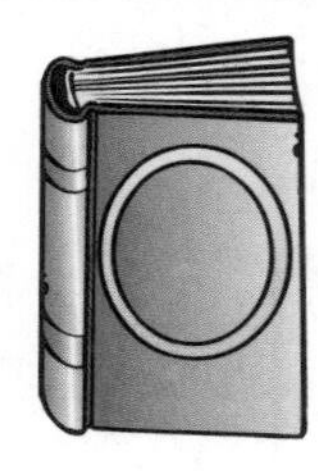

❍ ❍

F. Which shows equal parts?

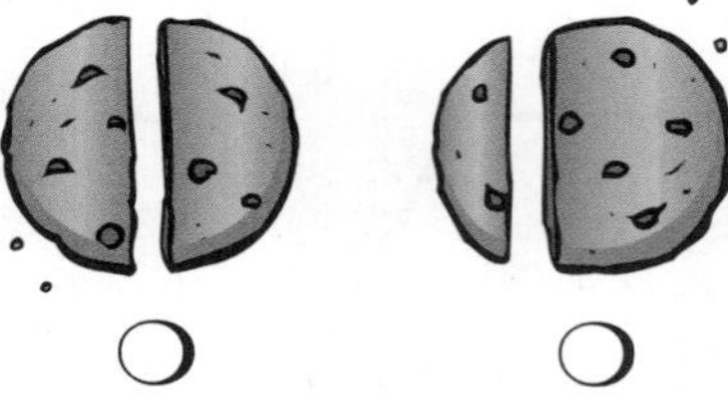

❍ ❍

C. About how many inches?

❍ 1
❍ 2
❍ 5

G. Mark the fraction.

❍ 1/2
❍ 1/3
❍ 1/4

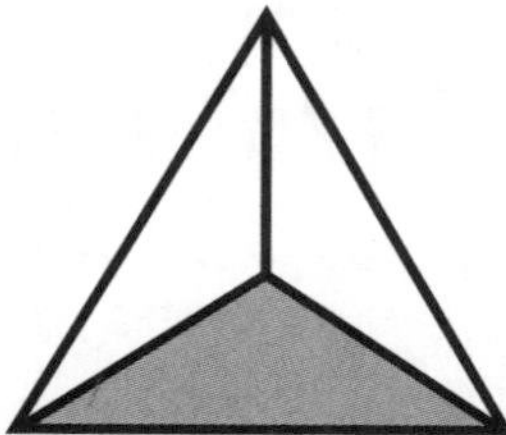

D. About how many centimeters?

❍ 12
❍ 2
❍ 6

H. Mark the picture that shows quarters.

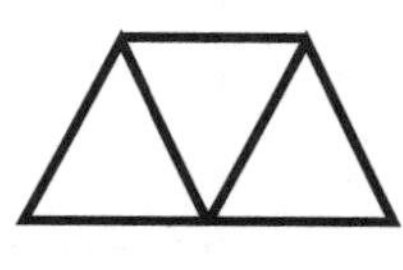

❍ ❍ ❍

Index